POPULATION TRENDS IN BRITISH BREEDING BIRDS

John H. Marchant, Robert Hudson, Steve P. Carter
& Phil Whittington

British Trust for Ornithology

The Nunnery, Nunnery Place, Thetford, Norfolk IP24 2PU

Based on work undertaken under contract to
the Nature Conservancy Council

NATURE
CONSERVANCY
COUNCIL

This book is dedicated to *Kenneth Williamson* (1914-1977), whose enthusiasm inspired so much of the work we now continue.

Marchant, J. H., R. Hudson, S. P. Carter & P. A. Whittington, 1990. Population trends in British breeding birds. Tring (BTO).

Published in April 1990 by the British Trust for Ornithology, Beech Grove, Tring, Hertfordshire, UK, with financial assistance from the Nature Conservancy Council

British Library Cataloguing in Publication Data

Population trends in British breeding birds.
1. Great Britain. Birds. Population
I. Marchant, John
II. British Trust for Ornithology
III. Nature Conservancy Council
598.252480941

ISBN 0-903793-03-2

Printed and bound by Maund & Irvine Ltd, Tring, Hertfordshire.

Contents

Foreword

by Dr Mike Pienkowski, Head of Ornithology,
Chief Scientist Directorate, Nature Conservancy Council.

Bird population trends – meeting information needs for conservation

One of the most frequent questions asked of conservation scientists is "are numbers increasing or decreasing?". This apparently simple question, which is applied to various animals, plants and their habitats, is remarkably difficult to answer. This is because of both the challenges in designing scientifically sound methods of measuring change, and particularly in finding a way of undertaking the large and regular amount of work required. Yet such information on changes is fundamental to the assessing of conservation needs and priorities, and to the monitoring of the effects of our actions. The answer to this dilemma is the combination of skilled amateur observers and professional biologists employed to coordinate and analyse their efforts. This is probably best developed anywhere for bird studies in Britain – and these are admired, envied and (where possible) emulated in many other countries. This success is based upon the long cooperation between the British Trust for Ornithology and the Nature Conservancy Council. The first major bird monitoring programme of this collaboration was the Common Birds Census, whose results to date provide the core of this book.

In the early 1960s, two major and widespread environmental impacts on wildlife were becoming apparent. These were the impacts of chemical pesticides and the effects of intensification of agriculture (often simplified at the time to just one element, hedgerow removal). The special feature of these two changes was their rapidity and widespread nature. They could affect wildlife (and people) over much of the country – and beyond – rather than in particular restricted sites. Bird populations provided a potential way of following related changes in wildlife, because of the "army" of amateur workers amongst the BTO's membership. Accordingly, the Nature Conservancy commissioned the BTO to undertake the Common Birds Census. After a pilot year in 1961, the CBC started on farmland in 1962 and in woodland in 1964. Further plots in a variety of other habitats were also undertaken. My own plot undertaken in the late 1960s in a Derbyshire gravel pit complex fell into this "special" category. Linear waterways joined as the Waterways Bird Survey from 1974.

Why do we need this information? The original reasons outlined above remain valid. Indeed, the Nature Conservancy Council Act 1973 places a duty on NCC "in the discharge of their functions, to take account, as appropriate, of actual or possible ecological changes." This includes necessary information in undertaking its licensing functions and advising Ministers on theirs, answering enquiries from the public and Parliament, and providing statutory annual reports nationally and in respect of international commitments. These are the bureaucratic but necessary activities which underpin the development of national policies to conserve populations and their habitats. Without sound data, the prospects of nature conservation being taken into account are minimal. Similarly, population trends provide important contextual information for local planning authorities in considering development proposals. Overall, data on trends are essential both in assessing whether our conservation measures are working, or whether further underlying causes need addressing.

Such analyses of causes are assisted by an extra benefit of the CBC: its application to habitat studies. Because of its map-based techniques, it has been possible to relate changes in bird populations to changes in their habitats. Many of these links are explored in *Farming and Birds*, and the application to farm management for birds in a further book resulting from collaboration between the BTO, the NCC and the Ministry of Agriculture, Fisheries and Food. Woodland CBCs have also been developed into fundamental studies of the relationships between birds and their habitats, with the results used for woodland management. The results of BTO work with that of the NCC on butterflies and other features combine in two NCC booklets: *Coppiced woodlands: their management for wildlife* and *Woodland rides and glades: their management for wildlife*. These will further promote practical application of the results of these studies to conservation management of woodlands.

The main results of the CBC featured in this book are its original ones of monitoring, in particular of man's effects on birds, so that appropriate action can be taken. The early years of the CBC indicated the success of measures to restrict the use of organochlorine pesticides. This is reflected in the increases in breeding success and/or population indices in seed-eating species such as Stock Dove and Yellowhammer and in birds of prey such as Kestrel and Sparrowhawk. The recovery of Buzzards has similarly taken place in the north and west, but a spread back to the southeast has not continued, illegal persecution being a possible cause. Still in the area of chemicals, pollution in rivers is suggested as a cause of the current disturbing decline in Kingfishers.

Whilst one original target of CBC monitoring, the effects of organochlorine pesticides, shows a generally satisfactory outcome, the situation is more negative in respect of land-use changes. Declining trends in a wide array of species can most reasonably be associated with the changing pattern of lowland agriculture. These changes include the regional specialization of farming, leading to a reduction in landscape mosaics and alternative feeding opportunities, affecting amongst other species Lapwing, Barn Owl, Green Woodpecker, Skylark, Rook and Corn Bunting. The shift from spring to autumn sowing, and consequent loss of winter stubble and spring tillage feeding opportunities, probably influenced some of these birds as well as Mistle Thrush and Linnet. Many of these species will have been affected also by the "tidying" of the countryside and the effects of increased use of herbicides on their food plants or indirectly via their prey animals. These may have been affected also by insecticides. These factors are implicated also in declines of Greenfinch and Grey Partridge. Loss of traditional farm buildings, which provided nest-sites, may have influenced Swallow and Barn Owl. Increased drainage has led to declines in Snipe and Redshank amongst others. There are clearly opportunities here to halt some of this alarming suite of declines, if changes in agricultural policies were to take account of conservation interest rather than simply reduction in food production surpluses. I should stress here that farmers have generally been responsive to changes in agricultural policies and incentives: it is these nationally and wider policies which need to be influenced.

There are, of course, also human-affected increases as well as decreases. The spread of Great Crested Grebes is clearly related to the provision of new water-bodies, especially flooded gravel pits. Magpies have benefitted greatly from tree-planting in towns. Siskins, Coal Tits and Goldcrests have probably benefitted from conifer afforestation – but the cost has been great in the losses of much scarcer and vulnerable open country species which, with a few exceptions like Raven, are outside the scope of this book. Some other man-induced increases are also not success stories. The rapid increase in Canada Geese following their translocation to enhance shooting (although the species is not a popular quarry) illustrates the folly of ill-planned translocations, and generally of introductions of non-native species.

The results in this book identify also changes which are the result of "natural" changes – or, at least, not directly related to human activities in Britain. This is important in identifying where conservation measures in Britain are unlikely to address the cause. The most striking example concerns the group of migrants which suffered in their winter quarters from the Sahel drought from the late 1960s onwards. These include Sand Martin, Redstart, Sedge Warbler and, most dramatically, Whitethroat which previously was possibly our most abundant warbler.

Climatic effects appear also to be a common feature of population trends of several resident species which tended to increase in the generally mild winter conditions of the late 1960s to early 1970s followed by a decline in the following period of more frequent cold winters. Small birds, including Treecreeper, Pied Wagtail, Wren, Goldcrest and Long-tailed Tit, are typical of this category.

The differences in recovery rates in different habitats have proven important in studies of habitat preference in many species, whether this concerns Garden Warblers, Wrens and many others filling woodland before farmland; Chiffchaffs preferring broadleaves to conifers; Reed Buntings increasing along waterways before farmland; or Shelducks staying constant in numbers on linear shores while varying in numbers in less suitable estuary breeding areas.

Of course, human-induced and natural factors often interact. For example, recovery of Grey Heron populations after cold winters was probably slowed by the effects of organochlorine pesticides when these were at high levels. Conversely, the creation of a wider range of water-bodies has probably helped Coot to survive severe winters. Regional differences in the population trends for some species, such as Sedge Warbler, may reflect breeding habitat losses superimposed on the problems in West African wintering areas.

Likely causes can be identified for many of the changes described in this book, a few of which are highlighted above, and these warrant further investigation. Others remain as total mysteries. Why are Nuthatches and Blackcaps increasing while Dunnocks, Marsh Tits and Tree Sparrows decrease? Are the decreases in Turtle Doves, Spotted Flycatchers and Song Thrushes linked respectively to usages of herbicides, insecticides and molluscicides? Surely there are the bases of many future studies here!

The pioneering cooperative work of the BTO and NCC in the CBC has been complemented in monitoring schemes for other groups of birds. These include the Seabird Monitoring Programme (NCC, RSPB, Seabird Group, Shetland Oil Terminal Environmental Advisory Group and others), Waders of Wet Meadows (BTO, Wader Study Group), the Rare Breeding Birds Panel (NCC, RSPB and others), Garden Birds Feeding Survey (BTO) and various single-species studies. Wintering waterfowl, for which Britain is internationally important, are monitored by the BTO/NCC/RSPB Birds of Estuaries Enquiry and the Wildfowl & Wetlands Trust/NCC National Wildfowl Counts. Where appropriate, results from these studies are used in this book to supplement CBC and WBS data.

Together, these schemes fulfil most of the monitoring needs for birds in Britain. However, none of the organisations concerned is complacent and we continue to look for ways of making even more use of the results depending on the efforts of the voluntary participants. Two current initiatives of NCC and BTO are particularly relevant in the present context. First, work is in progress on the Integrated Population Monitoring Programme, to pull together the results of the BTO/NCC schemes which monitor populations of breeding birds with those which assess their performance in terms of breeding and survival. We aim eventually to reach the stage of routinely reporting survival estimates obtained from the Ringing Scheme and breeding performance measures from the Nest Record Scheme and the Constant Effort Sites project alongside the population indices. With these, we shall be well on the way to an early warning scheme, as well as a pointer to possible causes of change. We plan also to extend the range of terrestrial habitats covered by the monitoring schemes. NCC plans to link these results to information on land-use and proposed changes, to predict consequences; this will develop further its advisory role in influencing policies, rather than simply follow changes.

The second initiative concerns the publication of the results of the bird monitoring programmes. This book brings us up to date on the results of CBC and related programmes. There is a large demand for regularly updated and widely available information on the state of the nation's birds. All the individual projects noted earlier produce rapid and valuable annual reports on their work, and these will continue. In addition, we need to bring the main features of each together in a convenient annual report on British birds. NCC and BTO, in conjunction with other bodies involved, are doing this as an appropriate development on the present book, as well as for the other monitoring studies.

My final task is the very pleasant one of congratulating the authors and editors on the production of what I am certain will become a key reference work. It will be a starting point for many further studies into the biology of these birds which fascinate us all. It provides also a firm basis for research into the causes of bird population changes, which we need to understand more fully in order to target our conservation efforts yet more effectively. In all these uses, it is in the fine tradition of BTO studies, combining the skills of amateur and professional ornithologists. Without the contributions of both, this would not be possible. Long may it continue: the need is quite clear.

Authors' preface

One popular image of "the birdwatcher" is of a solitary, unobtrusive figure, perhaps in a hide, watching the birds and waiting patiently for something interesting to look at or photograph. This is of course only one way of pursuing birdwatching as a hobby, and there are many others. In fact, hundreds of birdwatchers spend a great proportion of their leisure time in activities directed not at "bird spotting" or watching birds for the sake of doing so, but at counting and recording them. They do this because, by collecting numerical data on the birds they encounter, they can further both the biological study and the conservation of the various species. Collecting count data in whatever form, with a view to its use in this way, gives purpose to a day's birdwatching beyond the simple one of personal recreation.

This aspect of birdwatching represents teamwork rather than a solitary activity. It is at its best when counts from all observers at particular sites are gathered and co-ordinated at local, county, regional, national, or even international level, and summaries are produced which detail the results and publicise their importance. The observer may be alone in the field, but nevertheless part of a network.

One of the main functions of the BTO over more than half a century has been to organise network research in the United Kingdom on the national scale. The Heronries Census, which started in 1928, was taken over by the newly formed BTO in 1933 and is now one of the longest-running schemes of its kind in the world. Many new projects for collecting and collating bird data have been initiated by the BTO during its first half-century, mostly in association with funding bodies such as the Nature Conservancy Council, and these include the Common Birds Census and the Waterways Bird Survey whose results are the main subjects of this book. By means of such schemes operated by our organisation, amateur birdwatchers combine together to gather scientific information on birds on a co-operative basis. Data collected locally become, through the central organisation of the BTO, part of nationwide databases which are of great value to the scientific study of birds and thus to conservation.

This book is a documentation of the population changes and present status of most of the British breeding birds. Seabirds are not included, and neither are those rarities of which fewer than fifty pairs nest in the United Kingdom. The species texts discuss primarily the results of the Common Birds Census and the Waterways Bird Survey, but also summarise historical information where it is available and, in some cases, make use of other BTO data such as special surveys of single species. We have also made comparisons with population trends in continental Europe, where these are known.

The results of the CBC and WBS regarding annual changes in population levels have been published each year in *Bird Study* or (since 1983) in *BTO News*. Graphs of a full run of data have frequently been shown in these annual reports, but for only a few species at a time, and in general the long-term trends in populations have been given relatively little prominence. This book therefore represents a largely new approach because it treats the data not year by year, as do the annual reports, but species by species. It is our view that 27 years is a suitable period for recording index trends in this way. Sufficient data have been gathered to make worthwhile statements about the health of our bird populations up to the end of the 1988 breeding season. We cannot yet predict future trends, or estimate the extent to which new information will show our conclusions to have been wrong, but we have provided a firm baseline against which future results can be compared.

The subject matter of this book is of direct relevance to everybody in this country who has a concern for the well-being of our wildlife. We deal here with changes in the numbers and densities of common birds breeding in the United Kingdom – changes which affect our enjoyment of the countryside and of birds in particular. With the exception of seabirds, which are not covered by this book, bird species that are common are also relatively widespread and are familiar to a high proportion of our human population. These, not the rarities, are the species which the British people know and love, and the ones likely to be perceived as worthy of our finest conservation efforts.

The first chapter of the book explains what the Common Birds Census and Waterways Bird Survey are and do, and how they are integrated with other schemes for keeping track of bird populations. The second discusses the calculation of population indices and the reliability of the results. The third concentrates on the factors which have been shown to be important in determining population changes in a wide range of species, setting a background for the individual species accounts which follow. We hope that the whole will be both of interest to the general reader with an interest in birds and British natural history, and of value to the researcher.

A further hope is that it may provide a stimulus for readers to contribute to at least some of the many co-operative schemes in the United Kingdom for collecting and analysing information on birds, most of which are presently undersubscribed. Could *you* contribute to our national monitoring studies?

Acknowledgements

The primary acknowledgements in any publication based on CBC and WBS results must be to the many observers who give freely of their time and energy in gathering the data, and to the Nature Conservancy Council which funds the administration of the schemes at BTO headquarters. CBC and WBS observers are listed in Appendix 1.

A special tribute is due to Kenneth Williamson, who led the Populations Section of the BTO from 1964 until his death in June 1977. He was very largely responsible for putting the CBC onto a firm footing, earning for it the international respect it now enjoys. Further, he initiated the WBS and, in the absence of outside funding, was solely responsible for administration and territory analysis during its first four seasons. Ken was very enthusiastic about census work, and many observers, some still active with the CBC more than twenty years later, were inspired to contribute following a personal approach from him.

Many other staff have worked on the administration of the CBC and WBS during the years, either in a scientific or a clerical capacity. These include Dr R. S. Bailey, Miss J. L. Baker, Dr L. A. Batten, T. J. Bennett, Mrs G. Bonham, Mrs T. Bussell, H. M. Dobinson, Mrs C. Dudley, R. D. M. Edgar, Dr R. J. Fuller, D. E. Glue, Mrs R. Gray, R. K. Hicks, Miss C. A. L. Hunt, P. A. Hyde, Mrs Y. Lummis, Miss E. McHugh, R. A. Morgan, Mrs E. G. Murray, A. J. Prater, C. Purkiss, Mrs G. Rance, Miss C. M. Ray, K. D. Smith, Dr D. W. Snow, Mrs C. Taylor, Dr G. K. Taylor, Mrs J. Taylor, Mrs S. Taylor, Mrs M. Tourle, Miss G. Watts, Miss M. Wheeler, R. J. Wilmshurst and Miss S. M. Woodman.

Acknowledgements to referees

We are grateful to many people for their assistance in improving the interest, accuracy and clarity of the text. Any failings remain our own. Dr Mike Pienkowski of NCC read and commented on the whole text before publication, as did Drs Rob Fuller and Peter Lack of the BTO. Drs Stephen Baillie and Patrick Thompson improved substantial sections. The following people kindly refereed early drafts for particular species:

D. Alsop (Ring Ouzel), Dr S. R. Baillie (Song Thrush), Dr C. J. Bibby (Wood Warbler), Dr T. R. Birkhead (Magpie), M. Boddy (Whitethroat, Greenfinch and Redpoll), Dr K. B. Briggs (Oystercatcher and Ringed Plover), Dr M. de L. Brooke (Cuckoo), Dr D. M. Bryant (Sand Martin, Swallow and House Martin), Dr P. J. Dare (Buzzard, Carrion Crow and Raven), A. K. Davies (Mandarin Duck), Dr N. B. Davies (Pied Wagtail and Dunnock), P. G. Davis (Tree Pipit and Nightingale), Dr T. W. Dougall (Long-tailed Tit), S. P. Dudley (Quail), Dr C. J. Feare (Rook and Starling), Dr J. J. M. Flegg (Treecreeper and Hawfinch), Dr A. D. Fox (Teal, Mallard and Tufted Duck), Dr R. J. Fuller (Hobby), Dr P. J. Garson (Wren), Dr D. W. Gibbons (Moorhen and Jackdaw), Dr A. G. Gosler (Marsh, Willow, Coal, Blue and Great Tits), Dr R. E. Green (Red-legged Partridge, Snipe and Skylark), Dr P. W. Greig-Smith (Whinchat, Stonechat, Wheatear and Bullfinch), Dr D. G. C. Harper (Robin and Corn Bunting), Dr D. A. Hill (Jay), Dr G. J. M. Hirons (Woodcock), Dr J. A. Horsfall (Coot), R. J. Hubble (Jackdaw), Dr I. R. Inglis (Woodpigeon), Dr A. G. Knox (Redpoll and Common Crossbill), M. R. Lawn (Chiffchaff and Willow Warbler), Sir Christopher Lever (Mandarin Duck), Dr M. Marquiss (Grey Heron), Dr C. F. Mason (Lesser Whitethroat, Whitethroat, Garden Warbler and Blackcap), C. J. Mead (Stock Dove, Sand Martin and Pied Flycatcher), Dr D. Moss (Goldcrest), Dr I. Newton (Sparrowhawk, Little Owl, Goldfinch and Linnet), Dr D. Norman (Chaffinch), Dr M. A. Ogilvie (Mute Swan and Canada Goose), K. C. Osborne (Great Crested Grebe), Dr I. J. Patterson (Shelduck), Dr S. M. Percival (Barn, Tawny and Little Owls), S. J. Petty (Tawny Owl), Dr G. R. Potts (Grey and Red-legged Partridges), Dr R. P. Prŷs-Jones (Yellowhammer and Reed Bunting), N. J. Riddiford (Grasshopper Warbler), Dr P. A. Robertson (Pheasant), Dr D. C. Seel (Meadow Pipit), M. Shrubb (Lapwing, Turtle Dove and Collared Dove), Dr K. W. Smith (Curlew, Redshank, Green Woodpecker, Great Spotted Woodpecker, Lesser Spotted Woodpecker and Nuthatch), Dr D. W. Snow (Blackbird, Song Thrush and Mistle Thrush), R. Spencer (Hobby, Quail and Black Redstart), Dr T. J. Stowe (Redstart, Pied Flycatcher and Spotted Flycatcher), Dr J. D. Summers-Smith (House and Tree Sparrows), Dr I. R. Taylor (Barn Owl), Dr D. K. Thomas (Sedge and Reed Warblers), Dr P. S. Thompson (Siskin), Dr S. J. Tyler (Grey Wagtail and Dipper), Dr A. Village (Kestrel), K. E. Vinicombe (Little Grebe), Dr J. B. Wood (Yellow Wagtail) and Dr D. W. Yalden (Common Sandpiper).

Acknowledgements to artists

The cover design and painting are by Robert Gillmor, to whom we are very grateful. We also thank the following artists who provided vignettes to accompany the species texts:

Norman Arlott (Grey Wagtail), Kevin Baker (Wood Warbler), the late Leslie Baker (Blue and Coal Tits), Nik Borrow (Dunnock), Hilary Burn (Tree Sparrow, Hawfinch, Yellowhammer, Greenfinch and Bullfinch), Steve Cull (Robin and Magpie), Caroline Dudley (Pied Wagtail and Chaffinch), Robert Gillmor

xi

(Grasshopper Warbler), Peter Hobson (Redstart), Rob Hume (Red-legged Partridge and Garden Warbler), Alan Harris (Grey Heron, Sparrowhawk, Yellow Wagtail, Lesser Whitethroat, Blackcap, Chiffchaff, Carrion Crow, Raven, Siskin and Corn Bunting), Rodney Ingram (Buzzard), Mike Langman (Snipe, Whitethroat, Goldcrest, Woodcock, Little Owl, Sand Martin, Nightingale, Whinchat, Willow Tit and Redpoll), Anthony Murray (Quail, Curlew and Sedge Warbler), Brian Slade (Linnet), Julian Smith (Skylark), Barry Stuart (Black Redstart, Spotted Flycatcher and Reed Bunting), Thelma K. Sykes (Shelduck, Teal, Mallard, Moorhen, Oystercatcher, Ringed Plover, Lapwing, Collared Dove, Dipper, Wren, Stonechat, Wheatear, Blackbird, Mistle Thrush, Long-tailed Tit, Great Tit, Nuthatch and Jackdaw), David Thelwell (Little Grebe, Hobby, Turtle Dove, Cuckoo, Barn Owl, Kingfisher, Treecreeper and Rook), the late Charles Tunnicliffe (Pied Flycatcher), Donald Watson (Grey Partridge, Coot, Tree Pipit and Meadow Pipit) and Ian Willis (Common Crossbill, Kestrel, Tawny Owl, Green Woodpecker and Lesser Spotted Woodpecker).

The illustrations by Mike Langman, other than that of Snipe, are reproduced from the Devon breeding bird atlas by kind permission of Humphrey Sitters.

Vignettes for Great Crested Grebe, Mute Swan, Canada Goose, Mandarin Duck, Tufted Duck, Pheasant, Redshank, Common Sandpiper, Stock Dove, Woodpigeon, Great Spotted Woodpecker, Swallow, House Martin, Ring Ouzel, Song Thrush, Reed Warbler, Marsh Tit, Jay, Starling, House Sparrow and Goldfinch are by Steve Carter.

John Marchant, Bob Hudson, Steve Carter and Phil Whittington
Tring, 14th February 1990

1.
The monitoring schemes

Bird monitoring and surveillance

Birdwatching is growing rapidly as a pastime in Britain. While for many birdwatchers seeing and identifying a bird is an end in itself, for others it is the first stage in a process which may lead to advances in scientific knowledge and to the greater efficiency of bird conservation. A great deal of such ornithological study consists of surveys aimed, directly or indirectly, towards bird monitoring.

While it is still possible for single observers, working on their own, to produce useful advances, the value and significance of a study is much increased where results from several different observers can be brought together. Much valuable co-operative work is carried out on a local or county scale, for example by bird observatories and by the county and regional bird clubs. On a wider geographical scale, a number of schemes exist in which observers' efforts made on an individual or regional basis are co-ordinated nationally or even internationally, usually by paid staff. In Britain, well-known examples include the periodic BTO Atlas projects, which have recorded the distribution of both breeding and wintering birds. There are also several current and long-running programmes which measure annual changes in bird numbers, operated or supported by the BTO, the NCC, the Wildfowl & Wetlands Trust (WWT), the Royal Society for the Protection of Birds (RSPB), and *British Birds* (an independent monthly journal). Because the net is spread so wide, nearly all British birdwatchers participate in or help with some aspect of monitoring at some time or another. There are however many young people who have come to birdwatching recently through an interest in rarities, and have yet to begin contributing to their hobby in this way: we would encourage them to do so.

In its broadest sense, bird monitoring can be defined as any recording of statistics, for example about bird numbers or distribution, that gives a baseline against which later work can be measured. It is essential to the concept that there are repeat surveys which give a temporal component to the study, and that the study areas and methods are clearly defined. A more sophisticated definition of "monitoring", employed for example at the NCC, takes the concept of measuring against a standard and adds the stipulations that the aims of the project should also be clearly defined and that thresholds should be established beyond which action should be taken by conservation bodies. Such action may take the form of immediate conservation measures or further research into the causes of the observed changes. The related term "survey" implies a short time-scale for a project, while schemes that describe changes over time can be defined as "surveillance". Thus, surveys which are continuous or repeated using the same methods become surveillance, and surveillance is an essential part of monitoring.

The NCC is the government body responsible for promoting nature conservation in Great Britain. It was set up as the Nature Conservancy in 1949, and took its present form in 1973 under the Nature Conservancy Act. Under the Wildlife & Countryside Acts 1981-1985, the NCC has broad responsibilities which include the protection of bird species. It discharges some of its responsibilities in this area by funding or sponsoring schemes which keep track of bird populations in Great Britain as a whole. These include the BTO's Common Birds Census, Waterways Bird Survey, Nest Records Scheme and Atlas projects, the National Wildfowl Counts co-ordinated by the Wildfowl & Wetlands Trust, and the work of the Rare Breeding Birds Panel (RBBP) which is sponsored by the BTO, the RSPB and *British Birds*, as well as by the NCC. Some projects, such as the Seabird Monitoring Programme, are run by NCC staff.

The members and staff of the BTO have, since the organisation was founded in 1933, always given bird monitoring a high priority. With its national membership and with the support of other active fieldworkers, the BTO has been well placed to carry out surveys on a national scale. While some schemes, like the long-running Birds of Estuaries Enquiry, collect data on wintering birds, most BTO work has concentrated on the breeding season. The origins of this book lie in national schemes aimed at monitoring the numbers of breeding birds, carried out by the members and staff of the BTO and funded largely by the NCC.

The value of bird surveys

We need to know about bird population changes partly to satisfy scientific curiosity about the biology of particular species, and partly because as conservationists we may wish to try to influence those changes.

Public awareness of "green" issues, such as the health of species and ecosystems and the way these affect the quality of human life, has increased greatly in recent years. Pressure on government to pursue policies which benefit or are least harmful to wildlife has probably never been stronger, but such pressure is only likely to be effective where it can be backed up by sound scientific evidence about how and why populations are changing. For birds, the BTO can provide such evidence through its monitoring schemes.

Of course, people who enjoy the countryside differ enormously in their ornithological interests and abilities, and in their awareness of variations in the abundance of different bird species. However, a change such as the decreasing prominence of Song Thrushes in the dawn chorus is a loss to everyone who notices birdsong, even to someone who cannot put a name to any of the different species. Many people with only a passing interest in birds know the Spotted Flycatcher and that these occur much less frequently now, if at all, in the garden. The burgeoning of Magpies is a common topic of comment, even among non-birdwatchers and in the press. More active and more knowledgeable birdwatchers will be aware of many more subtle changes in bird populations, just by casual observations in their own areas. But all such personal observations must be backed up by firm evidence, from population monitoring, if they are to influence local or national government.

Why the breeding season?

Counting birds in the breeding season is a particularly efficient way of keeping track of the overall populations both of resident birds and of those avian visitors only here for the summer. Breeding birds are relatively stationary over a fixed period – because they have to leave their eggs somewhere! – and so counts made can be referred closely to a defined area. Repeat counts can be made of the identical area in the same or subsequent seasons. The number of breeding pairs of some species can be counted very accurately, or with known accuracy, by counting all active nests in a predetermined census area. Also, breeding populations can be considered as demographic units which have a relatively constant structure (because breeding adults at least are generally site-faithful between seasons) and where it is meaningful to talk of reproductive and survival rates. This is often not the case for wintering populations.

Birds can be surveyed in the winter months, but they tend to be distributed much less evenly than in the breeding season, and may gather in large loose flocks which can be very difficult to count (see Tucker, in press). Some species are much more mobile in winter: the location of flocks may vary from hour to hour and from day to day. Winter counts are much influenced by the local availability of food, the ambient weather, and to the relative success of the previous breeding season. In addition, populations of many resident species, such as Blackbird, Chaffinch and Starling, are supplemented heavily but to an unquantified and probably highly variable degree by Continental immigrants, while many species generally considered to be resident are actually partially migratory. Winter visitors can only be surveyed at that season, if we are to keep track of their British numbers at all. Surveys of resident species in winter would be very difficult to interpret in the absence of comparative data on breeding season numbers or productivity.

Inevitably, migration counts such as those collected at bird observatories suffer from variability introduced by the weather, by the behaviour of most species in flocking together to produce either falls of migrants or mass flights which pass undetected, and in autumn by the productivity of the preceding breeding season (see Darby 1985). However, they can be valuable supplements to monitoring of breeding birds, as for Blackcap (Langslow 1978), or help to indicate changes in status of otherwise poorly studied species, such as Grasshopper Warbler (Riddiford 1983). Counts of birds on spring migration can indicate major population changes rather earlier than censuses in the breeding season.

An introduction to the CBC

The Common Birds Census (CBC) is the main scheme by which populations of common breeding birds are monitored in the United Kingdom, and is one of the longest-running of BTO/NCC schemes. The CBC relies for its operation on the volunteer fieldwork of BTO members, and on funding from the NCC for staff and facilities at BTO headquarters. It measures changes in bird populations between years, by means of annual censuses of all species holding territory on particular plots of land. Between 200 and 300 plots are covered each year, and more than 40,000 territories are mapped in a typical season. Carrying out a census demands an appreciable amount of time for fieldwork and analysis, but CBC observers enjoy being able to put their bird finding and identification skills to good purpose, and in particular the intimacy they have, increasingly with each year's census, with the census plot and its birds.

The initial impetus for setting up this scheme came from widespread concern over habitat degradation on farmland and especially over the effects of agricultural pesticides following the serious poisoning of wildlife that occurred in the 1950s (*e.g.*Prestt 1970). Organochlorine seed dressings killed many seed-eating and predatory birds then, but in the absence of a national monitoring scheme the importance of the observed kills to bird populations could not be properly quantified. The Nature Conservancy (as it was then) resolved to set up a scheme which would measure both the natural background variation in bird numbers and the extent of any future reductions as a result of pesticide kills or habitat change.

3

Number of species

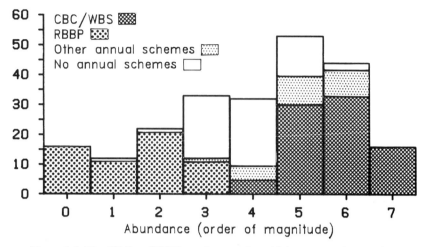

Figure 1.1. The CBC and WBS monitor species with between a thousand and ten million breeding pairs in Britain (orders 4-7), and are thus complementary to the work of the Rare Breeding Birds Panel. Other annual schemes are the Heronries Census and the Seabird Monitoring Programme.

For 75 of the commonest species on plots, the CBC produces a long-term and continuing population index which tracks changes in numbers on a national basis. In monitoring common landbirds in this way, the CBC is complementary to the work of the Rare Breeding Birds Panel and the NCC's Seabird Monitoring Programme (see Figure 1.1). The RBBP collects and publishes data on population sizes of all the rarer species breeding in the United Kingdom, mainly through the co-operation of county bird recorders, while the Seabird Monitoring Programme covers the common colonial seabirds. Only just over a quarter of species fall through the net of annual surveillance, and some of these, for example Peregrine, Little Ringed Plover and Nightingale, have been studied at longer intervals by special BTO surveys. While the word "common" is part of the name of the scheme, and only the more common species provide sufficient data for an index, the CBC in fact covers *all* bird species found on plots, including rarities.

Plots now accepted into the CBC fall into one of two broad habitat categories, farmland and woodland. "Farmland" plots can be any type of arable, horticultural or grazing land except unenclosed sheepwalk, but must be at least 40 and preferably 60 hectares in area. Small woods and copses are treated as integral parts of the plot, but must not exceed 10% of the plot area. "Woodland" plots include all kinds of seminatural broad-leaved and mixed woodlands, but exclude parkland, scrubby heathland and even-aged plantations of conifers. At least 10 hectares are required. Plots of each kind must be reasonably representative of the farmland or woodland in the locality. However, these criteria were not established until 1983, and plots started before 1984 do not always fit them precisely. Plots of other habitats, such as wetlands, suburban parks and moorlands, have also been accepted into the scheme, particularly before 1984. These all fall into a third habitat category, and are termed "special" plots.

A brief outline of the CBC method is given below. Because the CBC uses the method of territory mapping, it also gathers detailed information on the sizes and positions of breeding territories. Observers send habitat information, also in map form, on an annual basis. Censusing by the mapping method thus gives information in two main areas of interest: changes in breeding numbers (see the main systematic section of Chapter 4), and territory distribution in relation to habitat (*e.g.*Fuller & Whittington 1987, Hudson 1988). The latter aspect is of great value to research in various habitat-oriented and species-oriented areas, but falls mainly outside the scope of the present book.

Origins and early development of the CBC

After limited pilot work in 1960, the CBC began in the 1961 season. The first announcement to BTO members appeared in *Bird Study* of March 1961 (vol 8: 43), under the heading "Trust Aided Investigations", and is reproduced in part below.

"BREEDING SEASON CENSUS OF COMMON BIRDS
The object of this enquiry, which is being made at the request of the Nature Conservancy, is to investigate the status of about a dozen common species *in a variety of typical habitats*. The information is required primarily as a basis for studying the effect on normal bird population of toxic chemicals, in the form of sprays or seed dressings, and it is intended that the census should be continued for several years. So little pure census work of areas, as distinct from species, has been done in recent years that the results obtained should not only be of interest in themselves but should also be of value in studying the quantitative effect of environmental factors on bird populations . . .
The basis of the census will be singing males, the aim being a complete census and NOT a transect. An absolute minimum of four visits between 1 April and 15 June is required, and six visits should be made if at all possible.
Anyone willing to assist with the hope of being able to carry on for not less than three years is invited to write to the Secretary for full details which will be available later in the month. Help from clubs, schools or societies with good prospects of continuity of observations would be welcome.
This enquiry is regarded as being of considerable importance and with the financial support of the Nature Conservancy for this purpose the Trust hopes to appoint shortly an Assistant Secretary, one of whose duties will be to act as organiser of the scheme under the direction of the Scientific Advisory Committee."

Those who responded to this notice received with their set of instructions a strongly worded letter of encouragement from the BTO President, C.A.Norris. He pointed out that this was "not just another BTO request for information" but a full-scale inquiry of vital importance as part of a system to give early warning of adverse effects of new chemicals used in agriculture, horticulture or forestry:

"Detailed counts provide data against which change can be measured and the time has arrived when all of us with a real interest in ornithology must learn to count birds in a way which will have lasting value."

5

As described in a further *Bird Study* announcement in September 1961, now under the heading of "Permanent Enquiries" (vol 8: 158), the response in 1961 had been only moderate. About 27 plots had been surveyed, of which only 18 were on farmland, and half of these were below the requested minimum size of 200 acres. Thus, the 1961 season represented something of a false start.

The instructions which had been given for 1961, and the results for that year, provoked considerable debate in the CBC subcommittee of the BTO's Scientific Advisory Committee prior to the start of the 1962 breeding season. Instructions on how observers should arrive at their estimates of bird numbers were very brief and rather ambiguous (see Chapter 2), but discussion centred around the choice of habitats to be included, the nature of plot boundaries, and the species to be covered in 1962. The paramount issue of the day was still toxic chemicals, and so it was thought desirable to concentrate observer effort as far as possible onto farmland plots, including orchards.

An important development early in 1963 was the formation of a Populations Section within the BTO, and the transfer of Kenneth Williamson from the post of Migration Research Officer to head the new department. Support for the farmland side of the scheme was so encouraging in 1963 that further expansion in 1964 was channelled into other habitat types. Woodland studies in particular received a powerful boost. Plots of habitats other than farmland or woodland, termed "special" plots, were also welcomed, and included sewage-farms, wetlands, industrial and suburban areas, and moorland.

In the 1964 season, Ken introduced to the CBC a mapping census technique, based on that used by the Swedish ornithologist Anders Enemar (1959), in place of the previous ill-defined counting method (Williamson & Homes 1964).

The CBC today

The CBC was able to continue and consolidate the work carried out in its initial seasons, and is heading for its thirtieth season in 1990 as this book is published. Since 1961 it has built into a huge data-set, with about 7070 censuses made on over 1370 different plots by 1988. Through the CBC, the BTO stores data on about 1.4 million birds' territories. For probably over a million of these, we also hold records of their estimated position, to within a few metres, in relation to topographical features and the habitats locally available. These data have been used in over 400 publications by 1989 (see Appendix 6). Some have also been used in planning enquiries and for other purposes not resulting in a published paper.

Since 1978, computers have played an increasing role in CBC data analysis. Archiving and checking of plot data and territory counts on computer was completed in 1989. Computerised records for each census include territory counts, area, altitude, grid reference, number of visits made, total number of hours spent censusing, a quality code, and the presence or absence of four levels of habitat information. Further data are also stored on a plot basis. The positions of territories are not computerised: initial investigations showed that because of the time needed to digitise the data this would not be a cost-effective method for routine processing of CBC data (O'Connor & Fuller 1984).

Figure 1.2 shows how the numbers of farmland, woodland and "special" plots in 1988 relate to those in previous seasons. After its slow start, the farmland census built up rapidly to well over a hundred plots. Numbers of woodland and "special" plots grew more slowly, as primary effort was directed towards maintaining the farmland sample, and lagged behind until the late 1970s. All three samples fell during the 1980s.

6

Number of plots

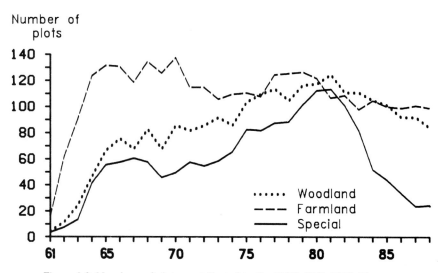

Figure 1.2. Numbers of plots contributed to the CBC, 1961-1988. New plots of farmland and woodland are now needed to reverse the current decline and allow monitoring to continue strongly into the 1990s.

For "special" plots, this was mostly as deliberate BTO policy, following a technical review of the CBC in 1983: it was decided that the limited staff resources were better used in concentrating on the two major habitat categories (O'Connor & Fuller 1984). The recent falls in both the farmland and woodland samples are not welcome, and we are currently very keen to receive offers of new plots of both these habitat types. About a dozen new plots of each category are needed each year just to maintain the samples at their present levels; and if samples shrink further, then so will the lists of species the CBC is able to monitor.

There is a long and successful history of bird population surveillance in the United Kingdom. However, there is a continuing need for new data in relation to environmental changes, and each additional year of census work adds to the value of the increasingly long-term data-set. Thus, it is imperative that the programme continues with at least its present strength for as long as fieldworkers and funding bodies are prepared to support it. Who knows what changes may occur in bird numbers in response to the "greenhouse effect" and continued growth of human pressure in the 21st century! Indeed, expansion of coverage in terms of species, habitats and geographical areas is of high priority, perhaps by means of additional methods such as point counts or transects.

The methods of the CBC

It is the essence of successful monitoring that the methods of fieldwork and analysis must be standardised and fully documented, so that repeat recording can be strictly comparable with the earlier work. Such strict comparability of results has been a feature of the CBC since 1964, and earlier with some individual observers, but subject to a few minor limitations described in Chapter 2.

The mapping method introduced in 1964 was first described to observers in

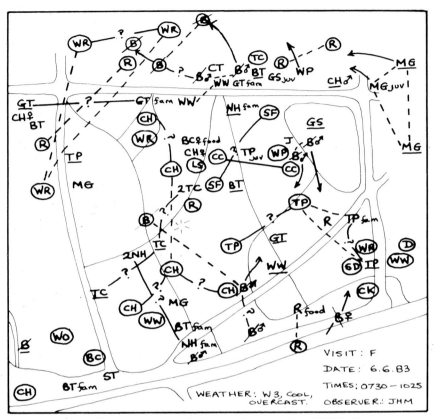

Figure 1.3. Part of a completed visit map for a woodland CBC, slightly reduced from the 1:2500 scale used in the field. It was a productive visit and all parts of the map are crowded with registrations. The dotted lines will be particularly helpful in the later analysis of territories. Blackbird registrations have already been copied to the species map (Figure 1.4) and cancelled with a light stroke of the pen.

cyclostyled instructions, of which the earliest dated version surviving at BTO headquarters was issued in January 1968 (Anon 1968). This went through a number of imprints, at which small improvements were made. In September 1983, following a technical review of the CBC earlier that year (O'Connor & Fuller 1984), the instructions appeared as a twelve-page printed booklet (Marchant 1983*b*). This incorporated both the instructions to observers and the guidelines to analysts, which had previously been an unpublished document internal to BTO headquarters (Williamson *et al* 1968). Although much longer and more detailed than the previous versions, they were effectively a documentation of what had been standard practice in fieldwork and analysis since at least 1968.

The basis of the method is a complete census of birds during the breeding season, March to July, on a defined area of land – the "plot". The observer makes a standard number of visits, labelled sequentially with letters, on each of which all birds seen or heard are mapped as accurately as possible on a large-scale map, called the "visit map". The CBC uses the 1:2500 scale, or 25 inches to the mile, at which one centimetre represents just 25 metres, and requests that ten visits should be made each year. When the visits have been completed, the observer transfers all the information obtained about each species onto a separate map, the "species map". Registrations on the species maps fall more or less neatly into clusters indicating the activity of particular birds or pairs throughout the season. The maps can then be "analysed" to assess the number of territories present.

A section of a real visit map is presented in Figure 1.3 as an example of the CBC mapping method in action. The position of each bird is represented by its BTO two-letter species code (Marchant & Lack 1984). Examples of these are CH for Chaffinch, WR for Wren, R for Robin, and MG for Magpie: the same codes are used in the Waterways Bird Survey and other BTO schemes, as well as by outside organisations such as the WWT and the RSPB. The activity of each bird is also represented, by a set of codes which are given in full in the CBC instructions. The ring around many of the letter-codes in Figure 1.3 shows that the bird in question was in song; an underline indicates that it was calling; arrows and solid lines indicate observed movements; a question-marked solid line represents a likely but unobserved movement; and the dashed or dotted line, which assumes great importance when the map is analysed, confirms that two different individuals were involved.

The blank outline maps on which the registrations are plotted are provided to the observers by headquarters. They show enough detail to allow the observer to be sure of his or her position, but not so much that the registrations need to be displaced. Also recorded on the visit map is the visit letter (in this case F), the date, times of observation, and a note of the weather. The Blackbird registrations, plotted as B, have been struck through because they have already been transferred to the species map (Figure 1.4).

Figure 1.4 shows the Blackbird species map for the same plot and year. The positions and activity symbols are exactly as on the visit maps, but each entry of the species code for Blackbird (B) has been replaced by the appropriate visit letter, A to L. Those Blackbird registrations made on visit F thus appear as F, not B, on the species map. Once the species map has been completed, the map can be analysed. This has already been done in this case, and a total of six Blackbird clusters has been detected. Some of these are partly beyond the plot boundary, but in the CBC all such clusters are counted as belonging to the plot, in order to maximise the index samples. The inclusion of these edge territories does, however, make density estimation from CBC plots less than straightforward (see Marchant 1981, Hudson & Marchant 1984). By including all edge clusters, the CBC differs from the international standard for the mapping method (International Bird Census Committee 1969).

A cluster is in general a spatially distinct group of registrations in which not more than one male and one female (or two adults) are represented per visit. Depending on the biology of the species, it usually relates directly to a breeding territory (see Chapter 2). Ideal clusters show a series of registrations of territorial behaviour spanning most of the visits, and dotted lines radiating out to neighbouring clusters. In practice, a small degree of duplication of males and females (or adults) is to be expected, particularly for species such as Dunnock and Long-tailed Tit which do not always hold territory in pairs, and for smaller birds like the tits and the *Phylloscopus* warblers which are mobile but inconspicuous and often move unseen.

Clusters are often difficult to differentiate and may sometimes overlap. For inconspicuous species, there may be few registrations per cluster and dotted lines may be lacking altogether. Thus, despite the existence of standard guidelines for species

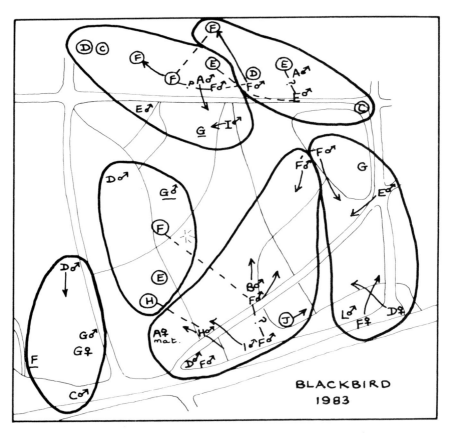

Figure 1.4. The Blackbird species map from the same census as the example visit map (Figure 1.3). The map has already been analysed, and six territories found on this portion of the plot.

map analysis, it is open to some subjectivity in interpretation. To minimise this problem, the final analysis of territories is always performed by a small number of specialist staff at BTO headquarters.

The result is a series of maps, for each plot, species and season, showing the numbers and positions of each territory or cluster detected. The total numbers of clusters on each map are the basis of the index calculations and population monitoring.

The choice of census method

It is widely accepted that the mapping method as practised by the CBC is the most accurate practical way of counting breeding birds on an area of land. It has often been the standard against which other, quicker methods such as point counts or transects have been compared (although the validity of such an approach is questionable). Mapping of individually colour-marked birds would give a better measure, but would be excessively time-consuming for most observers, and impracticable for those species

10

which are difficult to catch. A complete count of all active nests is another approach, but is not generally practicable because of the time that would be needed and the unusual nest-finding skills that would be required of the observers. It is of course a different measure from the CBC cluster total, which includes unmated and non-breeding territorial males, as well as those territories which contained active nests. In any case, a nest count is not straightforward to interpret, owing to the problems of separating late-starting nests from replacements of those lost at an early stage of the nesting cycle (see Chapter 2).

A comparison of mapping and nest-finding on farmland was attempted by BTO staff in 1965 (Snow 1965). Nests found showed the mapping censuses to be a good or an adequate indicator of nesting numbers for fourteen of the species investigated, but poor or very poor for six more. Thus it would be unwise to treat the results of CBC censuses as if they were accurate counts of nesting birds.

Mapping is a highly labour-intensive method for monitoring population changes. Point counts or transects are used in most other countries which operate national bird monitoring schemes, partly because there is insufficient manpower for mapping to be a possibility. These methods require far less effort per sampling unit on the part of the observer, and less input from headquarters staff. More observers feel able to take part and more contributions, each consisting of ten or more sampling units, can be dealt with by the organisers. Point counts can be carried out all year and in all kinds of habitats. However, mapping produces data of much higher quality than those from point counts. With more visits to each sampling unit, and hours rather than minutes spent on fieldwork, it is far better buffered than the other methods against environmental variations, for example in weather and in timing of visits in relation to the birds' breeding cycles. With mapping, the relationships between counts and the numbers of birds present are far better understood.

For population monitoring, there is a trade-off between the accuracy of the data that mapping provides, and the much larger samples that can be obtained using point counts. There is also the possibility that, with point counts, the representativeness of the population indices could be improved. For studies of community parameters and the relationships of birds with their habitats, the mapping method produces much more accurate information than is possible with either point counts or transects.

The Waterways Bird Survey

The Waterways Bird Survey (WBS) covers linear waterways: rivers, streams and canals. It surveys the populations of waterside birds, and measures both their use of different types of waterway and their relationship with particular habitat features (see Carter 1989b). Like the CBC it is a mapping census, but it differs in that it is linear and rather akin to a belt transect (Figure 1.5). It also differs in that the list of species covered is restricted to those which are mostly riparian, plus Grasshopper Warbler and Whitethroat, and in that 1:10,000 or 1:10,560 (6 inches to the mile) outline maps are used (Taylor 1982). The average length of a plot is about 4½ km. Because the plots are small and so few species are covered, it is a much simpler and less time-consuming census than a farmland or woodland CBC.

The scheme began in 1974, following pilot work by the Sheffield Bird Study Group the previous year. The origins of the WBS lie with the BTO's "Birds and Freshwater" conference at Swanwick in Derbyshire in February 1974, at which overwhelming support was expressed for the idea of the pilot waterways survey becoming a national scheme. Enthusiasm was such that well over 400 requests for instructions had been processed by May of that year. The main reasons for setting up the WBS were to

11

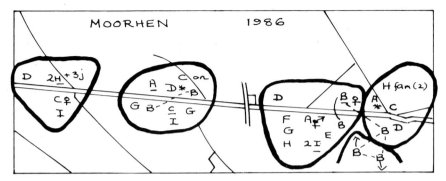

Figure 1.5. Part of an analysed species map from the WBS, reproduced at a slightly smaller scale than the 1:10,000 used in the field. The WBS is a linear mapping census with methods generally similar to those of the CBC.

gather information on the population changes of a number of common riparian birds for which CBC information was too sparse to be useful, and to document bird populations in a habitat greatly at risk. As pointed out at that conference, threats to birds on waterways included pollution by agricultural run-off or from industry, the increasing use of algicides and aquatic herbicides to clear vegetation, and increases in human disturbance, particularly by angling and boating (Smith 1975). Management of lowland rivers by River Authorities had involved deepening and straightening of the waterway, often with the removal of trees, shrubs and low vegetation from both banks to allow access to heavy machinery. The effects of such harsh management practices on birds were undoubtedly severe, but had not been documented, and so there was no hard evidence on which conservation bodies such as the RSPB and the County Wildlife Trusts could fight cases.

Initially the WBS was purely a BTO initiative, dependent on the enthusiasm of Kenneth Williamson and volunteer members such as Ben and Ann Bailey for its organisation and analysis, but it is now funded by the NCC. The list of publications from the scheme is growing steadily (Marchant & Carter, in prep). Since 1974, over 300 different stretches of waterways have been surveyed, from Ross & Cromarty in the north to Devon in the south. Typically about 100 are censused in any one year, and this sample gives sufficient data to enable 19 species to be indexed. For 15 of these, a comparative index is also available from the CBC, albeit generally based on fewer data. Up to 1979, some species for which neither the CBC nor the WBS samples were considered adequate were monitored by an index combining CBC and WBS counts (Marchant & Hyde 1979, 1980*a*), but this practice was subsequently discontinued because of uncertainty about its validity. All of the species covered previously by a combined index now have either a CBC or WBS index, although for Grasshopper Warbler the population had declined too far by 1987 for any census index to continue.

As with the CBC, the WBS is not solely concerned with following the changes in bird numbers from year to year. The mapping technique also allows investigation of the nature of bird distribution along rivers and canals, and the factors which affect it. Regional variations in territory density of waterways birds have already been documented for the early years of the scheme, as have the influences on bird density of waterway altitude and gradient (Marchant & Hyde 1980*b*). WBS data can aid site conservation by showing whether an individual waterway is especially valuable as a bird habitat at a regional or national level. They also provide a means of contrasting population changes in different regions or habitats, for example managed and unmanaged rivers (Marchant & Hyde 1980*b*, Taylor 1984). WBS information has helped the RSPB to prepare material for training Water Authority personnel. An RSPB film, "The Vital River" (1982), illustrates many of the techniques which are being developed to integrate the needs of wildlife with those of river management. Lewis & Williams (1984) have documented these techniques in detail, with reference to case studies.

The WBS is currently operating below its target number of plots, as is the CBC. Offers of new river and canal plots are always welcomed, particularly if they are in a poorly represented part of the country, or can provide a case study of the effects of watercourse management on birds.

Integrated Population Monitoring

Taking the more rigid definition of "monitoring", and the accepted hierarchy of "survey", "surveillance" and "monitoring", the CBC and WBS are schemes for surveillance, not monitoring, of bird population changes. Further, no schemes for monitoring in its sophisticated sense are yet in operation for bird populations.

With the support of the NCC, the BTO is currently establishing an Integrated Population Monitoring programme, which will combine data from the CBC and WBS, the Nest Records Scheme and the Ringing Scheme (including the Constant Effort Sites scheme) to produce ongoing population models for a number of common breeding species (Baillie, in press, *a*, *b*). Measuring changes in the population levels of common birds, as by the CBC and WBS, is an essential part of the Integrated Population Monitoring programme. Population trends detected by the CBC and WBS can be dovetailed with data on annual productivity, furnished by the Nest Records Scheme, and mortality data from bird ringing to give a year-round picture of how the population of a particular species works. Where the population of a species is changing in size, such a model will allow identification of the stage of the bird's life-cycle which is giving rise to the change. Further, it should eventually be possible to obtain indications of whether changes are natural or induced by man, and to establish realistic thresholds where action for conservation becomes desirable or necessary to safeguard a particular species.

2.
Indexing population levels

The nature of an index

Data from the CBC and WBS concerning bird population changes are usually displayed in the form of an index. An index is, in the present sense, a numerical scale by which the size of the bird population in a particular season can be compared with some baseline figure. For the species covered, there can be no firm baseline in terms of the real number of birds in the population. Instead, an arbitrary baseline figure of 100 is used for one of the years of the sequence, termed the "datum year". Index values are assigned to all other years according to how the population then relates to that in the datum year: if the population were half that of the datum year, then the index value would be 50, and if it were triple the new index value would be 300.

Index values are easily misinterpreted, and it is important that the pitfalls associated with their interpretation should be avoided. In particular, none of the above figures – 50, 100 or 300 – tells us anything about how many birds there are in the population. The index values are measures of the relative abundance of the species, but the relationship they bear to the actual size of the population is unknown and is different for every index. Thus, the index value has no meaning except when compared with other values in the same index sequence. Comparisons cannot be made between species in the size of their index values. Nothing is conveyed by index values about commonness or rarity: the rarest and the most abundant species have equal index values (100) in the datum year, and in any other year that of the rare bird may equally be higher or lower than that of the common one. Similarly, comparisons of farmland and woodland index values for the same species cannot tell us in which habitat the species is more abundant. The index value for a preferred habitat, for example woodland as opposed to farmland in the case of Goldcrest, may be either higher or lower than the index value for the same species in its secondary habitat. Numerical comparison of index values in the two habitats is entirely dependent on which year has been chosen arbitrarily as the datum. By their very nature, index values for different habitats or species will tend to converge approaching the datum year and diverge thereafter.

The indices are always presented on semilogarithmic graphs, log index against year. This is mainly because population changes are generally multiplicative processes rather than additive ones, and thus more easily studied on logarithmic plots (see Williamson 1972). With the logarithmic plots, the slope of any year-to-year percentage change is independent of the index values themselves: a 50% decrease from an index of 50 to one of 25 has the same slope as one from 600 to 300, and indeed they are equally important in biological terms. The year chosen as the datum becomes irrelevant. A change of datum year does not alter the shape of the graph at all, but it could do so very markedly if a linear scale were being used, and perhaps alter the apparent nature of the population trend. Zero of course never appears on the log index scale, because the log of zero does not exist.

Throughout the book, all index graphs have the same scale factors on both axes, so that it is valid to compare the slopes of year-to-year changes and of long-term trends both between and within species. When comparing different index graphs for the same species, it is sometimes possible to separate "preferred" and "suboptimal" habitats: in

14

preferred habitats, both increases and decreases in population trends tend to have shallower slopes than in suboptimal ones (Williamson & Batten 1977). This is because the preferred habitats are more likely to be fully occupied during a phase of increase, so that the extra birds spill over into suboptimal habitats, while during decrease there is net movement from suboptimal habitats to fill vacancies that arise in the preferred habitats.

How the indices are calculated

There are three main ways in which an index can be constructed from data such as the CBC and WBS provide:

1. *A simple method.* A simple index compares a parameter such as total species numbers or species density in each of the years under review, taking each year individually. For the figures to be sufficiently comparable, they should be taken only from those plots covered in all the years in question.
2. *A chain method.* This uses more information than a simple method. In a chain index, data from each plot are paired with those from the same plots in the previous season, and the counts summed across all pairs to produce an overall estimate of percentage change. This estimate is applied to the previous year's index value.
3. *The Mountford method.* This uses still more information than the chain method, by pairing each year's data not just with the immediately preceding year but with every previous year for which comparable data are available for the same plot (Mountford 1982, 1985).

The simple method is not very powerful, and in any case is inappropriate for the long runs of data held by the CBC. In 1988, only three plots were still current that had been covered every year since 1962 (see Appendix 2). These individual efforts are laudable, but do not in themselves provide a basis for nationwide monitoring.

The CBC and WBS indices presented in this book are based on the chain method. Each year's intake of data, in the form of numbers of territories found on each plot, is assessed carefully to see whether the plot was censused with similar effort and efficiency to that employed in the previous year, and data which have no comparable equivalent in the previous year are removed from the analysis. The remaining data are paired with their previous-year equivalents, and both are summed across all contributing plots. The overall percentage change is calculated between the two year totals, and applied to the index value for the previous year to give the new index level. Because a degree of turnover is allowed for in the plots used in the chain index, such an index can be continued indefinitely, as long as observers are prepared to continue supporting the scheme. The main disadvantage with this method is that, particularly with long runs of data, the uncertainty about each year's percentage change may accumulate to produce a kind of "random walk" (see below). However, there is no evidence that such effects are large enough to disguise the real pattern of population change. The long-term stability of many of our indices, and the typically close comparability between CBC and WBS indices or between indices derived from subsets of the CBC data, suggest that "random walks" are not important, at least for the more abundant species.

The Mountford method decreases the uncertainty about each percentage change, and may thus reduce the likelihood of "random walk". It has not yet been used for CBC data, mainly because its statistical model fits only modest runs of years, and a good method of splicing these runs together has yet to be devised. Also, for its maximum efficiency it requires new checks of comparability between different years on the same census plots. Disadvantages of the Mountford method are that each year's new intake of data is liable to alter the values of the index for all preceding years, and that huge computing resources are needed to cope with long runs of data. It is more likely to provide a substantial improvement on the chain index where a species is relatively scarce and, particularly, tends to occur in very small numbers on each plot: these are the species for which confidence intervals are widest and chance effects are most likely to cause the chain index to show a troublesome degree of "random walk".

In the CBC and WBS, therefore, each annual set of percentage changes is estimated by comparing *year 1* and *year 2* totals from a paired sample of census plots. The year totals are the sums of all valid and comparable pairs of counts obtained in each of the two years. A real but abbreviated example from the farmland index is given below: numbers in the left-hand column are plot-codes.

SPECIES CH	1987	1988
009	3	3
125	17	16
159	18	27
257	24	33
318	10	12
522	12	11
557	46	46
630	6	9

Thus, according to the example, there were eight plots with Chaffinches where coverage in 1988 was comparable with that in 1987 (in fact there were 81). Chaffinches were stable at 3 pairs on plot 009, in Lincolnshire, and at 46 pairs on plot 557 in Co.Tyrone, but changed in various ways on the other plots. Overall, the year totals in this example were 136 and 157, and the percentage change of Chaffinches on farmland between 1987 and 1988 was +15%. This percentage would be applied to the 1987 index value to obtain the 1988 index, so that an index of 100 would become 115, and one of 150 would become 173 (to the nearest whole number). Confidence intervals around the percentage change are assessed by statistical procedures which take account of the variation in changes detected on individual census plots, but these procedures are presently under review and are not discussed further here for that reason. The results of year-to-year comparisons are published in annual reports (*e.g.*Marchant & Whittington 1989, Carter 1989c).

CBC indices are produced separately for farmland and woodland habitats. There is also an all-habitats index, designed especially for scarce species, in which data from farmland, woodland and "special" plots are combined in order to achieve a sufficient sample.

Revision of the index figures

The index values from which the graphs in this book are plotted are different from those published previously in CBC and WBS annual reports, and supersede the old values for all purposes. There are three reasons why the index values have changed: these are plot reselection, changes in the species coverage, and a change of datum year. For the WBS, the change in datum year has been the only change. For the CBC, the differences between the old and new index values are mostly rather small, aside from the change of datum year, and it is most unlikely that conclusions based on the old index data will require modification. Because various anomalies of CBC plot selection have now been removed, the new values must be regarded as being a more accurate representation of bird population changes than those published previously, even where reselection has resulted in a reduction in the number of plots contributing to the data.

Many small differences stem from a complete reselection of the plots used to calculate the index data. Reselection was part of a major review, just completed, of all CBC data relating to population monitoring. There were two primary reasons why reselection of the plots was necessary. First, the older comparisons included some data which would latterly have been discarded, and the selection was thus inconsistent. Second, a substantial number of plots had been moved between woodland, farmland and "special" categories during an earlier stage of the review, and the paired counts now needed to be transferred into the index calculations for the new habitat division. A secondary aim of reselection was to supplement the original samples of plots with a small number of well-conducted censuses which had previously been omitted from the index calculations simply because they had arrived too late to meet deadlines for the annual reports.

During reselection, plots were excluded from annual comparisons if there were fewer than six visits in either year, or if there had been a large change between the two seasons in the number of visits or in the number of hours spent on fieldwork. Irregularities in the way that visits and times had been recorded, and the complete absence of visit data for many plots during 1961-1964, meant that many cases had to be dealt with subjectively. We now believe, however, that there are no major differences in the selection procedure across years. It was not considered necessary to review the selection of WBS plots for the index calculations, because all such selections had been made since 1979 using current criteria.

In addition to removing all data for particular plots from the index comparisons, pairs of counts for particular species were also excluded where they were not comparable. The usual case of this was where the erection of nestboxes on a plot had artificially inflated the numbers of hole-nesters.

Index values also differ from those published previously in that more species are covered, and a slightly different range of species is covered by the farmland, woodland and all-habitats indices. The reason for this is that we have reassessed the lists of indices that can validly be constructed, in the light of the new sample sizes following plot reselection. Farmland and woodland indices have been constructed in all cases where there is a long continuous run of years with the number of plots contributing to the data not falling below 15. This is believed to be adequate to produce meaningful long-term trends, although the accuracy of individual year-to-year percentage changes may sometimes be rather low. In a few cases, a run of index values has been allowed to continue despite the sample dropping temporarily a little below 15 plots, in the expectation that the level of support for the CBC will rise in future seasons. An all-habitats index has been calculated on a similar basis, but only for species for which samples were inadequate for the calculation of separate farmland or woodland indices. For four species only – Sedge Warbler, Lesser Whitethroat, Goldfinch and Reed Bunting – the farmland index is contrasted with one based on a combination of woodland and "special" plots. This index has the advantage of being completely independent of the farmland one.

In all, CBC indices are presented for 79 species, as opposed to the 60 for which such data have been published in annual reports. However, four or more of the indices have terminated in or before 1988 because of the decreasing numbers of plots contributing data on the species concerned. Sadly, these include at least two species (Snipe and

17

Grasshopper Warbler) which are strongly in decline, and for which continued monitoring would be highly desirable.

The third reason for the new index values being different is that the datum year for all CBC indices has been altered to 1980. The previous datum year was 1966, but with exceptions for two species (Sparrowhawk and Collared Dove) that were too scarce to be indexed in that year. The new datum year is more relevant to recent population changes. It also facilitates comparison of CBC trends with those from the WBS, which did not begin to produce index data until 1974. The datum year for all WBS indices is also now 1980.

A comparison of the old and new samples of plots used for the three main indices is given by Marchant (in press). For farmland and woodland, samples have become smaller than previously in most years, partly because reclassification of plots has led to net movements of farms and woods into the "special" category, and partly because of the loss of those pairs of censuses no longer regarded as comparable. Owing to these reductions in sample sizes, some indices given previously for the years 1962-1965 have now been excluded. In other years, however, the sample sizes remain adequate to support all the indices published previously. The sample of "special" plots has grown much larger than before in most years of the CBC. It has, however, decreased considerably since 1983 (Figure 1.2): this follows the recommendation of the 1983 Technical Review Group that observers should no longer be encouraged to census "special" plots (O'Connor & Fuller 1984). This decision was taken principally to concentrate CBC resources more into the farmland and woodland habitats, and to reduce the proportion of staff time needed for territory analysis.

The reliability of the index data

Because the index values are always calculated in the way described, they are a consistent reflection of the count data as collected by CBC and WBS observers in the field and interpreted by the headquarters analysts. However, these count data, derived as they are from censuses of a very tiny fraction of the available habitat, are not necessarily an accurate representation of the number of territorial males of a particular species in the United Kingdom. Any detailed interpretation of index trends should take account of the biases introduced by four classes of factors: the plots, the birds, the observers, and the analysts. These factors are discussed under separate headings below, although there are many interactions between them.

The CBC methodology has been subjected to a great deal of scrutiny (see O'Connor & Marchant 1981, O'Connor & Fuller 1984). All these investigations have been generally supportive of the method and its operation in producing population indices, with the reservation that the plots fall short of being truly representative of United Kingdom farmland and woodland as a whole. Following plot reselection (see above), an even greater degree of confidence in the CBC indices is justified. However, the recent review has highlighted two areas where extra caution should be applied when interpreting the long-term trends: these are, first, the changes made to the methods between 1962 and 1965 and, second, problems of scale, particularly relating to species with large territories.

For various reasons, it is unwise to treat the CBC or WBS indices as accurate and precise measures of changes in the entire United Kingdom population of a species. This is not what they claim to be, although for some species they may be a close approximation. The CBC index for Meadow Pipit, for example, is likely to represent United Kingdom Meadow Pipits as a whole relatively poorly, because the majority of pairs nest in habitats and geographical regions beyond the CBC coverage. In contrast, the concentration of CBC plots in the south and east of Britain is ideal for monitoring a species like Turtle Dove which is largely confined to that geographical area.

The CBC indices measure population changes in only two broad categories of habitat, farmland and woodland, and exclude others which may hold substantial sections of the population for some of the species covered. Similarly, the WBS indices are restricted to the habitat alongside linear waterways. The CBC all-habitats index combines several habitat types, but neither does this index claim to be a representative measure of changes in the entire United Kingdom population of the species concerned, although in some cases it may be. The farmland, woodland and waterways indices are aimed at those habitats alone, although, where a high proportion of the population breeds in the habitat being sampled (for example Dipper on waterways), the data have wider applicability.

The census plots – sampling problems

Ideally, to design surveillance of farmland or woodland in the whole of the United Kingdom by the mapping method, plots should be carefully selected to be representative of those habitats and that geographical area. Turnover in the sample of plots should be strictly controlled so that plots new to the index calculations are exactly equivalent to those leaving. In practice, it is not possible for the BTO to carry out a scheme so rigidly defined. Census work is entirely voluntary: no funds are available which might be used to send observers to census particular plots remote from their homes, or to persuade unwilling landowners to allow access to their land. In the CBC and WBS, plots are selected by the observers themselves, from the areas which are accessible to them, and according to the guidelines set out in the census instructions. Offers are usually gratefully accepted by headquarters staff, provided in the case of CBCs that they fit the size, shape and habitat criteria set down for either farmland or woodland.

The result has been an uneven geographical distribution of census plots, and a distribution of habitats within the broad categories which is not necessarily representative of the United Kingdom as a whole, but which is probably fairly representative of the main areas from which the plots are drawn. A typical example of CBC plot distribution is shown in Figure 2.1. There is, and has always been, a strong bias towards centres of human population. However, it should be borne in mind that habitat suitable for plots of both farmland and woodland, as defined by the CBC, becomes scarce in upland and northern regions.

Habitat distribution within the two broad categories is harder to define. To determine the degree to which farmland CBC plots were representative of land types and farming land use, Fuller et al (1985) examined the CBC plots in relation to the Institute of Terrestrial Ecology's system of land classification (Bunce et al 1981a, b) and the agricultural statistics for 1966 and 1981, issued by the Ministry of Agriculture, Fisheries and Food and the Department of Agriculture and Fisheries for Scotland. Their conclusions were that sampling of land-class types was highly consistent from year to year, and that the CBC farmland sample was representative of lowland land classes throughout England, excluding the extreme north and southwest. In terms of land use and cropping, CBC plots reflected the agricultural statistics closely, particularly in southern and eastern England. No parallel study has yet been carried out for the woodland CBC.

However, while topography and cropping of farmland CBC plots may not differ from that of the landscape being sampled, at the scale Fuller et al investigated, it is difficult to refute the suggestion that at the more local scale observers choose to census

19

sites which are better for birds than randomly selected plots would be. A prairie farmland, with long walks along fencelines or stunted hedgerows might well be passed over in favour of an adjacent area with smaller fields, and perhaps copses and ponds, which the observer would find more interesting to cover. Indeed, some sites are known to be rather special, for example because they are part of nature reserves, or because they are managed with unusual sympathy for wildlife. As yet, there is no evidence that either year-to-year population changes or long-term trends on sites known to be special are in any way unusual. Even on such sites, bird populations will be influenced by the weather and by habitat changes in the surrounding region.

Further, if censusing stops on a sample plot because the habitat has been degraded, for example by felling of trees, house-building or removal of hedges, and does not include at least one year's data from the altered plot, the population indices will remain artificially high. Effectively, the index will monitor the population level, not in

Figure 2.1. Distribution of farmland and woodland CBC plots in a typical year (1988). Farms are represented by spots, and woods by triangles. Relatively few census plots lie in the west and north of Britain.

the countryside as a whole, but in a shrinking area of prime habitat. This does not seem to be an overriding consideration, however: at most, 7% of plots become discontinued because of habitat change (O'Connor & Fuller 1984).

Long-term changes in the CBC index sample

The indices are built from series of samples of plots which are slightly different for every year-to-year comparison. It is essential for the validity of the indices that the characteristics of the sample of plots do not change in ways which are likely to influence the index values. To protect against this, the index samples are themselves monitored. Some comparisons of the index samples for the full run of years to date, 1962-1988, are tabulated in Appendix 3, along with similar data for the WBS.

The total numbers of plots of all habitat types grew very rapidly during 1961-1965, then increased more slowly (but not on farmland) up to the early 1980s (Tables A1-A3; see also Figure 1.2). Since then, numbers of "special" plots have fallen in accordance with new policy, and numbers of farmland and woodland plots have also fallen slightly. There are two important implications in these data. First, the proportions of plots of the three habitat types in the scarce species index have changed markedly over time (see below). Second, samples of plots during 1961-1965 are rather smaller than those for later years. This can be expected to make the index values for these years less reliable than later ones.

Tables A1-A3 also show the degrees of turnover in each sample and year, measured as the number of "new" plots (those not available or not used in the previous year-to-year comparison), and the mean areas of index plots. In general, plot turnover is rather small, and the majority of plots run for many years. The mean area of woodland plots has remained fairly constant, but for farmland and "special" areas, plots were larger up to 1965 than they were in subsequent years (see also Figure 2.2).

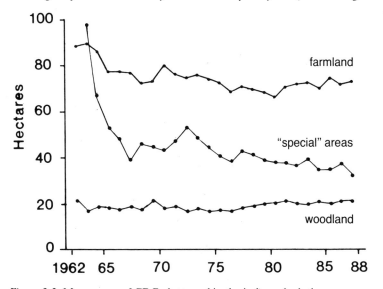

Figure 2.2. Mean areas of CBC plots used in the index calculations, 1962-1963 to 1987-1988. Changes have been small since 1965, but may nevertheless be relevant to analyses not based on paired data.

The long-term trends in plot area are also small, and in any case completely removed by the pairing of counts for successive pairs of years on the same plots (unless one postulates that percentage changes on small plots are consistently different from those on larger plots). But trends in plot area could certainly affect the results of analyses, such as the data on percentage occurrence presented in Chapter 4, which are not based on paired counts: as mean plot-size increases, the proportion of plots holding a particular species is also likely to increase.

Tables A5-A7 show the proportions of the index sample, in terms of the number of plots, in each of seven regions. These show that the geographical distribution of plots established in the first years of the scheme, although uneven, has remained relatively constant. The regions used for this analysis are those mapped in Figure 2.1.

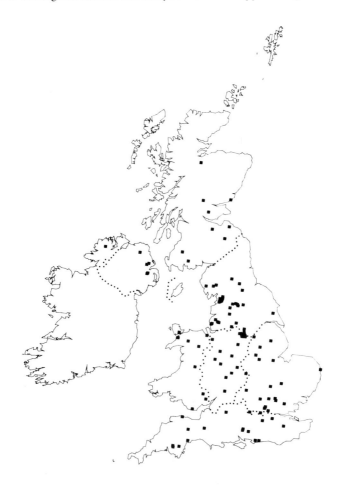

Figure 2.3. Distribution of WBS plots in a typical year (1988). The WBS has better representation than the CBC in northern England (see Figure 2.1).·

For farmland, Fuller *et al* (1985) found that, in terms of the area of CBC plots in each region, there were significant increases in coverage in Northern England and Northern Ireland during 1962-1982, but a significant reduction in Western England. Overall, however, there was a pronounced degree of regional uniformity in sampling effort throughout the study period. Whatever biases are introduced by the uneven geographical distribution of census plots, they will have affected all years more or less equally. It is most unlikely, therefore, that any population trends detected by the CBC or WBS are affected by temporal shifts in the pattern of sampling. On the other hand, population changes peculiar to areas poorly covered by the CBC and WBS will be under-represented in the national data.

Table A9 in Appendix 3 documents the more substantial degree to which samples for the all-habitats index have changed since 1963. These changes reflect the gradual increase in coverage of woodland and "special" plots which continued up to about 1981, during which period farmland coverage was roughly stable, and also the fall-off in "special" plots which followed the change in policy in 1983. The implications of these data have yet to be fully assessed. They could introduce biases into the all-habitats index, but only for species which occur in substantial numbers in more than one CBC habitat and which have experienced different population trends in the different habitats.

Characteristics of the WBS plot sample

The distribution of WBS plots (Figure 2.3) differs considerably from that of CBC plots. Most of the differences stem from the very major contributions made to the scheme by the Sheffield Bird Study Group and the Lancaster & District Bird Watching Society, in areas covered less well for the CBC. Trends over time in the composition of the WBS sample have been rather small (see Tables A4, A8 and A10 in Appendix 3). It is unlikely that changes in the nature of the sample have introduced any substantial biases.

Differences between bird species

Each index has the same nominal aim, to monitor the number of territorial males in a particular species and habitat. However, it is probably the case that the relationship between percentage changes in the index and real percentage changes in the population is slightly different for each species and every index. These differences arise from the biology of the species and, as has already been mentioned, from how closely the geographical and habitat distributions of the species correspond with those of census plots.

In general, a cluster of registrations represents one territorial male, whether or not it bred successfully or even attracted a mate. Such is the case for species such as Wren and Robin where, typically, males sing vigorously and persistently from small exclusive territories. However, what it is that observers record and analysts assess for each species depends on its biology: important biological differences between species include the degree to which the species exhibits territorial behaviour, whether males and females are readily separable in the field (either by plumage or calls), and the average size of a territory. For example, it is known that censusing Sedge Warblers, Reed Warblers and Reed Buntings may present special difficulties (Bell *et al* 1968, 1973). That such differences between species are known or suspected is probably immaterial in nearly every case for the interpretation of the index trend, because any species-specific difficulties are likely to have been constant over time, or any changes too small to influence the long-term population indices. Problems may arise where the conspicuousness of a species varies with its population level. It should be noted, however, that the mapping method is more robust against such problems than either point counts or transects: a conspicuous territory might have eight registrations from ten visits, and an inconspicuous one only three, but both count equally in the results.

Territorial behaviour affects the manner clusters are assessed for each species, probably in many subtle ways. Dunnocks, to take one example, have an unusual mating system which must make territorial boundaries (in CBC terms) rather fluid, but at least in this species song sometimes enables the sexes to be separated. Where the sexes cannot be distinguished easily by plumage or by calls or song, for example in Jay and Magpie, it is less likely that unmated territorial males will be located: more likely, their registrations will be drawn into adjacent clusters. On the other hand, some territories of these species may be based entirely on registrations of females, as may happen quite frequently for Sparrowhawks on farmland (where few are sexed, but most that are sexed are females). Probably many Sparrowhawks detected by the farmland CBC are in fact nesting in woodland, with females tending to hunt over open land as is their habit (Newton 1986).

Where the analyst finds it impossible to separate individual clusters, a multiple cluster is sometimes drawn which represents more than one territorial male or pair. This is the usual practice for some ducks, corvids and finches, which are often semicolonial. In such cases, it is not always possible to exclude transient birds or the non-breeding section of the population.

Counts for some species, particularly Starling, Carrion Crow, Rook, Magpie, and House Martin, tend to be more often counts of active nests than estimates of breeding territories. For Grey Heron, Rook, Sand Martin, Feral Pigeon, gulls and terns, only nest counts are acceptable as census estimates. Even within this group, however, there are differences in the way nest counts are collected. Those for Grey Heron and the corvids are usually made early in the season, before leaves make detection and counting of nests difficult, and so may include those which failed at an early stage and omit some which started late. In contrast, Starling nests are rarely found or proven to be occupied until attention is drawn to them by the begging calls of the young birds: thus Starling nest counts usually include only the successful nests. House Martin nests are easy to detect and count at all stages of the nesting cycle. In contrast, single Sand Martin nests are easily missed, and colonies are notoriously difficult to count: the usual measure is an estimate of occupied holes.

Species with large territories

In a subjective classification of ease of cluster analysis (Fuller & Marchant 1985), five headquarters CBC analysts voted Wren the easiest and Redpoll the hardest to analyse of the 60 species then indexed. The species described as straightforward were those relatively conspicuous birds like Wren, Robin and Willow Warbler which hold well-defined territories from which they rarely stray. The commonest problem with the more difficult species was absence of any natural clustering of registrations, and this feature was most frequent among wide-ranging and semicolonial species. Thus it is likely that CBC analysis is least accurate for species with territories which are large relative to the size of the study plots, or semicolonial birds where breeding groups occupy large areas communally.

Large territories may also present problems for population indexing. Because there is only a small number of likely cluster totals for each plot (0, 1, 2 or 3), the precision of the percentage change estimates between years is low, confidence intervals are wide, and chance effects are likely to enhance "random walks" in the population indices (see below). There will be no bias to the index, provided that the efficiency of mapping large territories does not change systematically with their density. But such a bias may well exist. Even when a wide-ranging species is at low density, it is likely that most census plots will record one territory, because the minimum requirement is only two or three registrations, and these could be almost anywhere within or even just beyond the plot boundaries. At higher densities, it is relatively unlikely that more than one territory will be recorded, even if birds from two territories are visiting the plot, because this will not happen unless there are simultaneous registrations of birds from both territories. Thus low numbers are probably overestimated, and high numbers underestimated. This would have the effect of buffering the population index against real population change.

In an important review of scale problems in bird census work, Wiens (1981) presented a theoretical "checkerboard" model which illustrates how imprecise estimates of both density and population change are likely to be where a species is scarce, relative to a more densely packed species. The conclusion most relevant to the CBC is that thinly distributed species should ideally be censused on larger plots than those used to monitor the more densely packed species, particularly those which saturate the available habitat. For practical reasons, all species are censused on the same sets of CBC plots, and these are better suited to the commoner species.

"Random walks"

The CBC indices are constructed by calculating overall percentage changes for adjacent years and then linking these serially, relative to an arbitrary level of 100 in one of the years of the sequence. The problem inherent in such a system is that sampling errors accumulate from year to year and can lead to "random walk" of the index, and false conclusions about population trends (Geissler & Noon 1981). These authors' findings led to a change away from the chain-index method in the North American Breeding Bird Survey (Robbins *et al* 1983).

In a similar investigation, Moss (1985) found that "random walks" in simulated CBC data were very much smaller than the estimated population changes, and not therefore a major cause for concern. The better quality of data provided by the mapping method, compared to the point transect method of the American scheme, and the larger CBC sample sizes and reduced plot turnover in the simulations, doubtless contributed to this result. However, Moss's simulated species held between 5 and 15 territories per plot: "random walks" could still be important in those cases in the CBC where trends are estimated for those scarcer species which never hold more than 5 territories per plot.

Observer effects

Differences in census efficiency between observers

It is known from several studies that the results of a census are dependent to some extent on the skills of the observer, and to a larger extent on the field effort in terms of visits made and hours spent. O'Connor & Marchant (1981) document a case where four observers, each performing an independent ten-visit census, differed in their assessment of the bird population of an area of scrub and woodland. The differences appeared to be due partly to the differing amounts of time the observers spent in the field. Combining their observations, an increase in number of visits over the range 10-40 gave a continuous rise in the total number of territories found, with "pseudoterritories" generated at the higher numbers of visits by the physical difficulties of mapping and analysis posed by censuses with high numbers of registrations.

Thus it appears that a true answer to the question, "How many territories are present on a plot?", may be impossible to obtain by the mapping method: the results may depend too much on the skill and effort of the observer. But in support of the mapping method, it should be pointed out that only one plot was used in this study, and the habitat was dense and difficult to work. Observers are likely to be much more consistent in their results on farmland, where territories are typically more widely spaced, more linear and more clearly defined.

From the birds' viewpoint also, there may be no simple answer to the question, in view of the problems set by the peculiar territorial or non-territorial behaviour of some species (*e.g.*Dunnock), deaths and replacements, sequential breeding by different birds in the same territories (already demonstrated for Golden Plover; Parr 1979), and nesting "out of season" (*e.g.*Woodpigeon). There is probably no firm dividing line between unmated, but territorial birds and the "floating", non-territorial birds believed to occur in some species, for example Blackbird (Batten 1977). Thus the relationship of CBC cluster total to population size is far from straightforward, but it is undoubtedly the best measure that can easily be obtained, and it has proved to be a very valuable one for population monitoring and for habitat-related studies.

Consistency of individual observers

Although it is recognised that observers differ in the results they obtain from censusing a plot, there is evidence to suggest that these differences do not affect observers' estimates of percentage change between years. In the O'Connor & Marchant study (1981), there were significant differences between observers in their census results, but none in their estimates of percentage changes between the two years of the study. This result suggests that differences in observer efficiency are not an important source of bias to CBC estimates of population change.

It is vital, however, that each observer is consistent between years in the time spent censusing and in the number of visits made, so that the known effects of these variables are removed. Results which are not consistent are in any case excluded from the index calculations.

Long-term changes in census effort

The method of selecting plots for use in the index calculations involves a check by the analyst that the number of visits and hours spent in the field are comparable between adjacent years. Small changes in these measures of effort are ignored, and this gives rise to the possibility of a long-term systematic change in census effort. A long-term increase in either the number of visits or hours could influence the bird population indices, unless the pairing process completely removes any trend. However, Marchant (in press) has shown that no such trends are obvious in the period after 1965. Fewer visits were made in 1961-1964 than subsequently, and this may have implications for the accuracy of the work done in those initial years. The average number of hours spent per hectare was also low during 1961-1964.

The numbers of species found on CBC plots were smaller during 1961-1964 than in later years, despite (on farmland at least) plots then being larger on average (see Figure 2.4). This is partly the result of changes in the instructions relating to the list of species observers should record, but is probably largely due to the lower census effort in those early years.

26

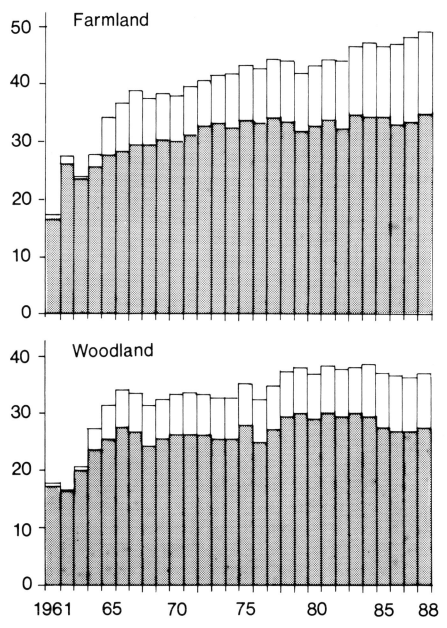

Figure 2.4. Mean numbers of territorial and visiting species recorded on CBC plots, 1961-1988. Shaded bars represent territorial species. Initially, records were requested only for certain species (see text). Upward trends have continued after the full introduction of the mapping method in 1965.

Improvements in identification skills

There may be another reason why there has been an upward trend in the number of species found on plots. Hildén (1979, 1981) has drawn attention to the better field skills of more recent ornithologists in Finland, the improvements in optical aids, and the greater readiness to accept specific identifications of birds seen or heard distantly. He drew comparisons between the 1930s, 1950s and 1970s. It is very likely that such advances have taken place in Britain during the period of the CBC.

The direction of any bias introduced into the CBC indices is clear, but the magnitude cannot be accurately assessed. It is likely to be relatively small for familiar and conspicuous species, and larger for the scarcer or more skulking species which may have escaped the attention of observers in the 1960s, or gone unidentified.

Analyst effects

The results of censuses are influenced by headquarters staff in two separate ways: these are the instructions given to fieldworkers and the ways in which the returns are "analysed".

Changes in instructions to CBC observers

Important changes in CBC methodology occurred during the initial development phase of the scheme during 1961-1965 (Marchant, in press). Changes in census method, especially the abrupt change in the field methods in 1964, must be borne in mind when interpreting the results for 1962-1965 presented elsewhere in this book.

The initial notice of the CBC in 1961 (see Chapter 1) gave the aims of the census and the recommended number of visits, but little other information on the methods to be employed: bird census methodology was in its infancy at the time. Further, the instructions for the 1961 season gave no advice on how the territorial males should be counted, beyond recommending that "as much counting as possible should be done from a distance", and that "frequent stops should be made to study the area ahead". Counts were required for only twelve species: Grey Partridge, Lapwing, Skylark, Wren, Song Thrush, Blackbird, Robin, Willow Warbler, Dunnock, Greenfinch, Chaffinch, and Yellowhammer. Results were to be presented as a table of counts by species and by visit, with the observer's assessment of how many different territorial males were present. In addition, a 25-inch map was requested describing the habitat and showing the approximate centres of territories of all the different species.

For 1962, it was decided that non-cultivated sections of farmland plots such as large areas of gardens, and small woods, copses and spinneys were to be left out "wherever possible", since they were considered not relevant to the possible effects of chemicals applied to the fields. On farmland only, all territorial species were to be included rather than just the original twelve. On woodland and other non-farmland plots, the 1961 list of species was expanded just slightly to include Whitethroat, Linnet and Goldfinch. In all habitats, the counting season was extended by a fortnight to the end of June.

These changes were written into the instructions for 1962, along with a few other small pieces of advice, but there was no further definition of the counting methods to be employed, beyond a statement to the effect that colonial species such as the corvids should be entered separately in the final table.

Strong criticisms expressed over the lack of a precisely defined and clearly described census method (*e.g.*W.B.Yapp, *in litt.*) were presumably a powerful

28

stimulus for the major improvements in methodology implemented in 1963 and 1964. According to Williamson & Homes (1964), the formation of the BTO Populations Section in 1963 came too late in the season to implement major changes in the field technique, and the necessary overhaul of the counting method had to be postponed until 1964. Despite some improvements being made for 1963, it was still the case that decisions on which birds or pairs were the same and which different were being made subjectively by each observer without any guidance from the Populations Section, for example on likely territory sizes in different habitats.

Only in 1964 was the standard mapping census technique introduced, based on that of Enemar (1959). Apart from being far less subjective, the mapping method was much simpler for the observer and more manageable for the analyst at headquarters. The new method resulted in far more detail being recorded about the distribution of each species (Figure 2.5).

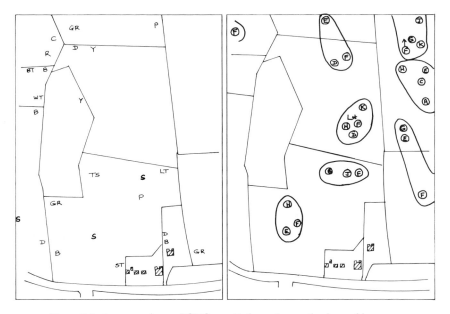

Figure 2.5. A comparison of CBC results from the methods used in 1961-1963 and from 1964 onwards, illustrated on a section of a farmland plot. The map on the left shows the total information on file for all species in 1963. The symbols are species codes, each representing the centre of a territory as determined by the observer. On the right is the species map for Skylark (S) in 1975, one of many submitted for that plot and year, as analysed at BTO headquarters.

A further change was made in 1965, when it was requested that *all* contacts with birds should be mapped, not just those relating to song or other territorial behaviour (Taylor 1965).

The index values for many species, both migrant and resident, increased strongly during the initial years of the CBC. Previously, the whole of the apparent increase in population levels, at least for resident species, was attributed to recovery from the severe winters of 1961/62 and 1962/63. Taylor (1965) found no evidence of inconsistency between observers in their detection of population changes in 1963-1964, but admitted that a small general upward bias could not be ruled out. In retrospect, and taking a much longer view, it seems very likely that there was a degree of upward bias in the early years of the census.

The extent to which these changes in methodology may have affected the population trends cannot now be estimated, but it seems likely that the improvement in methods will have led in many cases to the detection of more birds. Such apparent increases may be compounded by a "learning curve" effect by which the observers, nearly all in their first seasons of this kind of work, and with no guidance available from experienced census-takers, became more efficient at covering their plots.

While the CBC continues to offer index values for the years 1962-1964, these are likely to be less accurate than the figures for later years, and in some cases too low.

Changes in analytical procedures

If analytical procedures change over time, apparent long-term population changes could be generated by drifts in the way that species maps are analysed. While guidelines for territory analysis are laid down (Marchant 1983b), they cannot cover every case, and there is appreciable scope for individual variation in the way that analysts interpret them. In studies by Svensson (1974) and Best (1975), considerable variation was found between analysts working to the international guidelines (International Bird Census Committee 1969). Differences between untrained analysts are the main reason why CBC and WBS maps are analysed centrally rather than by the observers themselves. At BTO headquarters, territory analysis is carried out by a small team of specialist staff, who each undergo the same training and who are available to give each other second opinions in difficult cases.

Occasional small-scale checks suggest that differences between analysts in any given year are small compared with population changes, and are not a significant factor. In a more intensive study, the results of three analysts were compared for four independent censuses of the same plot: no significant differences were found between analysts (O'Connor & Marchant 1981).

A more insidious possibility is that the standards used or attention to detail might have varied systematically over time, within as well as between analysts, such as to bias the long-term population indices. We are not aware of any such biases, and indeed it is difficult to envisage such a bias operating strongly enough to influence the index trend.

Summary of strengths and weaknesses of the indices

The main weaknesses, limitations and justifiable criticisms of the indices are as follows.

1. The distribution of plots is biased geographically towards the south and east of Britain, and plots are not representative of the United Kingdom as a whole (see Figures 2.1 and 2.3).
2. Only the farmland and woodland sections of avian habitat are covered well, while the extensive moorland, urban and suburban habitats, which hold very large numbers of some species, are not sampled.
3. Despite farmland plots being representative of that habitat on the broad scale, at least in the southern half of Britain (Fuller et al 1985), on the more local scale plots of both farmland and woodland as selected by the observers may be rather better for birds than randomly selected plots would be.

4. Relatively few sites and observers contribute to the data, because the mapping method is more labour intensive than other methods for both observers and analysis staff.

5. Changes in the CBC method, and increases in observer and analyst experience, may have given an upward bias to the indices between 1962 and 1965. In particular, the CBC results may exaggerate the importance of the 1961/62 and 1962/63 cold winters.

6. Because the chain method is used for indexing all species, "random walks" may be occurring, especially in some indices for scarcer species.

7. The constitution of the samples for the all-habitats index has changed considerably (see Table A9 in Appendix 3).

It should be emphasised that, despite the limitations and caveats described in this chapter, that the CBC and WBS indices show a high degree of internal consistency and robustness, and that they are widely regarded as a useful and reliable set of biological data. Particular strengths of the indices are summarised below.

1. There have been no changes of any consequence in the field or analytical methods of the CBC or WBS since 1968 and probably 1965.

2. The mapping method used since 1964 is the most reliable of the practicable methods of taking a bird census of a particular study plot. Mapping results are far less likely to be influenced by the effects of timing of visits and weather during visits than those of point counts or transects.

3. There have been no major changes in the geographical distribution of census plots contributing to the indices.

4. The plots contributing to the farmland index have been shown to be representative of farmland land-classes and cropping, at least over most of the southern half of Britain (Fuller *et al* 1985).

5. Observers have been fairly constant since 1965 in the effort they expend on censusing, with no drifts in time spent or number of visits likely to affect the indices.

6. Evidence suggests that CBC observers are consistent in the way that they record percentage changes (O'Connor & Marchant 1981).

7. All censuses are analysed centrally, by a small number of trained staff. There have been no changes in analysis guidelines since at least 1968, and few changes in analysis staff.

8. Individual plots frequently contribute to the indices for long periods, giving stability to the plot samples. Two plots have been censused by the same observers each year since 1961 (see Appendix 2).

3.
Overall influences on bird numbers

The size of a bird population can be influenced by many different factors, often acting in combination. Many of these influences are poorly understood or even completely unknown. Some act across a broad spectrum of species, but others may affect only one species or a small group of species whose ecology is in some way similar.

Density-dependent factors, for example an increase in survival rates when population levels are low, typically regulate and stabilise populations. In contrast, those which are independent of bird density, such as winter weather, tend to disturb otherwise stable populations and cause irregular fluctuations. A third category of factors are those which change the carrying capacity of the environment in some way, so as to cause the population to fluctuate about a different level. Habitat loss and the creation of new habitat both fall into this category. Some factors, such as the changes which allowed species like Woodpigeon and Magpie to colonise urban habitats, or Collared Doves to invade Europe so successfully from the Near East, are apparently behavioural factors, internal to the species, rather than environmental ones.

Environmental changes which operate on bird populations at a fundamental level across a wide spectrum of species are summarised below. Where the nature of more specific factors is known in particular cases, their possible influences are discussed in Chapter 4 under the species concerned.

Patterns of climate and weather in Britain

Year-to-year changes in resident bird populations are often the direct result of weather conditions experienced by the birds during the previous winter. Just a few severely cold days and nights during which many birds die may be sufficient to depress the overall rate of survival through to the next breeding season. Population crashes following especially cold winters are clear in the index graphs for several small resident species (see below). The effects of weather during the breeding season on breeding productivity and the survival of newly fledged juveniles are likely to be important population determinants for some species, but have been little studied as yet.

Longer-term changes in bird numbers and distribution may be influenced not by short-term weather, but instead by changes in climate. Climate is standardly defined as the synthesis of weather over a long period – at least a decade and normally 30 years (Mason 1979). Population changes resulting from trends in climate are not readily detectable over the relatively short timescale of the CBC.

There is some information on the overall nature of the British climate as far back as the Middle Ages, but very little is known about birds at this early period. The long cold period known as the Little Ice Age lasted from about 1550 to 1810 or later, but it was not until the 1890s that our climate began to get appreciably warmer (Williamson 1975, Harrison 1988). The subsequent period of North Atlantic warming lasted up to about 1940, with the most striking temperature gains being recorded in the winter months. A strengthening of the Gulf Stream, bringing warmer waters to British coasts, was partly responsible. Summers from the 1920s to the 1940s were notably warm. In the 1940s, winter temperatures began to cool again, and summers also began to cool around 1950. The decrease in winter temperatures continued to about 1969/70, with one winter, 1962/63, as fierce over the Midlands and south of Britain as any since 1740 (Williamson 1975, Elkins 1983). There was then a short series of milder winters, but since 1976 there has been an increased frequency of severe ones, although the three at the end of the 1980s have again been unusually mild.

Geographical variations in climate within Britain are likely to be an important influence on bird distribution, and they may also influence the nature of population fluctuations in different parts of the country. Temporal variations in climate have brought about many changes in bird numbers and distribution, even during the course of the 20th century (Parslow 1973, Williamson 1975). The most marked of these changes are described under the relevant species (see for example Nightingale and Blackbird). The ways in which climate influences the population changes of a particular species are rarely understood. It may act more-or-less directly, for example on survival rates of fully grown birds, or on nest success, or indirectly, perhaps through the distribution and numbers of invertebrate prey.

Winter weather

The most obvious effect of weather on the size of breeding bird populations is that of the varying severity of winter conditions in Britain on the overwinter survival rates of resident species. For some species, for example Wren and Goldcrest, winter weather is a major determinant of population level, while for many others the population trend can be linked to the frequency of severe winters over a period of years. Short-distance migrants to France or Iberia, such as Grey Wagtail and Goldfinch, normally escape severe conditions but may also show large reductions in numbers after hard winters if the unusually cold weather extends to these areas as well.

Severe weather is easiest to quantify in terms of temperature, but the degree and distribution of wind, snowfall, freezing rain and freezing fog may at times be of greater significance to the birds. Snow can make food on the ground inaccessible or difficult to find, particularly if strong wind has forced drifts into hedge bottoms and other sheltered corners, while an ice coating or rime on trunks and branches creates severe difficulties for birds which normally feed in the trees. In January 1940, rain falling from warmer upper layers into frosty air near the ground formed ice coatings on vegetation up to 10 cms thick in many areas of southern Britain. As well as reducing opportunities for birds to feed, ice formed also on the plumage and feet of the birds themselves, seriously impairing their ability to fly (Ticehurst & Witherby 1940). It may be crucial whether a cold spell is continuous for a long period, or interrupted by warmer interludes during which birds are able to replenish their fat reserves.

Using temperature as the indicator of conditions, Figures 3.1 and 3.2 show the relative severity of each winter from 1960/61 to 1987/88. The data plotted in Figure 3.1 are the differences from the overall average for the whole period, 1960-1988, of the means of the four monthly means, November, December, January and February. Each monthly mean is averaged across 27 meteorological stations throughout Britain, three from each of the nine climatological regions considered by the Meteorological Office to experience approximately similar weather. Thus the data are broadly representative of Britain as a whole, but do not take account of regional differences in winter severity.

The use of an average figure for each calendar month may understate the importance of cold spells spanning parts of two months. This happened in 1961/62, a winter often referred to as unusually cold, when a short but severe spell of freezing weather from 22nd December to 5th January hardly affected either monthly average.

33

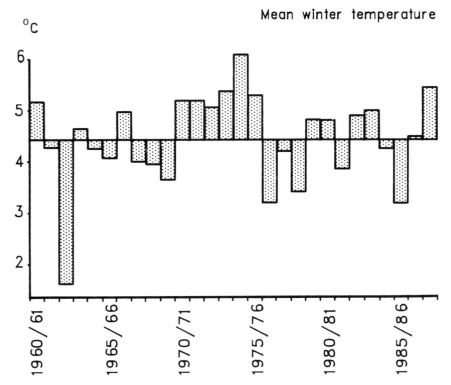

°C   Mean winter temperature

Figure 3.1. Mean winter temperatures in Britain, 1960/61 to 1987/88, as defined in the text. 1962/63 remains much the coldest so far of the CBC period. There was a run of mild winters in the early 1970s, during which population sizes of many resident birds rose to a peak.

The same applied to another short, harsh spell from late January to early February 1976.

The coldest months of the CBC period, in chronological order, were January and February 1963, February 1969, January 1979, December 1981, January 1985, February 1986, and January 1987 (Figure 3.2). After 1963, the only month in which the mean temperature fell below freezing was February 1986.

Taking both diagrams together, it is clear that the 1962/63 winter, the first after CBC indexing began, is still the coldest of the CBC period by a considerable margin. A December which was itself colder than usual was followed by the two coldest months in the whole 28-year period. Because the CBC was still undergoing some changes in field and analytical methods up to 1965, and because both observers and analysts were growing in experience during these initial years of the scheme, the extents to which bird populations decreased between the 1962 and 1963 breeding seasons may in some cases have been exaggerated by the CBC indices (see Chapter 2). However, it is clear from the CBC results that the effects of 1962/63 were greater and more widespread across species than those of any subsequent winter.

Another conspicuous feature of Figure 3.1 is the long run of mild winters during the

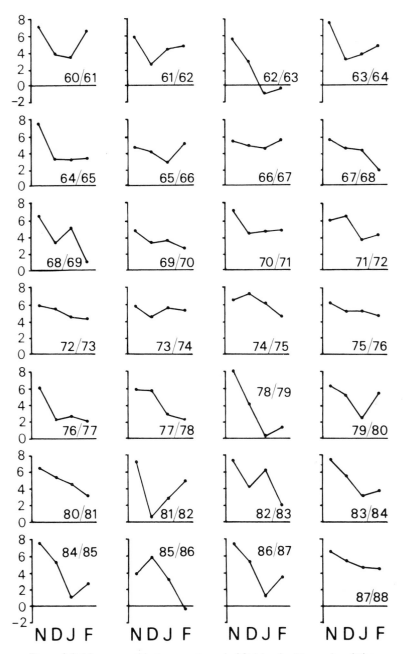

Figure 3.2. Mean monthly temperatures in °Celsius for November (N) to February (F), winters 1960/61 to 1987/88, averaged from 27 weather stations across Britain.

early and middle 1970s, with that of 1974/75 being much the mildest of the 28-year period. Many resident species were able to increase then, beyond the level they had reached after recovering their losses in 1962/63. Since the mid-1970s, there has been a fairly high frequency of colder winters, but the most severe of these have been followed by unusually mild ones which enabled populations to recover very quickly. Goldcrest is the only species for which the effects of a recent winter, 1985/86, are known to have been greater than those of 1962/63.

The effects on birds of unusually cold winters this century have been well documented (Jourdain & Witherby 1918, Witherby & Jourdain 1929, Ticehurst & Witherby 1940, Ticehurst & Hartley 1948, Dobinson & Richards 1964, Cawthorne & Marchant 1980, O'Connor et al 1982, Davidson & Clark 1985, Lack 1986). It is clear that there are a number of species which are especially susceptible to cold weather, and suffer high mortality when severe conditions occur. Cawthorne & Marchant (1980) demonstrated, for the 1978/79 winter, that it was the smallest birds that showed the largest percentage reductions following harsh weather. In general, those species especially susceptible to cold are able to recover their previous population level within two or three breeding seasons following a crash, provided that there is no recurrence of severe conditions.

However, it is now apparent, particularly after several cold winters during the CBC period, that each winter is unique in its effects on bird populations. While the Kingfisher was the species worst affected in 1962/63 (Dobinson & Richards 1964), and its numbers fell sharply again in 1981/82, hardly any change was detected following 1985/86, the season in which Goldcrests suffered exceptionally high mortality. Differences between cold winters might result from differences in the weather conditions actually experienced by the birds, in terms of temperature, wind-chill, snow cover and icing of trunks and foliage. The availability of food at the time of the severe weather must also be important in determining survival. The period of the winter at which severe conditions occur influences food availability, the length of daylight during which birds can forage and the length of the night-time period for which they must roost. The geographical extent of the severe conditions and the proximity of milder refuges also differ between winters.

Rainfall patterns in the western Sahel

In spring 1969, following a severe drought in parts of West Africa the previous summer, only one-third of the expected number of Whitethroats returned to Britain from their winter quarters. It was this that initially drew the importance to birds of rainfall in West Africa, and particularly the Sahel zone, to European attention (Winstanley et al 1974, Berthold 1974, Berthold et al 1986). The Whitethroat crash, one of the most striking of population changes measured by the CBC, was a demonstration that climate and weather geographically remote from Britain may also affect the numbers of our breeding birds.

The Sahel occupies a band across northern tropical Africa which is intermediate in rainfall and vegetation between the desert conditions of the Sahara and the generally lusher and wetter forests and savannas farther south (Figure 3.3). Annual rainfall averages between 100 and 600 mm. The western part of this zone contains the first and last potential areas of good feeding for birds crossing the Sahara from or to Europe, and includes the sometimes vast wetland formed by the flooding of the River Niger upstream from Tombouctou in Mali. Several species of European migrants often spend the whole winter in the Sahel, while others move further south. The rain falls mostly between May and October, but determines the state of the vegetation and the availability of food during September to March when the European migrants are present in greatest strength.

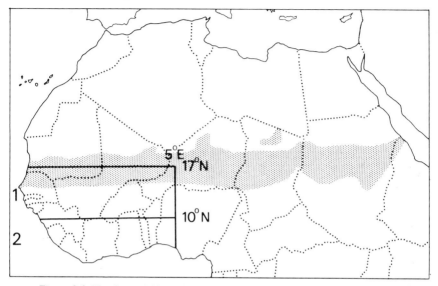

Figure 3.3. Northern Africa, showing the extent and position of the Sahel zone, and of Regions 1 and 2 from which rainfall data are presented in Figure 3.4.

Recent variation in the mean rainfall anomaly for two sections of West Africa is plotted in Figure 3.4. The mean rainfall anomaly provides an index of annual rainfall relative to the average for the period 1941-1970 (G. Farmer, *in litt.*). Positive values indicate wetter years than normal, and negative values drier ones. While both Regions 1 and 2 lie mostly to the south of the Sahel, Region 1 contains most of the southwestern part of the Sahel zone.

Between 1900 and 1950, rainfall in Region 1 varied around the long-term mean without any definite pattern. During 1950-1958 there was a continuous period when rainfall was well above average. There was then a return to average levels, but in 1968 there was less rain than in any year since 1941. Precipitation was as much as 70% below normal in some parts of the Sahel and adjacent savanna zones (Winstanley *et al* 1974). Rainfall in 1969 was average in Region 1, but deficits, many greater than that of 1968, were recorded in each year from 1970 to 1988. Rainfall was particularly poor in 1983. There has been more rain since 1986, allowing some respite to the affected species. On the broad scale, from Senegal to the Sudan, 1988 was the wettest year in the Sahel since 1969.

The pattern has been rather different in Region 2, further south. Here, years with less than average rainfall have predominated since the mid-1960s, but deficits have been less severe than in Region 1. Runs of drought years have been interrupted by seasons when rainfall amounts were average or even much higher than usual. The wettest years were 1968 and 1979. Since the Whitethroat crash occurred following a failure of rains in Region 1 in 1968, it seems likely that rainfall in Region 2 is or was at that time largely irrelevant to Whitethroat survival. The numbers of contributing

37

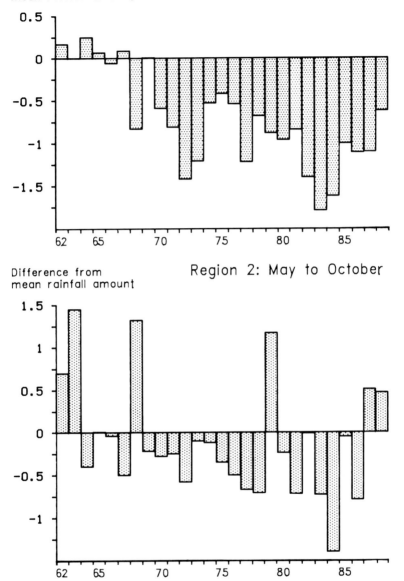

Figure 3.4. Rainfall in two regions of West Africa during 1962-1988, as mapped in Figure 3.3. The number of contributing weather stations in Region 1 varied between 21 and 78. In Region 2, the figures are drawn from around 60 stations up to 1974, but from fewer than 10 in most years subsequently.

weather stations in Region 2 were very small in the 1980s but, taking the two regions as a single unit, it appears that the driest years of the whole period were 1983 and 1984. Among the species which winter in or pass through the Sahel, seven (Sand Martin, Swallow, Grasshopper Warbler, Sedge Warbler, Whitethroat, Chiffchaff and Spotted Flycatcher) showed their lowest recorded CBC indices or occupancy of CBC sites in 1984 or 1985. Others, however, exhibit a different pattern: for example, Redstart and Garden Warbler were at their lowest in the mid-1970s and increased throughout the 1980s.

Now that two decades have passed since the onset of the drought, the circumstantial evidence is very strong that the amount of rainfall in the western Sahel is a major determinant of subsequent breeding population levels in Britain, 6500 km to the north, not just for Whitethroat but also for Sand Martin, Redstart, Sedge Warbler and other long-distance migrant passerines. A recent finding from the Constant Effort Sites scheme is that the year-to-year return rates of individually marked Sedge Warblers are positively and very highly correlated with the amount of rain in Region 1 in the previous season (W. J. Peach, pers. comm.).

The differences in the patterns of population change between species which visit the Sahel may perhaps be explained by geographical variations in rainfall patterns south of the Sahara. Drought conditions were and still are most severe along the northern edge of the Sahel, next to the desert, with the effects tending to diminish southwards across the savanna zones. The impact on ground vegetation has often been exacerbated by overstocking of these fragile terrains with domestic grazing animals. Thus the drought conditions hit hardest at those bird species wintering farthest north in tropical Africa, notably Whitethroat, Sand Martin and Sedge Warbler (Winstanley et al 1974). Using the overall annual ringing totals to give a crude measure of population changes between 1983 and 1984, a close correlation has been demonstrated over a range of fourteen species between the mid-latitude of the wintering area and the degree of population change, such that those species wintering furthest north showed the greatest decreases (Mead & Hudson 1985).

Loss of winter habitat for tropical migrants

In North America, the Breeding Bird Survey has recently revealed declines in many migrant bird species, particularly those which both breed and winter in forest habitats. American birdwatchers are beginning to ask "Where have all the birds gone?" (Terborgh 1989). The continuing rapid destruction of forest in the American tropics is likely to be the main cause of the problem, although forest fragmentation in North America may also be contributing.

Despite its importance across the Atlantic, loss of tropical forest does not appear to be a problem now for European migrant birds: most West African deforestation has already taken place. In any case, few European species are known to winter in African forests. Pied Flycatcher is one to which continuing deforestation may be detrimental (Grimmett 1987). Desertification associated with drought and overgrazing in the Sahel is likely to be a far more important problem.

Habitat change in the British countryside

A substantial level of breeding productivity, as well as good overwinter survival, is necessary for a bird population to maintain itself. Whether productivity is sufficient to offset mortality depends partly on the amount of breeding habitat available, and the quality of that habitat. The availability of suitable habitat determines the maximum number of individuals which can establish territories, and influences the survival of adults through the breeding season.

The conversion of Britain's natural forest, floodplain and moorland to the present-day countryside, dominated by farmland and by human dwellings and artefacts has brought about enormous changes in our avifauna over the last five millennia (Harrison 1988). But widespread habitat changes are still occurring, perhaps at a faster rate than ever before, and continuing to affect the numbers and distribution patterns of birds.

It is difficult to draw a firm line between habitat changes and habitat loss. From the human perspective, habitat loss brings to mind gross changes such as urbanisation, the clear-felling of a wood, hedgerow removal, or the conversion of moorland to grass field. However, from the birds' viewpoint, far more subtle changes may constitute habitat loss: thus building a new road through a wood could destroy the capacity of the habitat to support some species of nesting birds (for example Woodcock and Hawfinch), as could felling standard trees from a hedgerow (Chaffinch), or opening a new footpath across moorland (Golden Plover). Draining a field may be good management to a farmer, but could represent a total loss of habitat for bird species of conservation importance (particularly Snipe and Redshank), even if the farmer makes no other changes. It generally happens that the loss of habitat for some species involves the creation of new habitat for others, but the species lost from an area through habitat change are more likely to be ones of conservation interest than those enabled to move in.

Changes in woodland bird habitats

The total area of woodland in Britain has increased markedly during the present century, and it is likely to continue to do so. Measured as the total of woodland blocks larger than 0.25 hectare, British woodland has increased from 6.7% of the total land area in 1947 to 9.4% in 1980 (Locke 1987). Over this period there has been a major shift towards conifers, with their total area increasing more than threefold. The Farm Woodland Scheme and "direct set-aside to woodland" (MAFF 1988) may eventually increase the number of small woods on farmland. The expansion of afforestation has enabled some woodland birds, notably Siskin and Common Crossbill, to expand their breeding ranges considerably. Most new plantings have been even-aged monocultures of non-native species of conifers. While some conifer plantations support high densities of a few species, particularly Goldcrest, Coal Tit and Chaffinch, there are many woodland species which are rare or absent in these woods, including Hawfinch, Marsh Tit, Nuthatch and Redstart.

There have been important losses of woodland bird habitat through the replacement of native trees by introduced conifers, and by fragmentation of larger woods. The extent of Britain's surviving ancient woodland declined by between one-third and one-half between the Second World War and the mid-1980s, mainly through felling and replanting with conifers. There is ample evidence to confirm that larger woods hold more species than smaller ones (e.g. Fuller 1982). In part this is because some woodland birds, such as Woodcock, require large areas of continuous habitat and do not breed in small woods. Fragmentation of woodlands provides more woodland-edge habitat, but reduces the availability of the secluded woodland interior which is necessary for the presence of some of the scarcer birds.

Most areas of woodland are viewed as economic resources and managed for profit, although the numbers of woodland nature reserves are increasing. The value of woodland to birds depends to a large extent on the species of trees grown and on how the woodland is designed and managed, but profit and conservation motives can be integrated. CBC studies have shown the value of the retention of mature trees as landscape fringes or island refuges when a wood is cleared for replanting (Williamson 1970). More detailed advice on conservation-minded management of woodlands is given by Smart & Andrews (1985), Fuller & Warren (in press) and by Warren & Fuller (in press).

Rivers

Alluvial land along lowland rivers is very productive for agriculture but, in its natural state, subject to occasional floods which may damage homesteads or crops. Over the centuries, floodplains have been reduced by embankment and drainage, and rivers more or less confined to artificial channels. Pressure continues from landowners and water authorities to increase drainage further by dredging and straightening ditches and river channels.

Lowering of the water table by increased drainage can result in a sudden and complete loss of wet meadow habitats for birds. The drainage of wet meadows is currently causing very severe losses to inland populations of breeding waders such as Snipe and Redshank (see species texts).

Where management alters a river from its natural state, when perhaps there were meanders, ox-bow lakes and steep earth banks, to a straight dredged channel with graded banks and no emergent or bankside vegetation, then the bird community associated with the river is greatly depleted (Williamson 1971, Smith 1975). Among other species, Kingfisher and the *Acrocephalus* warblers are likely to suffer. On two WBS plots, one river and one canal, Taylor (1984) showed that, although Moorhens were still present after management had taken place, their breeding performance was much lower than on unmanaged sections. Alternative, less damaging techniques of river management are available in many cases, by which the channel retains some of its original character and some wetland habitat can be created between the flood embankments (Lewis & Williams 1984).

Loss of heathland and moorland

Britain has experienced very considerable losses of heathland and moorland habitats during the last half-century, and these losses have reduced the available habitat for several of Britain's rarest breeding birds, including Wood Sandpiper, Red-necked Phalarope, Stone-curlew and Dartford Warbler. Commoner species such as Skylark, Wheatear, Lapwing and Snipe are also among those adversely affected (NCC 1986).

By the mid-1980s, about 40% of Britain's original lowland heath had been destroyed, mostly by afforestation, new building development, or conversion to farmland. Much of the remainder has become too disturbed or too fragmented to retain the original species richness or to support birds at their former densities.

The main losses of upland moorland have been to coniferous afforestation, although particularly in earlier decades there was much conversion of lower moorlands to enclosed grassland, and this process is still continuing in Shetland (Thom 1986). The increase in afforestation has been most marked in Scotland, where the bulk of the planting has been on open moorland. The species which have benefited from afforestation of moorland are mainly woodland birds which were already abundant, such as Woodpigeon and Chaffinch, but Common Crossbill and Siskin are examples of

41

birds which have been enabled to increase their numbers and expand their range considerably (NCC 1986). Open-country species, such as waders and many raptors, cannot use the plantations, and decline.

Habitat changes on farmland

Over thousands of years, agricultural development has been a major force for change in the British countryside. It has created new habitats for birds, such as open fields and hedgerows, and increased the diversity of a previously largely wooded landscape. But the presence on farmland of wild birds, other than those shot for sport, has almost always been incidental to the main economic purpose of food production. During the present century, the development of new crops and methods of management, new machinery, drainage and pesticides has resulted in a very considerable loss of habitat diversity on farmland.

The initial reason for setting up the CBC was to help quantify the deleterious effects on wildlife that were expected in the 1960s in view of continuing hedgerow destruction and the use of persistent organochlorine pesticides. It was realised that fashions in agricultural practice, like the use of organochlorines in the 1950s, could spread very fast across Britain and perhaps produce sudden widespread decreases in bird populations.

Losses of farmland birds have not occurred to the extent that was feared in the early 1960s. However, this book documents the continuing strong decreases of Snipe and Redshank in lowland England resulting from increased drainage, the effects (particularly since the late 1970s) of farm chemicals on both seed-eating and insectivorous birds, and other instances where changes in farmland management have resulted in reductions in bird populations.

Recent positive developments in the conservation of birds on farmland are the general increase among farmers in awareness of conservation issues, and the ready availability of advice through the county Farming and Wildlife Advisory Groups and the Agricultural Development and Advisory Service. A new book now being prepared in the BTO's Agricultural Birds Unit will be a further source of practical conservation advice (Lack, in prep.). "Set-aside" and Farm Woodlands, among other new proposals, may go some way towards reversing the losses of bird habitats on farmland since 1950. The primary purpose of the set-aside scheme, however, is to reduce surpluses of arable crops, rather than to benefit wildlife (MAFF 1988).

Loss of bird habitat features on farmland

Hedgerow removal has been an issue in wildlife conservation on farmland for many years, although perhaps exaggerated in importance relative to other changes in farmland management (O'Connor & Shrubb 1986a). Although hedges occupy only a tiny fraction of the land area, they are used extensively by the majority of farmland birds.

Since 1949, an estimated 225,000 km (140,000 miles) of hedgerow have been lost (NCC 1984). Clearance of hedgerows removes shelter and nesting places for birds, and also destroys potential food plants and insects. Hedges have often been seen by farmers as unnecessary and undesirable – a waste of land, expensive to maintain, no longer needed to restrain stock, a refuge for pests and an obstacle to the economic use of heavy machinery. Post-war rates of hedgerow removal appeared to peak in the early 1960s (Pollard et al 1974, O'Connor & Shrubb 1986a). A high rate of loss still continues, however, in regions where livestock and mixed farming are giving way to arable (Lack, in prep.). Joyce *et al* (1988) have shown that the rate of hedge loss in north Hertfordshire has continued to increase into the mid-1980s.

A related loss of hedgerow habitat has occurred since 1969 through Dutch elm disease, which resulted in the loss of many millions of hedgerow trees. The death of elms probably benefited such birds as woodpeckers and tits that were able to feed on the scolytid beetles that are the vectors of the disease, but the subsequent felling and clearing of dead elms has reduced the structural diversity of hedgerows, and reduced feeding and nesting opportunities for a variety of bird species (Osborne 1982, 1983, 1985; O'Connor & Shrubb 1986*a*). In areas badly affected, there were losses of bird species, redistributions of territories and increases in territory size. There has generally been little attempt to replace the elms with other hedgerow trees, and in some cases the loss of elms has been followed by complete removal of a field boundary.

Farm ponds are an important breeding habitat for some birds, particularly waterside species such as Moorhen and Sedge Warbler, and a source of food and water for many others. In previous centuries they were an important source of water for both humans and livestock, but with the advent of piped water many ponds have become neglected and polluted, or have been filled in. Surveys of England and Wales show a major decrease in numbers of farm ponds between the 1880s and 1920s, with perhaps 60% destroyed during that period (Rackham 1986). A recent survey in Hertfordshire has estimated that the number of farm ponds in the county fell by nearly one-half between 1882 and 1978, while in 1986 the biological condition of the remaining ponds was very poor (HCC 1987).

Changes in farming practice

Technical innovations in farming and the resulting changes in land management have been very important but much underestimated influences on farmland birds (O'Connor & Shrubb 1986*a*, *b*). Among the recent management changes these authors highlighted were increased mechanisation, regional specialisation, the intensification of cereal farming, the change from spring sowing to autumn sowing of cereals with the consequent loss of spring tillage, the increase in stocking rates on grassland, and the switch from hay to silage. Each of these has taken its toll of bird populations, and their effects are discussed further in Chapter 4 under the relevant species headings.

Intensification and specialisation are the trends most evident in agriculture over recent decades. Much land farmed at low intensity, or not at all, has been brought into intensive use, while there has been a marked increase in the farming input and output in areas already in agricultural use. Specialisation into arable or livestock enterprises, evident regionally as well as at the level of individual farms, has tended to destroy the previous mosaic-like pattern of farmland, in which many different kinds of field-use were to be found within a relatively small area. Farmland "mosaics" have been established as being of particular value to several bird species, for example Lapwing (Redfern 1982; Galbraith 1988; Shrubb & Lack, in press), Rook (Brenchley 1984) and Skylark (Schläpfer 1988). Intensification also leads to loss of "mosaics" because, with high input of fertilisers, the previous systems of rotational cropping and fallow years are often no longer necessary.

Agricultural chemicals

The use of chemicals as agricultural fertilisers or pesticides has changed the nature of farmland radically and in various ways in recent decades, and continues to do so.

While the background effects of chemical usage are not easy to distinguish from other causes of change in farmland bird populations, there are historical cases where high mortality and population declines among birds were directly attributable to the widespread use of particular chemicals. In the 1950s and early 1960s, many deaths of farmland birds were caused by ingestion of organochlorine insecticides, particularly the cyclodienes such as aldrin and dieldrin which were used as seed-dressings. The Stock Dove in particular suffered a decline estimated at 90% during the 1950s, and appears not to have regained its former abundance (O'Connor & Mead 1984). Pesticide residues spread through the food-chain and reach highest concentrations in raptors such as Peregrine and Sparrowhawk. By 1962, only about 360 pairs of Peregrines remained in Britain, and many of these were failing to breed (Ratcliffe 1963). Merlins also decreased then, and have since shown little sign of recovery.

The most damaging organochlorine chemicals were withdrawn from general agricultural use in the mid-1960s, and since then both Peregrine and Sparrowhawk have largely recovered. However, both aldrin and dieldrin are still approved for certain specialised uses in the United Kingdom, despite the known dangers: while all MAFF approvals for dieldrin were withdrawn in March 1989, it is still sanctioned for use in timber treatment. It is likely that both chemicals are also being used illegally. Organochlorine residues are still evident in Merlins, and may be depressing breeding success even now (Newton & Haas 1988).

The use of fertilisers has tended to reduce the diversity of plant communities such that only the planted crop or a few species of grass are able to thrive. Since 1949, 95% of Britain's former herb-rich meadows and lowland grassland had lost their wildlife interest, and only 3% had been untouched by agricultural improvement (NCC 1984). Animals dependent on these plant communities directly or indirectly, including many birds, have also been reduced in number.

Generally, fertilisers are not directly poisonous to animals and plants, at least in the concentrations applied to the land, although there is mounting concern at the effects of run-off on water quality. Pesticides on the other hand are designed to be lethal, if only to a restricted group of species. The term "pesticide" comprises a wide range of chemicals aimed at controlling different kinds of pests and diseases which would otherwise deplete the harvest, including seed dressings, herbicides, fungicides, insecticides, rodenticides and molluscicides. However, the effects of many pesticides are broader than is desirable, insecticides for example killing neutral or beneficial insects as well as those causing damage. It has been shown relatively recently that some molluscicides and fungicides are in fact directly poisonous also to earthworms, and to some insects and other classes of invertebrates (Henderson 1989). This is cause for considerable concern, especially because earthworms play a vital role in aerating the soil, to the benefit of both wildlife and crops, and are a major component of the diet for many farmland birds.

While chemicals for agricultural use have to pass many safety checks before they are allowed into general use, there has been very little study of their long-term effects. A further concern is that, while farmers may legitimately use a very large number of different combinations of chemicals on the farm, there has been very little study of the effects of mixtures of chemicals on wildlife. It may be that the long-term use of pesticides is actually counterproductive from the farmer's point of view. Some insects are able to develop resistance within a remarkably short time to the chemicals aimed at controlling them. Recent figures suggest that since the 1940s the usage of insecticides has increased tenfold, while insect damage to crops has doubled over the same time period.

The effects of pesticides on birds in recent years have rarely involved instances of large-scale lethal poisoning, and certainly nothing to compare with the incidents in the 1950s and early 1960s. However, it is almost certain that the indirect effects of these chemicals, acting through the food chains, are evident in the declines in some bird species on farmland. Without doubt, the widespread use of pesticides has greatly reduced the diversity of the farmland ecosystem, to the short-term profit of the farmer and in some cases the consumer, but to the detriment of birds and other wildlife.

Grey Partridge numbers on farmland have decreased by more than 80% since the CBC began. The most important single cause of the decline is believed to be the effects of herbicides and insecticides on the arthropods which are the staple diet of the chicks. Potts (1986) estimated that since 1968 at least 10,000 Grey Partridge chicks had died from the indirect, ecological effects of herbicides in his West Sussex study area of 29.2 sq.km. Work by Rands (1985) has demonstrated that chick survival rates are improved where cereal fields are given "conservation headlands" – six-metre bands around the margins which are left unsprayed with herbicides or where spraying is severely restricted. For passerines in the same study area, no differences were found in the densities of territories between hedges adjacent to sprayed headlands and unsprayed headlands in their first year (Fuller 1984), but such differences could perhaps develop over time. The NCC (1987) has suggested that the development of rough grass strips and other non-agricultural habitats along field margins could be of considerable benefit to nature conservation.

Since the late 1970s, there have been a number of sustained decreases among seed-eating birds on farmland. Skylarks have decreased by 40%, Linnets and Reed Buntings by more than 50%, Corn Buntings by 60%, and Tree Sparrows by 75% over the period 1977-1988. Winter finch flocks on farmland are now almost a thing of the past in many parts of Britain. Circumstantial evidence suggests that these declines are associated with the increased efficiency and greater use of herbicides, decreasing the availability of weed seeds for winter food (O'Connor & Shrubb 1986a). While not an instance of direct poisoning of birds by agricultural chemicals, nevertheless it appears that the current level of use of herbicides is having a very severe effect on farmland bird populations. It remains to be seen whether the new fallows due to appear as a result of "set-aside", albeit a tiny proportion of farmland area, will begin to halt the declines.

Against this background, the current moves towards reducing chemical usage, and towards running farms organically without using agrochemicals at all, would be expected to benefit natural animal and plant communities, including birds. The value to Grey Partridges of "conservation headlands" has already been established (Rands 1985). More significantly, a recent Danish study has found that 24 of the 35 farmland bird species studied, including all the characteristic birds of farmland, were more common on organic farms than on conventionally farmed land, and that bird numbers overall were more than double on the organic farms (Braae et al 1988, Nøhr 1989). This is a strong indication that reductions in use of agricultural chemicals, as are now planned on a large scale in Denmark, would benefit bird populations. But more research is needed to establish the full value of organic farming to wildlife.

4.
Population trends

The selection of species for review

The systematic section of the book is in two parts. The first is a detailed treatment of main species with vignettes, tables and graphs, and the second a set of briefer accounts for some additional species.

Species are included in the main section only if there is some information worthy of publication from either the CBC or the WBS, or in a few instances from other BTO censuses. This could be index data of the kind traditionally associated with the CBC and WBS, or trends drawn from the percentages of plots occupied by the species. On this basis, we have been able to include in the main section species as rare as Hobby, Quail and Black Redstart, each of which is so scarce as to be monitored by the Rare Breeding Birds Panel. However, there are a few very common and familiar species which do not qualify for detailed treatment because they are poorly covered by BTO censuses. Swift and Feral Pigeon are the most abundant and widespread of these, but seabirds also fall into this category.

Since the birds treated in the main part of this book were chosen partly because they are easy to survey, the selection of main species has arguably been somewhat inconsistent. In order to bring species coverage to a standard criterion – all terrestrial and freshwater species with British breeding populations of at least 50 pairs – we have added a series of short paragraphs for an additional 59 species. None of these has more than very marginal CBC or WBS input, though some have been investigated by the BTO in other surveys. In all, population trends for 164 species are discussed in this book. Estimated population sizes for all bird species known to have nested in Britain since 1970, 228 species in total, are listed in Appendix 4.

The main systematic section

The 105 species texts which follow describe what we know of the changes in population level in the various species, and the factors which were or may have been responsible. Data from the CBC, WBS and other long-running BTO schemes are integrated with the information available from other sources, including BTO single-species surveys. We also summarise, with reference to the literature, what is known of trends before the CBC began.

While the monitoring schemes give clear and mostly straightforward information about what is happening to the size of a breeding population, the reasons for particular trends are almost always speculative. We have drawn attention to factors which we believe may be implicated in particular population changes, but in most cases formal evidence of a causal link is lacking. Many more investigations remain to be made into the reasons for population change, and it has not been possible to carry out new researches especially for this book. The planned BTO/NCC programme of Integrated Population Monitoring is certain to lead to huge advances, because it will establish whether observed population changes are linked to any known disturbances to breeding productivity or to seasonal mortality.

Regional differences in population trends or densities within the United Kingdom are discussed under a separate subheading. There are relatively few species where sample sizes allow regional indices to be validly compiled, even combining all habitats. Generally, however, there is a remarkable similarity between regions in population trends.

Trends in other European countries, including the Republic of Ireland, are also discussed under a separate subheading. The United Kingdom was the first country in Europe to instigate a national monitoring scheme for common birds, but we have been followed now by six others: Sweden (1969), Denmark (1975), Czechoslovakia (1981), Estonia (1983), and Finland and the Netherlands (both 1984). Recently, a number of developments have been made in co-operation between monitoring schemes in different European countries, including the establishment in 1988 of a twice-yearly newsletter, *Bird Census News*, by the International Bird Census Committee and the European Ornithological Atlas Committee. A report has appeared describing the seven European schemes and listing all their published population index values (Hustings 1988), although for Denmark as well as the United Kingdom these figures have since been superseded (DOFF 1989). For many species the information on population trends across Europe remains sparse.

Explanations of the introductory tables

Each species text begins with a standard table of data which gives a ready summary of some important population parameters.

Present population trend is summarised in a few words for quick reference. An expansion of the bald statement given here will be found in the body of the text.

Percentage of plots occupied is defined here as the percentage of plots on which the species was seen or heard, whether or not it was holding territory: the percentages of plots on which the species was holding territory will almost always be lower. Both are measures of how widespread a species was. They are sometimes referred to as "ubiquity" measures, although strictly the word "ubiquity" is an absolute which cannot be qualified with percentage measures. Figures are given for all habitats combined, or separately for farmland and woodland plots, and for three widely spaced years, 1968, 1978 and 1988. In some cases these reveal a temporal trend which may represent further evidence of a change in status. WBS data are also given for those species which are covered by that scheme, but these are not available for 1968 because the scheme was then not yet in operation. Percentage occurrence, unlike index values, can be compared directly between species, although it should be remembered that in all cases the figures refer directly to census plots. Between-habitat comparisons are also valid provided that it is noted that farmland plots are, on average, more than three times larger than woodland ones. There have been no temporal trends in the composition of farmland or woodland plot samples which would be likely to influence trends in percentage occurrence (see Chapter 2, and the tables in Appendix 3).

Latest estimate of breeding population applies in general to Britain alone, but for several species estimates are available only for Britain and Ireland together. In some cases more detail on how the estimate was arrived at is given in the text. Appendix 4 lists all breeding species with their estimated British population sizes.

Regional density rankings give letter-codes for seven regions of the United Kingdom in decreasing order of the mean density of the species, as calculated from 1988 CBC returns. Rankings are given for farmland, woodland, or for all habitats combined, for all species present on 30 or more plots of the stated category. The regions are denoted by the following codes: SE Southern England, EE Eastern England, WE Western England, NE Northern England, W Wales, S Scotland, and NI

Northern Ireland. The counties included in each English region are mapped in Figure 2.1 and listed in Appendix 3. Omission of a code indicates that no birds were recorded on CBC plots in that region in 1988. In some cases, the rankings suggest a gradient in density across the United Kingdom, but farmland and woodland data sometimes disagree. The rankings given are derived from only a single year's results and may not be representative of the full CBC data-set.

Mean densities are not quantified because of the difficulties in providing such data from CBC plots. Dividing the number of clusters by the area of the plot gives a comparative measure, which indeed has been used in ranking the regions, but such estimates of density are too high because the cluster totals include all edge territories and refer effectively to an area rather larger than the plot itself. Even when corrections are made for edge territories according to the international guidelines (International Bird Census Committee 1969), CBC density data are still too high and remain influenced both by the area of the plot and the nature of its edges (Marchant 1981).

Index and "ubiquity" graphs

In introducing the index graphs, it should be emphasised that index values cannot give numerical comparisons between species or between habitats for the same species. The actual value of an index relates solely to the relationship of that year's population level to that of the same species in the same habitat in the datum year (see Chapter 2). Only the way in which the index values change, for example a steep *versus* a shallow decline, can be compared between species or between habitats. Our use of the same logarithmic scale for plotting all the index graphs ensures that comparisons of rate of change can be made directly. The benefits of using a logarithmic rather than a linear scale are discussed in Chapter 2.

For species not indexed by the CBC or WBS, a graph of percentage occurrence is presented instead. These graphs have linear (not logarithmic) scales on the vertical axis, with scaling factors chosen as appropriate for each. The horizontal scale is uniform on index graphs and graphs of percentage occurrence throughout the book. Percentage occurrence is a far less reliable indicator of population change than an index, because the percentages are generally rather small and thus especially subject to chance variation, and because the plot samples are not paired year-on-year in the way that index samples are. The trends are thus subject to an extra range of biases, such as the variations in mean plot size and changes in the overall composition of the CBC sample referred to in Chapter 2. However, these data are in several cases (for example Hobby and Quail) among the best available for the species concerned: county reports and similar sources often show increases in scarce species as a result of long-term improvements in observer coverage and reporting, but the CBC data, based on standardised methods, are independent of these biases. No percentage occurrence data are presented for years before 1965, when plots were larger and observer effort lower than subsequently, and most observers recorded only a restricted list of species (see Chapter 2).

Little Grebe *Tachybaptus ruficollis*

Present population trend: uncertain; little evidence of change.
Percentages of plots occupied 1968/78/88: all CBC habitats 6/13/11; all WBS plots -/33/28.
Latest estimate of breeding population: 9000-18,000 pairs in Britain and Ireland (Sharrock 1976); 73% of occupied squares were then in Britain.

During the last century and a half the British population of Little Grebes has undoubtedly shown an overall increase, but the timing and extent of this increase are obscured by a general shortage of good quantitative data.

Although Alexander & Lack (1944) considered that over the preceding century there had been no evidence of wide-scale changes in status, other authors, (*e.g.* Temperley 1951, Oakes 1953, Baxter & Rintoul 1953), noted substantial increases in central and southern Scotland and also in northern England from about the 1880s onwards. Numbers further south also appear to have increased over this period (Noble 1906, Norris 1947, Homes 1957). It has been suggested that these widespread changes are the result of climatic amelioration (Parslow 1973, Sharrock 1976).

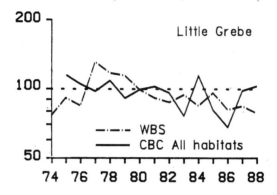

Data collected by the WBS since 1974 are limited but suggest that the breeding population increased considerably over the period 1975-1977. However, the extent of this increase may have been exaggerated by the index because this period seems to have coincided with an expansion by the species into rivers and canals, where alone it is monitored by the WBS (Marchant & Hyde 1979). Since 1980 the population index shows fluctuating values but suggests a slight downward trend. This apparent decline is perhaps the result of recent cold winter weather, there having been particular dips following the winters of 1981/82, 1983/84 and 1985/86. Additionally, some data are available from CBC plots having aquatic boundaries; an index has been constructed for the years since 1975, though this is not a robust one since plot samples are small for some years. This CBC index shows fluctuations which only partly correspond with cold winters, but it agrees with the WBS in showing a small overall downward trend recently. Population levels were no doubt higher during the 1970s, when most winters were relatively mild.

Many Little Grebes are resident in Britain, though outside the breeding season there is much internal redistribution into river systems and coastal waters, plus an unknown amount of emigration. Hence the species is vulnerable to cold winter conditions, which depending on their severity, can result in both hard-weather movements and increased mortality. Reports received by Dobinson & Richards (1964) indicated that the particularly prolonged freezing conditions in the winter of 1962/63 had "exterminated" breeding Little Grebes north of a line between the Severn and the Wash; south of this line there was little or no change in status. Cold winter weather is thus likely to be a major factor influencing the numbers and distribution of this species. However, none of the cold winters of the 1980s affected the Little Grebe so badly as did that of 1962/63.

The increased availability of both reservoir and gravel-pit sites, particularly those offering a range of depths and with fringing vegetation sufficient to conceal a nest, has undoubtedly provided new breeding sites for this species and contributed at least to the earlier increases. Recently, there has also been expansion into new habitats created by environmentally sensitive waterway management: Raven (1986) has described how the development of dense emergent vegetation on low-level flood berms on the River Roding in Essex, constructed as part of flood-alleviation works, resulted in an increase in nesting cover for a range of riparian species including Little Grebe.

Thom (1986) considered that flooding was one of the main threats to successful breeding. The nest, built as an anchored floating platform (Campbell & Ferguson-Lees 1972), must be positioned so as not to flood when heavy rain raises the water level, yet not to be left high and dry during drought. A study at Chew Valley Lake in Avon during 1970-1979 (Vinicombe 1982) showed that the best nesting seasons were cool, wet summers when water levels remained high into August.

Regional variation

For Scotland, Thom (1986) mentioned that there were suggestions of periodic declines or increases, although no systematic or significant trends were evident. Parslow (1973) emphasised the importance of newly available gravel-pit sites in central and eastern England, implicit in which is the suggestion that numbers were increasing in those regions. Quantitative data are lacking, however.

Trends elsewhere in Europe

Very little information is available. In northern Europe, populations are especially liable to be severely depleted by hard winters. Dutch census data record a strong decrease between 1984 and 1985 (Hustings 1988).

Great Crested Grebe *Podiceps cristatus*

Present population trend: increasing.
Percentages of plots occupied 1968/78/88: all CBC habitats 3/6/3; all WBS plots -/10/13.
Latest estimate of breeding population: 6000-7000 adult birds in Britain (Hughes *et al* 1979).

Archaeological and historical data suggest a chequered past for the Great Crested Grebe in Britain. They indicate that the species was widespread some centuries ago but had become scarce by the second half of the 18th century. By the mid-19th century it had regained its earlier status, but subsequently declined to a total of only 42 pairs in England by 1860 (Harrisson & Hollom 1932). The decrease can be partly attributed to human persecution to satisfy the British and European market in "grebe furs".

Egg-collecting was also widespread and serious. Harrisson & Hollom considered that had it not been for private ownership providing refuges from hunting, the bird would have become extinct in this country. With the introduction of a series of Bird Protection Acts between 1870 and 1880 the population began to recover.

The national survey conducted in 1931 (Harrisson & Hollom 1932), estimated a population of 2650 adults in England and Wales and an additional 80 pairs in Scotland. Further sample surveys (Hollom 1936, 1951, 1959) revealed continued increases, steepest in southern Britain, and a full national survey in 1965 estimated 4137-4737 birds to be present (Prestt & Mills 1966). These authors noted that recent population increases were greatest in those counties with the largest areas of newly created wetlands such as gravel pits and reservoirs. The expansion of the population may, in some areas, have led to saturation of standing-water sites and a diversion of further increase onto rivers and canals, where the species is now more numerous than in former years (Youngman 1977, Harvey 1979). The most recent national survey, in 1975, estimated the British population at almost 7000 adult birds (Hughes *et al* 1979).

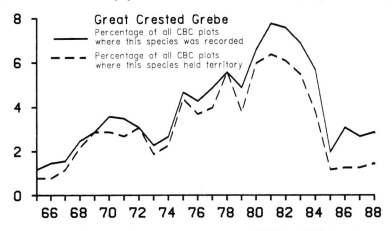

The Great Crested Grebe does not occur on enough WBS or CBC plots for regular monitoring. However, CBC ubiquity values showed an increase during the 1960s and 1970s, which was partly due to the species' overflow onto linear waters (as mentioned above). The fall in ubiquity values in the early 1980s was due to the decrease then of "special" plots, many of which contained standing water.

The increase this century is attributable mostly to legislative protection, which has promoted adult survival, and to the provision of much new habitat by the flooding and restoration of pits previously used for gravel extraction, which has presumably aided the survival and recruitment of young birds into the breeding population. This trend began at a time of climatic amelioration, which is thought to have resulted in a northerly or northwesterly expansion in range of many wetland species across Europe (Sharrock 1976). The results of a Danish study (Asbirk & Dybbro 1978) may also be relevant to Britain. These authors found that densities of grebes increased with enhanced eutrophication of a water-body, and also to some degree with lessened boat disturbance: there was no correlation, however, with the area of reed bed present.

Regional variation

A comparison of the data from the 1965 and 1975 national surveys shows that over that decade the population increased by about 50% in England and Wales but by only about 9% in Scotland. England and Wales together show the greater increase in availability of new freshwater habitats: in 1975, 60% of the English and Welsh population occurred on gravel pits and reservoirs, while in Scotland most pairs were found on natural lakes.

Within England and Wales, population changes between 1965 and 1975 have not been uniform: notable decreases in Essex, Leicestershire, Staffordshire, Cheshire and Gwent contrast with stable or increasing numbers in other areas. These regional differences are unexplained, but they may be linked to changes in habitat availability.

Trends elsewhere in Europe

There has been a general increase in the total European breeding population and a northward range extension into Scandinavia during the present century (Lack 1986). Increases have been noted in Ireland since the turn of the century (Ruttledge 1966, Preston 1976, Hutchinson 1989), the largest concentrations being on the shallow lakes of the midland counties and around Lough Neagh and Lower Lough Erne in the north.

Grey Heron *Ardea cinerea*

Present population trend: increasing.
Percentages of plots occupied 1968/78/88: all CBC habitats 4/15/32; all WBS plots -/75/82.
Latest estimate of breeding population: about 10,155 pairs in the United Kingdom in 1985: England and Wales 5770 pairs, Northern Ireland 585 pairs (Carter *et al*, in prep.); Scotland 3800 pairs (Marquiss 1989).

The Heronries Census is the BTO's longest-running population monitoring scheme, and provides the longest continuous series of population figures for any European breeding bird. This is the basis for the accompanying population graph. Data are available from 1928 in the form of annual counts from a large sample of heronries across the country, and are used to produce an annual population index. This has been augmented by complete censuses in 1928 (Nicholson 1929), 1954 (Burton 1956), 1964 (Stafford 1979) and 1985 (Marquiss 1989; Carter *et al*, in prep.).

Grey Herons today are more numerous than at any other time during the history of the census, but the upward trend is slight and is punctuated by large population crashes. These follow severe winter weather which reduces the accessibility of prey, at least on inland waters, and leads to increased mortality. The magnitude of these effects is related both to the duration of freezing conditions and to the absolute minimum temperature, such that short cold snaps have less effect on survival rates than prolonged spells, even if the latter are less extreme. This relationship between survival and winter conditions has been described in detail by North (1979) for birds in their first year. Mead *et al* (1979) have shown, based on ringing recoveries, that mortality for first-year birds is two or three times greater than that of older ones. This is likely to be related to the inexperience of birds of the year in foraging and dealing with problems of food shortage. North (1979) has suggested that the reason why Grey Herons breed so early in the year is so that they maximise the period from fledging to the first winter.

Mead *et al* (1979) also showed that mortalities varied over three separate time periods, 1909-1941, 1942-1954 and 1955-1975, for different age classes. Specifically, their work illustrated that the survival rates of first-year birds had increased from 1954 onwards (coincident with legislative protection), whereas that of adults had decreased

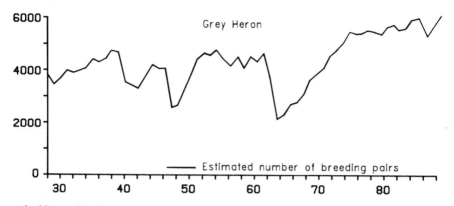

Grey Heron

Estimated number of breeding pairs

6000
4000
2000
0

30   40   50   60   70   80

coincident with increased pesticide use. They considered that, without the Bird Protection Acts which preceded the pesticide era, the Grey Heron population would have declined seriously in the 1950s and 1960s.

Possible pesticide effects are also manifest in the rates of population recovery following hard-winter crashes. Declines in the early and late 1940s were made good within two or three years, aided by greater recruitment into the breeding population of birds in their second year. Following hard winters in the 1960s, however, numbers took more than twice as long to recover (Stafford 1971, Reynolds 1979). Poorer adult survival may have been responsible for this, and possibly also a decrease in reproductive rate due to pesticide contamination: Grey Heron carcasses examined at that time contained large residues of organochlorine compounds (Cramp & Olney 1967, Prestt 1970).

Some problems remain with the data used to produce the population graph. Current work aimed at discovering counts that have not previously been included, and at the methods of estimating population changes, may result in some revision to this graph in the future.

Regional variation

Comparison of the 1985 census results with those from previous national censuses showed that in England, Wales and Northern Ireland there was a tendency for there to be more medium-sized colonies and fewer very large or very small colonies (Carter et al, in prep.). The reasons for this are unclear but may include a decrease in direct persecution, and perhaps a general improvement in water quality. A similar tendency was noted in Scotland at the turn of the century as the range expanded into areas north and west of the Great Glen (Marquiss 1989).

Grey Heron numbers rose in all regions of England for the decade preceding the 1985 census, with data suggesting that increases were greatest in the southwest and the Midlands. Welsh numbers fell slightly over the same period (Carter et al, in prep). Inland in Scotland, numbers rose to a peak in 1981 but then declined by about 30% by 1985; in contrast, the colonies along the north and west coasts of Scotland appeared to be stable during that period, without significant trends being discernible (Marquiss 1989).

More recent data show that the numbers increased at a rate of about 8% a year throughout England between 1986 and 1988. This is particularly encouraging in the light of fears that many heronry sites in southern and eastern Britain may have been damaged irreparably in the hurricane-force winds of October 1987 (Carter 1989a).

53

These data also show that the downward trend in Wales has been reversed.
For Northern Ireland, Wells (1978) reported an increase of 11% between 1964 and 1977 but added that part of that rise might have been an artefact arising from better coverage. A total of 619-630 nests were counted there in 1977, compared to an estimated population of 585 pairs in 1985 (Carter *et al*, in prep.). It must be borne in mind that regional variations are of necessity based on small sample sizes, which reduces the likelihood of detecting change. For example, recent Scottish changes could only be proven over several years, with variation of less than 30% not being detectable in annual figures (Marquiss 1989).

Trends elsewhere in Europe
During the present century, the Grey Heron has expanded its European range northwards into Norway, Sweden and Finland, and this has been attributed to climatic amelioration (Cramp & Simmons 1977). Cramp & Simmons also reported increases throughout central Europe (after declines earlier in the century), whereas data from the southern part of the Continent suggest a decline.

Mute Swan *Cygnus olor*

Present population trend: stable.
Percentages of plots occupied 1968/78/88: all CBC habitats 5/12/15; all WBS plots -/54/47.
Latest estimate of breeding population: 3150 breeding pairs in Britain, plus 12,600 non-breeders (Ogilvie 1986).

Despite the long history of royal and private "ownership" of Mute Swans (dating from the year 966), information on the numbers in Britain over recent centuries is very limited. However, what data there are suggest that large numbers, almost certainly greater than those of today, were present from the 13th to the 15th centuries, when these birds were farmed to provide food. With the domestication of the Greylag Goose and the introduction of the Common Turkey as a farm animal in the early 16th century, swan-keeping declined, and numbers are likely to have fallen considerably as a result. Subsequently, good data are available on swan numbers on the River Thames, from Crown and other records; adults and young are still caught for marking during the traditional annual "swan-upping" (Birkhead & Perrins 1986).
It is only in recent decades that systematic surveys of the national population of Mute Swans have been carried out. The first of these, in the springs of 1955 and 1956, followed widespread reports of increases in swan numbers. Swan-upping records from the lower River Thames, for example, had shown an increase in the number of swans caught from 412 in 1948 to 1311 in 1956, equivalent to an annual increment of over 15%. Such population growth led to complaints from farmers about an increased incidence of crop damage, and from fishermen concerned over the impact of swans on fish reproduction. The BTO survey estimated a British population of 17,850-19,250 birds in 1955-1956 (Campbell 1960), although these figures were later revised by Ogilvie (1981) to 19,900-21,600, in view of some local under-recording. An additional partial survey in 1961 gave similar results (Eltringham 1963).
Subsequently Ogilvie (1967) showed that there had been a 25% decline in the

national population between the winters of 1960/61 and 1964/65. Several suggestions may be made to explain this, such as increased disturbance due to pleasure craft, and loss of suitable habitat following drainage or navigation and flood-alleviation works. Of the reported causes of death of Mute Swans, collision with overhead wires was found by Ogilvie (1967) to be the most important, accounting for over 44% of cases. However, the cold winters of 1961/62 and 1962/63 must have temporarily increased the mortality rate.

After this, total numbers remained constant, though there were marked regional variations: increases in the north compensated for declines in the Midlands and west. Concern over these large and well-publicised declines prompted additional survey work to be undertaken in 1978, and a new census estimated the total number of swans in Britain as 18,400 (Ogilvie 1981). This represented a decline of 8-15% from 1955-1956, the fall being most pronounced in parts of the English Midlands and along the River Thames. Urban flocks in particular were much reduced (Bacon 1980, Hardman & Cooper 1980).

Towards the end of the 1970s evidence began to accumulate of a particularly insidious threat to swan populations, through lead poisoning. Lead weights lost and discarded by anglers were being ingested by swans along with the grit they needed to aid in their digestive process, and were quickly ground down in the muscular gizzard and absorbed into the blood. This affected the neuromuscular system, the birds showing a characteristic kinked neck due to weakened muscles. Death resulted from starvation because, although the swan may have been feeding normally, the lead inhibited the action of those muscles which carry food through the gut. Post-mortem analyses and studies of blood lead levels showed, for instance, that 90% of swan deaths on the River Trent in the east Midlands, and 77% at Stratford-on-Avon in Warwickshire, between 1973 and 1980 were due to lead poisoning (NCC 1981). Of 94 dead swans from the River Thames examined between 1979 and 1981, 57% were found to have died from lead poisoning as a result of ingesting anglers' weights (Birkhead 1982). Based on these findings, Birkhead & Perrins (1986) estimated that between 3370 and 4190 Mute Swans had died annually in Britain from this single cause.

Against this background, and on recommendations from the NCC for the regular monitoring of Mute Swan populations, another national survey was carried out in 1983 (Ogilvie 1986). Results showed that, since 1978, overall numbers had risen by about 7% to 18,750, although it was considered that an increase of this size was within the margin of error of the census method.

In the light of these results, the sale of lead weights was prohibited under the Control of Pollution (Anglers' Lead Weights) Regulations 1986 which came into operation on 1st January 1987. Since then there has been a significant reduction in the incidence of lead poisoning of Mute Swans, at least on the River Thames, but almost certainly elsewhere too (Sears 1988).

WBS indexing of the Mute Swan population since 1974 shows that there was a decline following the winter of 1981/82 and then recovery, but no general trend over the whole period. This is not inconsistent with the results previously described from the 1978 and 1983 censuses. It should be noted that the WBS samples are small for this species. Also small are the samples of CBC plots which have an aquatic boundary. Compared to the WBS index, that constructed from CBC data shows a more pronounced fall in 1977 and 1978, a more continuous period of subsequent recovery, and a clearer upward trend over the last few years.

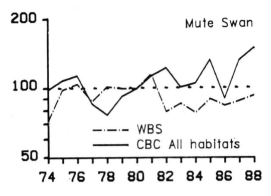

Mute Swan

200

100

50

—·—·— WBS
———— CBC All habitats

74 76 78 80 82 84 86 88

Regional variation

The stability or small increase recorded during 1978-1983 masked marked regional variations in population trends; swans had increased in counties bordering the south coast, in parts of eastern and northern England, northeast Scotland and North Wales, but elsewhere were either stable or in decline (Ogilvie 1986).

Trends elsewhere in Europe

A large increase in breeding populations throughout Europe has occurred since the 1950s. Increase continues in many areas, despite temporary halts or reversals in hard winters (Rüger *et al* 1986).

Canada Goose *Branta canadensis*

Present population trend: strong long-term increase.
Percentages of plots occupied 1968/78/88: all CBC habitats 3/9/15; all WBS plots -/25/39.
Latest estimate of breeding population: approaching 50,000 birds in Britain, including non-breeders (Salmon *et al* 1988).

The Canada Goose was first introduced into Britain in the 17th century as an ornamental bird in the collection of King Charles II in St James's Park, London. It flourished, and by the end of that century had been introduced onto private estates and park lakes in many parts of England. Escapes from collections were inevitable; the first record of a free-living bird was one shot on the Thames in Middlesex in 1731. Between then and the end of the 19th century many feral populations became established in scattered localities as far north as Rydal Water in Cumbria: Lever (1977) documents their history in detail. During this period, however, it remained predominantly a bird of private estates and parkland.

The first national census was conducted in 1953, and found that the total British population, estimated at 2200-4000 birds, was divided into a number of isolated groups within each of which the geese were sedentary (Blurton-Jones 1956). These units appeared to remain discrete and self-contained at all seasons, to the extent that this author reported some pairs failing to breed within them due to competition for nest sites, despite suitable habitats being available nearby.

In their native North America, some populations of Canada Geese undergo long-distance migrations, south to winter and northwards to breed, but this behaviour has not been transferred to this side of the Atlantic. However, Dennis (1964) established the existence of a moult migration of Yorkshire-bred Canada Geese to the Beauly Firth, Inverness, in late summer. Walker (1970) described the development of this moult migration in detail and showed that approximately half the birds in the flock were immature, the remainder being failed breeders or non-breeders. This moulting flock had increased to 1000 birds by 1983 (Thom 1986).

As the population groups increased in size during the 1950s and early 1960s, conflicts with agricultural interests soon became evident. To alleviate this and to provide birds for shooting, approximately 1400 were caught and transplanted to vacant sites elsewhere (Ogilvie 1969). This had little benefit to agriculture but did aid natural dispersal and provide greater opportunities for population expansion (Owen et al 1986). Additionally, some transported birds wandered from their new locations and must have given rise to spontaneous colonisation in many areas (Ogilvie 1969). The colonisation of many newly available freshwater sites such as gravel pits and reservoirs occurred at this time. A repeat census in 1967/68 estimated the population at 10,500 birds (Ogilvie 1969), and by 1976 the estimate had risen to 19,400 (Ogilvie 1977). The trend continued, and during the Winter Atlas period 1981-1984 the population was estimated to be 30,000-35,000 (Lack 1986), with a projected increase to 50,000 birds by 1990 assuming the rate of increase then current was maintained (Owen et al 1986). The latter figure had almost been reached by the winter of 1987/88 (Salmon et al 1988).

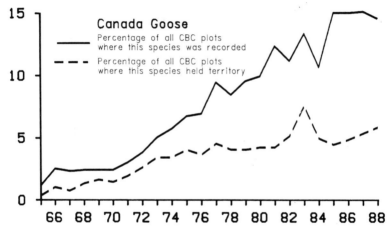

The Canada Goose is not monitored by the WBS or CBC, which do not cover the larger standing waters favoured by this species. Yet the species' upward trend is apparent in CBC ubiquity values (see graph), as more pairs occupy peripheral sites in southern and central England where the CBC has its strongest representation. Nationally, Owen et al (1986) commented that there was no reason to believe that habitat shortage would limit numbers since large parts of the country, for example in northern England and Scotland, appear suitable and are currently unoccupied. They warned that only co-ordinated action could prevent this species from assuming pest proportions, a view endorsed by Thom (1986). Several authors have suggested winter shooting as the best method of control (e.g.Ogilvie 1969, Lever 1977), but Owen et al (1986) pointed out that to maintain the population at its 1980 level an additional 2000 birds would have to be killed each year.

Regional variation
   The annual rate of population increase, about 8%, is the same nationally as for the long-established population groups (Owen *et al* 1986).

Trends elsewhere in Europe
   Following introductions in Sweden in 1933, and later in Norway and Finland, the Swedish population at least is increasing rapidly: the index values there increased tenfold between 1975 and 1985 (Hustings 1988). The Scandinavian total now exceeds 50,000 birds (Owen *et al* 1986). Lever (1977) cited "considerable numbers" breeding in the park at Versailles, France, from the mid-17th century to the late 18th century, but no feral populations are now known elsewhere in Europe.

Shelduck *Tadorna tadorna*

Present population trend: probably still increasing.
Percentages of plots occupied 1968/78/88: all CBC habitats 4/11/15; all WBS plots -/13/18.
Latest estimate of breeding population: 12,000 nesting pairs in Britain, and 26,000 non-breeders (Owen *et al* 1986).

   The breeding habitats of the Shelduck are mainly coastal and estuarine, the preferred sites being linear shores adjacent to intertidal feeding areas that are small enough for single pairs to defend as feeding territories. More extensive intertidal areas are an overflow habitat for breeding birds. The function of territory in the Shelduck appears to be to provide an exclusive feeding area for the female from the pre-laying period to the time of hatching; territories are established only when prey abundance exceeds a critical minimum (Patterson 1982). Although it might be expected that a given site could support more breeding Shelducks, each with a smaller territory, when prey abundance is high compared to seasons when it is low, this has been shown not to be true (Buxton 1975). It is freedom from disturbance by conspecifics which seems to be important; and where feeding conditions are good, the territory-holders may have more time to chase away other Shelducks (Pienkowski & Evans 1982*a*).
   Shelducks breed colonially as well as in dispersed pairs, the latter being more successful due to higher duckling survival. In colonial situations there is more interference at nests, including nest parasitism and egg-dumping, leading to desertions (Pienkowski & Evans 1982*b*), and more predation of ducklings by gulls while parent Shelducks are fighting, while gathering of young in crèches at colony sites also depresses duckling survival (Evans & Pienkowski 1982, Pienkowski & Evans 1982*a*). Hence colonies are not self-maintaining, but depend upon immigration. Population regulation in the Shelduck occurs in the breeding season, through territorial behaviour and its effects on the production of young.
   Nationally, this species has shown a considerable increase over the course of the present century. Parslow (1973) noted that since the mid-1940s the Shelduck had colonised several parts of the coasts of eastern, southern and southwest England. In part this may be viewed as a recovery, aided by legislative protection, following declines during the 19th century attributable to persecution and habitat loss, but real

range expansion has also occurred. In addition to coastal increases, a symptom of the success of this species has been the tendency, summarised by Sharrock (1976), to colonise inland waters. Nisbet & Vine (1955) reported that Shelducks had nested at Wisbech sewage-farm (on the borders of Norfolk, Cambridgeshire and Lincolnshire), six miles from the mouth of a tidal river, since at least 1923, and that several other sites in the Fens had since been occupied. The breeding range has also extended inland from other coasts, and some land-locked counties now support breeding Shelducks. Nesting was first noted in Berkshire in 1950 (Walker 1955), Warwickshire in 1970, Worcestershire in 1978, and Staffordshire in 1979 (Harrison *et al* 1982). While there is no reason to believe that the movement inland will cease, this is unlikely ever to become a major sector of the national breeding population.

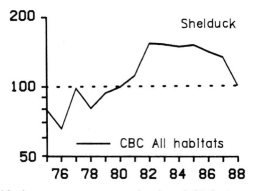

Breeding Shelducks are present on a minority of CBC plots, more particularly those which are close to a coast or estuary. Since 1975 the samples have been large enough to construct a population index. This reveals initial increases up to a brief plateau between 1982 and 1985; but since then the index has fallen somewhat, back to the 1980 level. The winter of 1985/86 was a severe one, which may have influenced the trend; but the CBC index actually rose after the previous hard winters of 1978/79 and 1981/82.

Associated with the population increase in Britain is the recent development of new moulting sites here. Previously, almost all the Shelducks from northwest Europe undertook a moult migration from their breeding areas to the Heligoland Bight in the West German Wadden Sea, where up to 100,000 birds have been recorded in July/August (Owen *et al* 1986), but many now moult in Britain. The first moulting group was found here in 1951, at Bridgwater Bay in Somerset (Eltringham & Boyd 1960), and others have since been located on the Firth of Forth in 1975 (Bryant 1978), the Wash in 1977 (Bryant 1981), and the Humber in 1978 (Tasker 1982). Pienkowski & Evans (1979) gave some evidence that it is immature Shelducks which tend to establish new moulting areas. It is likely that more new moulting sites will be established if the breeding population continues to increase.

Regional variation

Increases in the breeding population have been most marked in the east and south of England. Local reductions have occurred however, most notably in South Wales, Lancashire, Northumberland and Ayrshire, due to coastal disturbance (Parslow 1973).

The overall increase in the winter population (Owen *et al* 1986) masks a considerable decline in Scotland over the period 1960-1982, coincident with large increases in England and Wales.

There has been a widespread increase throughout Europe over the course of the present century. associated with legislative protection, leading to higher densities at coastal sites plus increased inland nesting (Cramp & Simmons 1977).

Mandarin Duck *Aix galericulata*

Present population trend: increasing.
Percentages of plots occupied 1968/78/88: all CBC habitats 0/1/2; all WBS plots -/8/7.
Latest estimate of breeding population: about 7000 individuals in Britain (Davies 1988).

The Mandarin Duck is a native of the Far East, breeding in Japan, northern China and extreme eastern USSR, but it has long been a popular bird with aviculturalists throughout the world. It was first brought to England before 1745, into a private waterfowl collection at Richmond, Surrey, but the first record of a wild-living bird was not made until over a century later, in 1866, when a bird was shot on the Thames in Berkshire (Lever 1977). In the early 1900s, Mandarin Ducks were introduced into the Duke of Bedford's estate at Woburn in Bedfordshire, where they flourished: numbers had increased to over 300 birds by the time of the First World War. By the end of the Second World War, numbers there had halved, and today the population appears stable at 10-15 pairs (Fuller 1988). While this is certainly the oldest established population of this species in Britain, the best known is probably that at Virginia Water, a major stronghold of the species on the Surrey/Berkshire border. Birds at this site derive from escapes from the Ezra waterfowl collection, near Cobham in Surrey, and from introductions into the London parks in the 1930s (Lever 1977). Many less successful introductions have been made elsewhere: the distribution of these, and of waterfowl collections (from which birds can escape), best explains the patchiness of the current breeding distribution, as described comprehensively by Davies (1988).

The Mandarin Duck is typically shy and secretive, and its preference for secluded and undisturbed waters in mature open deciduous woodland makes censusing very difficult. Davies (1988) has shown the Mandarin Duck to be far more widespread than was thought at the time of the Breeding Atlas (Sharrock 1976): the species is scattered over much of central and southern England, with particular strongholds in Surrey, Berkshire and Buckinghamshire. Isolated populations are also known from central Wales, Tayside and elsewhere. However, Davies (1988) attributed this apparent change in status to under-recording during earlier surveys, rather than to range expansion. The species occurs on too few WBS or CBC plots for population monitoring, though CBC ubiquity values (see graph) suggest that there may have been genuine increase since the Breeding Atlas years.

The Mandarin Duck is a hole-nester, with three-quarters of recorded sites being in cavities of oak and ash trees (Davies & Baggott 1989). Nestboxes are also widely and readily used, and in areas where the availability of natural sites is limited, their provision may be important in allowing further growth of the population. Populations may also be limited by competition with native birds for nest sites. For example, Fuller (1988) considered that Mandarin Ducks at Woburn were unlikely to increase because of competition with a thriving local population of Jackdaws. Even so, the breeding range of the Mandarin Duck is likely to continue to expand because, as a hole-nester feeding principally on aquatic insects in the summer, and acorns, chestnuts and beechmast in the winter, it exploits a vacant ecological niche (Cramp & Simmons 1977). However, since Mandarins are relatively sedentary residents, further expansion of the population in terms of both range and numbers may be temporarily halted or reversed by severe winter conditions, and limited overall by a naturally slow rate of expansion.

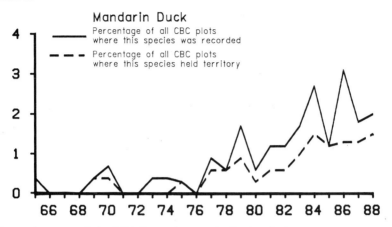

Mandarin Duck

Revered as a symbol of fidelity and mutual affection in its native Far East, the Mandarin Duck is nevertheless threatened and decreasing there, due to loss of nesting habitat as a result of deforestation, and it is speculated that the British population may already be larger than that in the original range outside Japan (Davies 1985). The Japanese population still probably equals or exceeds the numbers in Britain (Sir Christopher Lever, *in litt.*).

Regional variation

No regional differences are known in long-term trends. Winter flocks tend to form where food is provided for game or for wildfowl, and the distribution of such sites is likely to affect population trends locally.

Trends elsewhere in Europe

No self-supporting feral populations elsewhere in Europe were known to Cramp & Simmons (1977), but the species was noted as an escape from waterfowl collections. There are recent reports of more than fifty free-flying Mandarin Ducks in Berlin, and of the species nesting among sand-dunes in the Netherlands (A.K.Davies *in litt.*).

Teal *Anas crecca*

Present population trend: uncertain; little evidence of change.
Percentages of plots occupied 1968/78/88: all CBC habitats 6/6/7; all WBS plots -/21/21.
Latest estimate of breeding population: 3000-4500 pairs in Britain (Owen *et al* 1986).

The Teal is thinly distributed as a breeding species throughout Great Britain and Ireland, becoming generally more abundant in the north and west. Its favoured breeding habitats are boggy moorland pools, though it also nests in lowland marshy vegetation fringing lakes and slow-flowing rivers. In Sutherland and Caithness, where this is the commonest breeding duck on moorland pools and peatland *dubh-lochain*, it shows a distinct preference for acidic environments, selecting waters with lower pH values where there is a choice (Fox *et al* 1989). Its retiring behaviour makes censuses difficult and accurate assessments of populations and trends almost impossible. Broods are seldom seen on open water, preferring to stay concealed among emergent vegetation (Sharrock 1976). Though Teal are recorded in WBS and CBC data, the registrations are too few for annual indexing. CBC ubiquity values (see graph) show an overall increase in the numbers of plots on which the species is seen; but the corresponding values for pairs certainly holding territory have not changed overall, despite being temporarily higher for a period in the middle of this span.

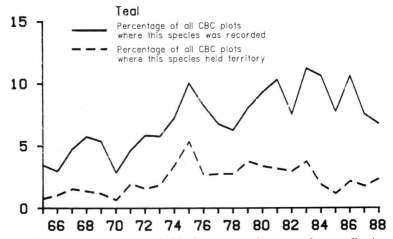

Rainfall and temperature are probably the two most important factors affecting the timing and success of the Teal's breeding season (Ogilvie 1983). Migration back to the breeding grounds may be delayed by cold weather conditions in spring, leading to a later start to nesting. Suitable breeding habitat is less extensive in a dry spring than in a wetter season, and if drought continues, the drying out of breeding pools will force the female to lead the ducklings on a hazardous overland journey. Conversely, if rainfall is high during laying and incubation some nests may be lost due to flooding; later in the season heavy rain renders ducklings liable to chilling (Owen 1977).

At a local level, it is possible to increase the breeding population by active habitat management. Fox (1986) described how the blocking of ditches on a coastal raised mire in Wales, creating deep linear pools with abundant emergent vegetation, led to a three- to four-fold increase in the number of nesting Teal over two years. This demonstrates that, at least in some areas, the availability of suitable breeding habitat is limiting the population, despite the apparently wide range of habitat types used.

Native breeding Teal are largely resident but their numbers are augmented during the winter months by immigrants mainly from Scandinavia (Cramp & Simmons 1977). National Wildfowl Count data show that the number of Teal wintering in Great Britain has increased considerably over the period 1960-1982, giving a recent average peak of about 100,000 birds (Owen et al 1986). This parallels an increase throughout Europe where the total population is estimated to have trebled between 1967 and 1983 (Rüger et al 1986). That this has occurred despite extensive habitat loss due to drainage, may in part be due to legislative protection but may also be partly attributable to enhanced feeding opportunities within the breeding range, perhaps most notably in Scandinavia; an increased abundance of aquatic insects occurs during the early stages of nutrient enrichment and acidification (Eriksson 1985, Rüger et al 1986). A preference by Scottish Teal for acidic environments has already been mentioned. However, there are no data to suggest that breeding populations have increased in those parts of Britain where the acidification of fresh waters has been shown to have occurred (Harriman & Morrison 1982).

Winter conditions have an important influence on the size of the breeding population. The Teal, the smallest of the European waterfowl, is more susceptible to severe winter conditions than are other species, and cold-weather movements occur more frequently and over greater distances as a result (Ogilvie 1983). Similarly, since the duck is smaller than the drake, females are more cold-sensitive than males and move sooner and further under the stress of cold conditions (Bennett & Bolen 1978). This results in a greater preponderance of males in the north, and females in the south of the wintering range. Tamisier (1974) suggests that wintering populations are also regulated by water level (which affects food availability), and that hunting pressure plays an important role too.

Regional variation

Atkinson-Willes (1963) reported that parts of the former counties of Aberdeenshire, Perthshire and Fife, which had previously been regarded as breeding strongholds, had been abandoned since the 1930s, but no reason was suggested. He noted no major changes elsewhere, but Parslow (1973) commented later on probable decreases in parts of Galloway and in Suffolk since about the 1930s. He also considered that breeding in Cornwall and Dorset occurred more sporadically then than in recent decades. Cox (1984) reported that breeding numbers of Teal on Old Hall Marshes, previously the Essex stronghold, had declined from about 30 pairs in the mid-19th century to no more than eight by the 1950s and only one or two pairs since. However, breeding Teal in lowland Britain are probably opportunistic in their use of individual sites; local concentrations of pairs dwindle when those sites lose their attraction, but without such instances necessarily being symptomatic of an overall regional reduction.

Trends elsewhere in Europe

It is not known whether the widespread increases in wintering numbers stem from increases in the breeding population in northern Europe. A strong decrease of Swedish index values during 1975-1986 (Hustings 1988) argues against this idea.

Mallard *Anas platyrhynchos*

Present population trend: apparently now stable after period of increase.
Percentages of plots occupied 1968/78/88: farmland 58/76/89; woodland 27/40/46; all WBS plots -/97/100.
Latest estimate of breeding population: 70,000-150,000 pairs in Britain and Ireland (Sharrock 1976); 74% of occupied squares were then in Britain.
Regional density rankings 1988: farmland S>WE>SE>W>EE>NI.

The Mallard has always been the most abundant and ubiquitous of our breeding ducks, showing a continuum from the wary inhabitants of rural wetlands to the full-winged birds of urban parks which have learned to live in close proximity to man. So far as is known, there had been no major changes in the species' modern status prior to the start of the CBC. Quantified data are few, but duck counts in late winter (when fewer immigrants are present) suggest that the Mallard population level remained virtually unchanged between 1949 and 1964 (Parslow 1973). The severe winter of 1962/63 caused regional redistribution at the time, but little reduction in the size of the 1963 breeding population, perhaps because there had been less wildfowling in the harsh conditions of that winter (Dobinson & Richards 1964).

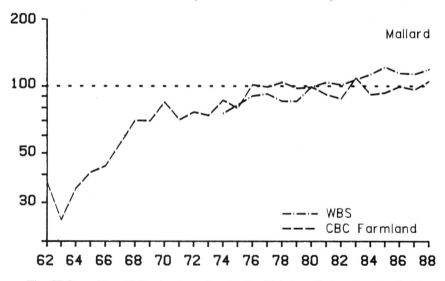

The CBC monitors Mallard only on farmland, which is unlikely to be a key habitat for the species. There, index values were lower during the early years 1962-1966 than subsequently. They almost doubled between 1967 and 1976, and since 1976 have stabilised around a new, higher level, with only slight disturbances following the cold winters of 1978/79 and 1981/82. These recent twelve years of stability, following ten of increase, suggest that maximum capacity has been reached on farmland. The WBS recorded increase from its outset in 1974 up to 1985, since when there has been little change. This temporal difference between the two sets of data is puzzling, for one would expect waterways to be a preferred habitat which filled up before overspill occurred onto farmland.

The cause of the increase since the mid-1960s is uncertain: there is no evidence that it was recovery from a previous decline (Parslow 1973). It may have owed something to an expansion of release programmes. Because of its abundance, the Mallard is a major quarry species for wildfowlers, who have long pursued the practice of releasing artificially reared birds to provide more birds for shooting. When released directly onto shooting preserves, 90% or more are shot in their first autumn; however, some releases are made into protected areas, where first-year survival will be higher, when the objective is to supplement the wild population (Harrison & Wardell 1970, Sharrock 1976). The scale of this rearing and releasing has increased over the years. By the 1980s around 500,000 birds were being liberated each year, though Mallard hunting statistics suggest that over 80% are shot during their first season (Harradine 1983, 1985). Allowing also for other causes of mortality, the contribution made by released birds to the breeding population must be relatively small, though it is presumed to be a regular increment. Alternatively, large-scale releasing of artificially reared birds may simply serve to reduce hunting pressure on the wild stock.

There is evidence that density-dependent control of the British Mallard population operates during the winter period (Hill 1984). Overwinter losses are highest following years when large numbers of young are reared, and the degree of density-dependence determines the extent to which the birds are able to compensate for shooting and other causes of death. The latter include poisoning through ingestion of lead pellets, which is (or has been) a notable factor (Mudge 1981).

Regional variation

There is little evidence of any regional variation in CBC trends. The largest post-1966 increases in the farmland CBC appear to have been in eastern and northern England, though these still appear low down in the 1988 density ranking.

Trends elsewhere in Europe

Cramp & Simmons (1977) report that despite local increases across the European range, all main geographical populations (defined by migration flyway catchments) are thought to be declining due to hunting pressures. Hutchinson (1979) disputes this, however, and suggests that in most countries the species is actually increasing. Winter count totals for northwest Europe presented by Rüger (1986) indicate a slowly increasing population.

A marked expansion northward has been noted in Norway since the 1870s (Haftorn 1971), and post-1945 increase in Finland (Grenquist 1970). Recent declines were reported from Sweden and throughout France by Cramp & Simmons (1977), but subsequent index values from Sweden have shown an increase (Hustings 1988).

Tufted Duck *Aythya fuligula*

Present population trend: fluctuates, but still increasing.
Percentages of plots occupied 1968/78/88: all CBC habitats 4/11/14; all WBS plots -/40/36.
Latest estimate of breeding population: over 7000 pairs in Britain (Owen *et al* 1986).

From the first British report of breeding, in 1849 in Yorkshire, the Tufted Duck has increased rapidly and expanded its breeding distribution, and it is now our most common and widely distributed breeding diving duck. A graphic illustration of the increase during the early phase of this colonisation is provided by Baxter & Rintoul (1953). They reported that the first nest on Loch Leven (Kinross) was found in 1875 and that by the end of that decade over 100 broods were present there.

The species is now widely distributed over most of the country but is largely absent from areas more than 400 m above sea level, or where there are no standing water-bodies larger than one hectare. Much of Wales, southwest England, and north and west Scotland are therefore sparsely populated. In Caithness and Sutherland it shows a preference for those lochs with low acidity; this is probably linked to the calcium requirements of bivalve prey (Fox *et al* 1989).

At least two factors are important to the success of this colonisation, which is still continuing. First, the initial expansion was probably stimulated by climatic amelioration; second, it is likely that the momentum of expansion was maintained by the opportunistic use of newly created freshwater sites such as reservoirs and gravel pits, which have proliferated since the 1930s. Its tolerance of disturbance (see Cryer *et al* 1987) and its tameness enable the Tufted Duck to establish itself close to human habitation and activity, and thereby to utilise areas unsuitable for other more wary species. The success of colonisation may also be related to the expansion, during the mid-19th century, of the zebra mussel. This mollusc was first recorded in the Surrey Commercial Docks (Greater London) in 1824, from where it spread quickly throughout the then new canal system; by about 1850 it had attained its current distribution, which comprises much of England (not the southwest) northwards to a line joining the Humber and Morecambe Bay (Kerney & Morton 1970; M.P.Kerney, *in litt.*). Olney (1963) reported that where the zebra mussel occurs it is usually abundant, and in some cases is fed on by Tufted Ducks to the virtual exclusion of other animal matter. Nevertheless, the Tufted Duck is a generalist omnivore and is probably highly adaptable to local conditions; it does not seem to have many competitors in base-enriched waters.

Tufted Ducks occur on relatively few WBS plots, and censusing by the WBS is not likely to be very accurate (Marchant & Hyde 1980*b*). Many of the birds recorded may be nesting well away from the waterway, while at some sites summering birds may be mostly non-breeders. Broods are seldom seen, and this species is so often a late breeder that broods may appear only after the census season ends in mid-July.

WBS index values for Tufted Duck are available from 1974, and others are available from CBC data for a limited period, 1978-1986, within which annual plot samples are adequate. Both sources show wide fluctuations. These may be due more to annual variations in food availability, and to overall habitat conditions such as result from variations in rainfall, than to overwinter mortality as a result of severe weather. The freezing of inland wintering sites induces hard weather movements to open waters, and only in exceptionally prolonged cold conditions is mortality likely to increase significantly. However, the Tufted Duck's preference for enclosed waters

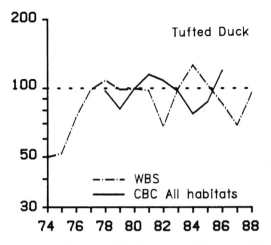

Tufted Duck

WBS
CBC All habitats

such as lakes, reservoirs and gravel pits almost certainly means that the linear WBS plots are not typical for this species. Hence the known trend towards continuing increase is inadequately reflected in WBS and CBC figures.

Regional variation

Thom (1986) suggests that the Scottish breeding population has now stabilised, even though numbers continue to increase in England.

Trends elsewhere in Europe

A widespread increase across Europe in the late 19th and early 20th centuries is attributable to climatic warming then (Parslow 1973). This has contributed, along with an increased native population, to a doubling in the midwinter peak since the early 1960s (Owen *et al* 1986).

Sparrowhawk *Accipiter nisus*

Present population trend: sustained recovery from earlier major decline probably now completed.
Percentages of plots occupied 1968/78/88: farmland 11/33/61; woodland 10/32/43.
Latest estimate of breeding population: 25,000 breeding pairs in Britain, plus 30,000 non-breeders (Newton 1986).
Regional density rankings 1988: all CBC habitats NE>EE>NI>W>SE.

Prior to the modern agricultural changes which began in the 1950s, Sparrowhawk fortunes were linked to levels of persecution from gamekeepers. These birds increased during the First World War, when the temporary virtual cessation of keepering effectively ended the heyday of the big sporting estates: fewer gamekeepers were employed thereafter. Sparrowhawks increased again in many areas during the Second World War, and only part of these gains was lost with a post-war return of gamekeepers. But after the mid-1950s there was a serious national decline. From a questionnaire survey of both amateur and professional ornithologists in 1964, Prestt

(1965) concluded that the Sparrowhawk had declined from being one of the commonest and most widely distributed of our diurnal birds of prey, to the extent that there was not a single county remaining in England where it could be considered a common breeding bird.

The decline, which occurred chiefly in the period 1957-1963, followed the introduction of several new organochlorine pesticides (Newton & Haas 1984). Residues from these accumulated in prey species which fed in treated areas, and were finally concentrated in the bodies of predators at the top of the food chain. Such contamination had not only a direct effect by lethal poisoning of adults, but also more insidious sublethal effects, which included eggshell thinning (leading to breakage during laying or incubation) and reduction of hatching success (Newton 1979).

Newton & Haas (1984) showed that, in any given region, the extent of the population decline was related to the proportion of tilled land there. The higher the proportion, the more pronounced was the decline, since it was in such areas that the use of these pesticides was most intensive. Thus in eastern and southeastern England the Sparrowhawk had been virtually extirpated by 1960, but further north and west, the populations were less affected. This general pattern was evident in fieldwork for the Breeding Atlas during 1968-1972 (Sharrock 1976).

Sparrowhawk populations were quick to respond to restrictions imposed in the early 1960s on the use of aldrin, dieldrin and heptachlor, the most toxic of these agrochemicals. Increasing numbers were noted first in those areas where populations had been least severely depleted (the north and west), with a wave of recovery rippling eastwards towards those areas where the species had been effectively exterminated (Newton & Haas 1984). In Kent and Sussex the main recovery, dating from the mid-1970s, occurred when there was a major reduction of DDT use in orchards (Shrubb 1985). At the time of the Winter Atlas there were still some eastern arable regions where Sparrowhawks remained sparse or absent (Lack 1986), but even there recovery seems to have been completed during the last three years (I.Newton, *in litt.*).

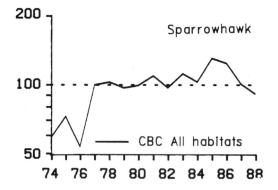

Prior to 1974 a CBC index for Sparrowhawk could not be calculated, because there were too few pairs on census plots, although an overall trend could be obtained from the annual proportions of CBC plots where the species was recorded (Marchant 1980). These ubiquity values, for both farmland and woodland, rose from less than 5% in the early 1960s to over 25% in the late 1970s. Since 1974, CBC registrations have been sufficient to allow index values to be calculated. These show big increases up to 1978 (despite a temporary, unexplained fall in 1976), followed by a much shallower rate of growth. This slowing of the rate and its cessation in the last three years probably indicate that Sparrowhawk densities on CBC plots are now at or close to their maximum, which accords with the view (see earlier) that recovery is now virtually completed. Some further increase is likely as additional suitable sites become available in new forestry plantations; and there is every prospect of pairs overflowing into the timbered parks and large gardens of towns and cities (Newton 1986). Indeed, the species is already well established in such cities as Bristol and Edinburgh.

Regional variation
See above. CBC data are too few to permit regional subdivision.

Trends elsewhere in Europe
Cramp & Simmons (1980) recorded widespread and marked declines in the 1960s or earlier in all European countries, the use of organochlorine pesticides being the most important factor. Subsequently, various degrees of recovery have been reported widely across northern Europe, from North Sea countries eastward to Germany and Finland (Newton & Haas 1984). In the Netherlands, for example, a population collapse in the 1960s due to agrochemicals had been virtually made good by the mid-1970s, and the Sparrowhawk continued to increase through a spread into lowland habitats previously unoccupied; only now is saturation level being reached (Bijlsma 1989).

Buzzard *Buteo buteo*

Present population trend: modest increase, mainly through in-filling; perhaps late stage of slow recovery from earlier decline.
Percentages of plots occupied 1968/78/88: all CBC habitats 9/9/16.
Latest estimate of breeding population: 12,000-15,000 territorial pairs in the United Kingdom in 1983 (Taylor, K., *et al* 1988); at least 100 pairs in Northern Ireland in 1986 (Hutchinson 1989).

The Buzzard was the subject of BTO and BTO-aided surveys in 1954 (Moore 1957), 1964 (Prestt 1965) and 1983 (Taylor, K., *et al* 1988). Because of its mainly northern and western distribution the species occurs on rather few of the CBC plots, though it is possible to present an index for 1977 onwards. However, the indicated trend of increase to a 1981 peak, and then subsequent decline, is at variance with knowledge of the Buzzard's status obtained from the special surveys already mentioned. Presumably the discrepancy arises because the CBC sites include atypical ones peripheral to the species' main range.

Though the Buzzard was widespread in Britain in earlier centuries, by the peak in the popularity of field sports in the years immediately preceding the First World War it was virtually restricted to the western Scottish Highlands, Galloway, the Lake District, the Welsh uplands, and the English Southwest Peninsula. The economic and social changes which followed 1918 removed some of the pressure from birds of prey, with fewer gamekeepers being retained in employment. Buzzards were able to regain some of the territory they had lost, but they remained excluded from eastern counties of England and Scotland. By 1954 the population was estimated at 12,000 breeding pairs.

Then the Buzzard's fortune took a downward turn again. In 1955 and the years

69

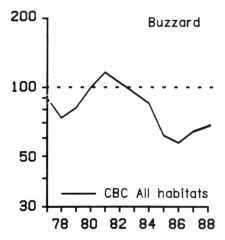

which followed, an epizootic of myxomatosis decimated the numbers of rabbits, the Buzzard's main prey in Britain. The effects on Buzzards were uneven geographically, but breeding success was affected in most areas and numbers fell. Subsequent recovery through the 1960s and 1970s was slow in some areas, possibly as a consequence of organochlorine residues (Prestt 1965), although it is more likely that food supplies remained suboptimal (P.J.Dare, pers.comm.). By 1970 the breeding population was estimated at 8000-10,000 pairs (Tubbs 1974).

A further BTO survey in 1983 found evidence that the slow increase was continuing. Comparison of numbers of occupied 10-km squares with those found in 1968-1972 during fieldwork for the Breeding Atlas revealed that in the traditional strongholds the occupancy rate had risen from 91% to 98% by 1983, while along the edge of the range (where Buzzards are more thinly distributed) the occupancy of 10-km squares had risen from 44% in 1970 to 73% by 1983. However, expansion was mainly through in-filling; there was little sign of pioneering spread into new districts, except in Northern Ireland where a recolonisation which began in the late 1950s had been consolidated. The 1983 estimate of 12,000-15,000 territorial pairs (*i.e.* breeding pairs plus territory-holding immatures) is very close to the 1954 figure, which suggests that the 1983 survey recorded a late stage of recovery from the 1950s-1960s setback.

It is evident that Buzzards are failing to recolonise much of the lower ground they once occupied in central and eastern England and in eastern Scotland, though the reasons for this are by no means clear. The number of professional gamekeepers had fallen from over 20,000 in 1911 to around 5000 in the 1970s. Yet there is good circumstantial evidence that illegal activity by gamekeepers is still limiting Buzzard distribution in northeastern Scotland and Northumberland, and this has often been assumed to apply elsewhere. Local outbreaks of myxomatosis still occur and rabbits have generally not returned to their former abundance. Consequently, Buzzard breeding success in many areas, for example northern and central Wales, is still well below that achieved in the years before myxomatosis, despite reduced levels of persecution. With annual breeding success averaging less than one young fledged per pair (but adult mortality rates unknown), it may be that there are few "surplus" youngsters available to initiate range expansion (P.J.Dare, pers. comm.).

Extensive afforestation of uplands, when trees have grown up, reduces the amount of open country available to Buzzards for hunting. This may affect populations in the northern half of Britain, where afforestations tend to be large. In Wales, however, moorland and mountainside plantations are relatively small. Buzzards may even benefit from these, since they create a mosaic of habitats which the birds can exploit for the different requirements of nesting and hunting.

Regional variation
CBC data cannot add to what is known from the national surveys (see above).

Trends elsewhere in Europe
Declines during the 20th century have been reported from many countries, attributed to persecution, habitat loss and toxic chemicals, but also some small improvements in the 1970s. Declines were estimated at 50% in Finland, 30-50% in West Germany, and 50% in France, though in the last two countries there has been recent stability or small improvement (Cramp & Simmons 1980).

Kestrel *Falco tinnunculus*

Present population trend: stable or declining slightly, after earlier increase.
Percentages of plots occupied 1968/78/88: farmland 54/78/64; woodland 25/50/42.
Latest estimate of breeding population: 70,000 pairs in Britain (Newton 1984).
Regional density rankings 1988: all CBC habitats NE>EE>S>SE.

The Kestrel is our most common and familiar raptor, and this has been the case since ornithological recording began. Though it declined on cereal farmland in eastern England during the height of the organochlorine pesticide era, 1959-1963 (Prestt 1965), this was against a national trend towards increase which included a spread into suburban areas and even cities. The overall increase became more pronounced during the 1960s, doubtless enhanced by recovery in eastern England after restrictions were placed on the usage of the more toxic agrochemicals.

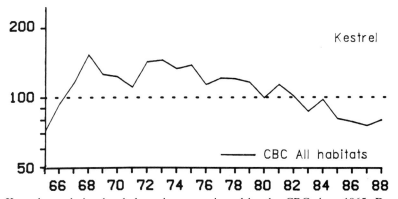

Kestrel population levels have been monitored by the CBC since 1965. Despite short-term peaks and troughs (the significance of which is discussed later), the trend was for increase during the 1960s and early 1970s, followed by a plateau period, but then a decline in the early to middle 1980s (see under *Regional variation*). Since 1985 the index has been stable at a new, lower level which is only slightly higher than that which applied when the CBC began. That the earlier increase was not maintained may have been due to numbers having reached or exceeded the carrying capacity of the available habitats (Newton 1984). The recent decline has been uneven regionally (see below).

Two other attempts have been made to index Kestrel populations, both of which were based on the numbers of nestlings ringed annually. Snow (1968) presented index values (the number ringed expressed as a percentage of an 11-year running mean) for 1925-1962 which showed a generally stable population with marked fluctuations but rising towards the end of the period. Mason & Hussey (1984) calculated a different index (number of chicks ringed in a year, divided by the number of ringing permits issued for that year), for the period 1950-1980. This showed a general increase, but with marked annual fluctuations, particularly prior to 1970, which agreed closely with those demonstrated by Snow, probably because they used the same ringing data. Both of these studies concluded that the observed population fluctuations were cyclical, with a periodicity of three to five years. Comparable cycles are detectable in the CBC results. They occur also in other raptors and owls which feed on those small rodents that fluctuate in numbers in irregular cycles (Newton 1979). (See text for Little Owl.)

Why such fluctuations in ringing totals should have been of smaller amplitude since the early 1970s (Mason & Hussey 1984) is unclear, but it might be related to changes in the population dynamics of prey species, for example as a result of changes in agricultural landscapes and practices. More likely, however, it is an artefact of change over time in the geographical distribution of Kestrel ringers. Snow (1968) showed that cyclical fluctuations in Kestrels were most marked in Scotland and northern England; indeed, since the mid-1940s they had been barely detectable in data from the southern half of the country. Up to the 1960s, Kestrel ringing was pursued most vigorously in upland areas of the north and west, so that the indices derived from ringing totals did not reflect the decline of Kestrels in eastern England during the period when organochlorine pesticides were being used. During the 1970s and 1980s more Kestrels have been ringed in central and southern England, encouraged by the Kestrel's increase and also by ring-price subsidies; and it is believed that it is the higher contribution now made by southern ringers to national ringing totals which has made the cyclical fluctuations seem smaller of late. Similarly, CBC fieldwork is strongest in central and southern England, leading to fluctuations in these data being smaller than those shown by the ringing indices. However, the CBC does show additional (though small) cyclic peaks in 1981 and 1984, to extend the series given by Snow and by Mason & Hussey.

Population levels indicated by the various indices rose approximately five-fold between 1950 and 1980. O'Connor (1982) showed that this was accompanied by a quadrupling in the numbers of nesting habitats used, and by evidence of density-dependent variation in the timing of onset of breeding and in clutch sizes.

Regional variation

A major decline in eastern England around 1960, and the subsequent recovery, are discussed above. Regional indices show that the recent decline at national level is largely due to decreases in western England and in Wales; indeed, the species was absent from sample plots in both in 1988 (see regional density rankings).

Trends elsewhere in Europe

Cramp & Simmons (1980) report that European populations fluctuate following changes in rodent populations and the effects of severe weather. Declines in the Netherlands have been linked to habitat changes and pesticide use.

72

Hobby *Falco subbuteo*

Present population trend: CBC data add to evidence for overall increase.
Percentages of plots occupied 1968/78/88: all CBC habitats 1/2/5.
Latest estimate of breeding population: over 500 pairs in Britain (Fuller *et al* 1985).

The Hobby, our only long-distance migratory falcon, has often been regarded in Britain as a bird of lowland heaths and downland, and therefore as having a restricted distribution in the southern counties of England. On that basis, Brown (1957) estimated the British population at 60-90 pairs and Parslow (1973) offered a figure of 85-100 pairs, both these authors believing that the bulk of the breeding population was located in central southern England from Wiltshire and Dorset to Surrey and Sussex. That impression is now known to have been wrong: there are more Hobbies breeding in Britain than had previously been suspected, with pairs widely distributed in farmland and woodland habitats as well as those regarded as traditional (Parr 1985).

Fieldwork for the Breeding Atlas detected the presence of Hobbies in a total of 261 10-km squares during 1968-1972, with the distribution extending into the southern English Midlands, mainly south of a line from the Severn to the Wash, and the Southwest Peninsula (Sharrock 1976). Since that period, the known breeding range has expanded, especially eastwards into Essex, Suffolk, Norfolk, Cambridgeshire and Lincolnshire (county bird reports), but also into southeast Wales, notably Gwent (Tyler *et al* 1987).

Fuller *et al* (1985) studied two areas of mixed and arable farmland in the south Midlands, lying between the Cotswold and Chiltern hills. There, Hobbies adopt the old nests of Carrion Crows, which used to be mainly in elms but now (since Dutch elm disease) are in a wide variety of tree species. In these two study areas the minimum Hobby densities were 3.8 and 4.8 pairs per 10-km square, with nearest-neighbour distances of 2.0-9.6 km (average 4.6 km). These densities are close to those reported from the southern counties (Fiuczynski & Nethersole-Thompson 1980, Parr 1985). The question arises whether these farmland pairs had previously been overlooked or whether they represent an extension of range. Fuller *et al* (1985) traced evidence for the presence of breeding Hobbies in their areas back to the late 19th and early 20th centuries, such early reports indicating that the species may already have been well established there. Their conclusion was that an important segment of the British breeding population had been largely overlooked for half a century or more.

Although the 261 occupied 10-km squares found during the five years of the Breeding Atlas included a high proportion in the lowest (possibly breeding) category, breeding is not easily established on farmland and nests and broods must often be overlooked. On the other hand, many of the records will undoubtedly have related to migrants or to squares not occupied every year. A perhaps conservative estimate of 2 pairs per occupied square would mean an English population of over 500 pairs. Were the average density (4.3 pairs per occupied 10-km square) found in the south Midlands study to be applicable nationally, then there must be in excess of 1000 pairs breeding in England (Fuller *et al* 1985).

The species is included in the annual reports of the Rare Breeding Birds Panel. However, the numbers of pairs and sites notified to the Panel each year vary considerably, probably reflecting variations in reporting effort rather than real population fluctuations. The Panel's best year so far was 1986, when a possible maximum of 291 pairs was reported from 32 counties as far north as Derbyshire and Yorkshire (Spencer *et al* 1988), but even this total is well below the estimated size of the British population.

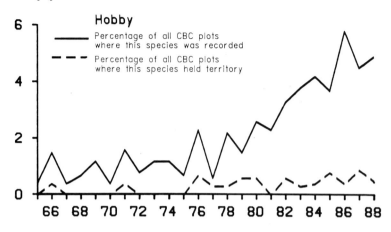

The Hobby is not indexed by any BTO monitoring scheme. Ubiquity figures from farmland CBC returns show a distinct upturn since about 1976 in the number of plots known to have been visited by Hobbies (see graph). In addition, a tendency in recent years for RBBP and county bird report sources to produce more breeding records peripheral to the main range indicates that some overall increase is taking place. In the past, Hobbies have suffered from habitat loss, shooting while on migration and egg-collecting (Fiuczynski 1978), and direct persecution at least may have lessened in recent years as a result of protective legislation.

Regional variation

Numbers appear to be stable on traditional southern heathlands such as those of the New Forest in Hampshire, are perhaps declining on downland as a result of habitat changes there (Parr 1985), and are probably increasing in the English Midlands and eastern counties.

Trends elsewhere in Europe

Numbers fluctuate in many countries, this being not unusual in a migratory species; but over the last three or four decades there have been marked declines in France, Denmark, Finland and Hungary, plus small ones in West and East Germany, and increases in the Netherlands and USSR (Cramp & Simmons 1979, Fiuczynski 1987).

Red-legged Partridge *Alectoris rufa*

Present population trend: fluctuates; the trend has been upwards since the mid-1950s, latterly due to artificial stocking.
Percentages of plots occupied 1968/78/88: farmland 24/42/44; woodland 1/10/13.
Latest estimate of breeding population: 100,000-200,000 pairs in Britain (Sharrock 1976). No reliable estimate is possible due to the large scale of rearing and releasing, compounded by the hybrid problem (see below).
Regional density rankings 1988: farmland EE>SE>NE.

The Red-legged Partridge was introduced successfully into Britain in 1790, earlier attempts having failed, and became established in southeastern England. Over sixty cases of supplementary releases were recorded between 1830 and 1958, with more probably going unreported, and since then such liberations have been made regularly; numbers have risen since 1974 with the growth of commercial game farms to supply the stock. It is estimated that over 800,000 birds are now being released each year by organised shooting syndicates and estates, and about 400,000 are being shot annually (G.R.Potts, in Lack 1986).

The present species prefers light, dry soils in low rainfall areas and in regions where arable farming predominates; in Britain these conditions are best met in eastern and southern England, where Red-legs are most common. Introduction attempts in western and northern regions are invariably unsuccessful, owing perhaps to an aversion to high rainfall (above 87 cm annually) (Howells 1962), or to the different farm cropping patterns there (R.E.Green, pers. comm.). Hence the British breeding distribution remains rather similar to that of 50 years ago, with east-to-west and south-to-north gradients of declining density.

Since at least 1971, released birds from game-farm stock have included hybrids between Red-legged Partridge and its Middle Eastern relative the Chukar, and in some cases pure Chukars, and these have predominated over pure Red-legs in recent years. The release of non-indigenous bird species, including Chukar but not the long-established Red-legged Partridge, was prohibited by the 1981 Wildlife & Countryside Act, though a licence was issued by the Department of the Environment to allow releases of Chukars and hybrids to continue for a limited period until they were phased out of game-farm stocks (Wilkinson 1987). This licence was due to expire in October 1989, but pressure for a continuance has resulted in an extension of the licence until October 1992. In the wild, these hybrids have poor reproductive performance; moreover, there is field evidence of assortative mating, with true Red-legs preferring to pair with their own kind (Potts 1989). Thus the Chukar type should decline rapidly if releases of such birds are stopped.

Nationally, Red-legged Partridge numbers increased in the late 1950s, as shooting pressure was relaxed following the decline of Grey Partridges (Potts 1980). The latter species had previously outnumbered the Red-leg by 20:1 in eastern counties, though by the late 1950s their densities were close to parity. Subsequently, the wild stock of Red-legs has declined considerably, though this trend has been largely masked by the rising scale of releases of game-farm birds.

CBC data are available from 1964, and these include released hybrids as well as true Red-legs. Up to 1976, numbers fluctuated at around the 1964-1965 level. Since then there has been an upward trend (and continuing fluctuation); this increase

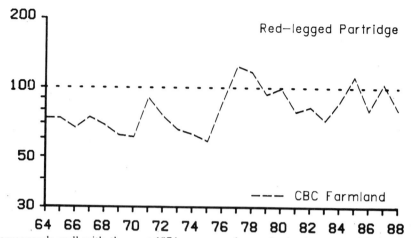

```
200
            Red-legged Partridge


100   - - - - - - - - - - - - - - - - - - - - - - - -



 50


                                      --- CBC Farmland
 30
     64  66  68  70  72  74  76  78  80  82  84  86  88
```

corresponds well with the post-1974 upsurge of organised releases, and is in stark contrast to the fortunes of the Grey Partridge. However, Game Conservancy Trust data reveal that the feral "background" population of pure Red-legs has fallen greatly since the mid-1970s, especially in areas where large numbers of hybrids are reared or where gamekeeping is no longer practised (G.R. Potts, pers. comm.). Whereas densities of 20 pairs per sq.km were normal in eastern counties in the late 1950s, nowadays wild stocks seldom exceed 5 pairs per sq.km. Without continuing releases, the Red-leg's density would soon become far lower than it was before large-scale rearing began.

Breeding success in this species is influenced in part by the availability of food for chicks, in terms of insects and other foods, including grassland weeds (Green 1984); these are subject to chemical control on modern farmland. However, Red-leg chicks are less dependent on insects than are those of the Grey Partridge. More importantly though, Red-legged Partridge stocks are limited by the availability of nesting cover, which itself is often related to changes in farmland cropping patterns (Potts 1980, Green 1983). Adequate cover is important since nest predation (by corvids, hedgehogs, stoats and rats) is high in this species, in part because the birds leave their eggs uncovered during laying. In one Norfolk study, daily nest loss was three times higher than in Grey Partridge and, despite the double-clutch strategy of some pairs which would tend to offset this, the net effect was that the Red-legs fledged 40% fewer young than did the Grey Partridges (Green 1981, 1984). Hence the level of gamekeeping is vitally important to this species in Britain, since keepers have responsibility for habitat quality as well as for control of nest predators.

Regional variation

Against the national trend, index values for western England have shown progressive reduction since the mid-1970s; this reflects the unsuitability of western counties as well as the distribution of modern release points. The national graph shows that a decline occurred between the late 1960s and mid-1970s, before index values rose again; this temporary fall was more pronounced in southern England than elsewhere.

Trends elsewhere in Europe

In the natural range there was southward retreat in the 19th century (and earlier) in West Germany, France and Switzerland. Introduction attempts to various countries in central Europe have been unsuccessful (Cramp & Simmons 1980).

Grey Partridge *Perdix perdix*

Present population trend: severe long-term decrease is continuing.

Percentages of plots occupied 1968/78/88: farmland 73/68/52; woodland 16/17/10.

Latest estimate of breeding population: about 500,000 pairs in Britain and Ireland in 1968-1972 (Sharrock 1976); 89% of occupied squares were then in Britain. The CBC index has halved since that period.

Regional density rankings 1988: farmland NE>EE>SE>WE>W>S.

The modern decline of the Grey Partridge can be traced back to the closing decades of the 19th century, as is apparent from old records in game books. Only in regions such as East Anglia where game-bird management, with gamekeeping, was paramount were maximum population levels maintained into the 1940s. By the mid-1940s the decrease was general, and it has accelerated in recent times.

The beginnings of the Grey Partridge decline coincided with the onset of agricultural recession, which affected cereal farming in particular. The downward trend became more noticeable during the First World War, when changed conditions started a reduction in the numbers of gamekeepers employed which became drastic during and after the Second World War. The decline in the number of gamekeepers was crucial, because the level of nest predation is an important factor in the population regulation of the Grey Partridge (Aebischer & Potts 1989).

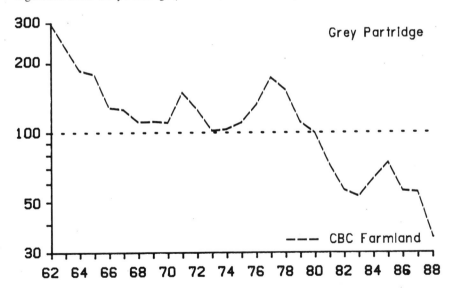

The CBC has documented the scale of this decline since 1962. There was a temporary improvement between 1975 and 1977, believed to have been due to a short series of seasons favourable to the insects on which partridge chicks feed, but the decline then resumed and index values plunged to even lower levels. The average early autumn stock is now less than a million birds, adults and juveniles together, though formerly more than twice that number were shot annually (G.R. Potts, in Lack 1986). Approximately 200 man-years have been invested in partridge studies (*e.g.* Potts 1980, 1984, 1986; Green 1984; Rands 1985; Aebischer & Potts 1989), and the large quantity of data gathered has allowed an accurate modelling of the population. Nest predation has emerged as a significant proximate factor, accounting for about half of the post-1940 decline. Not only are eggs taken by corvids and small mammals, but each year about a quarter of incubating females are killed on the nest by predators such as foxes. Nests placed close together are more easily found and predated, so predation levels increase where pairs cannot space themselves adequately due to a low density of hedgerows; thus the amount and quality of nesting habitat is an ultimate underlying cause of decline.

The other major modern impact on Grey Partridges, estimated to account for 43% of the observed decline, is the effect of farm chemicals (at first herbicides, more recently insecticides) on the June densities of the arthropods on which the chicks are dependent for their food. Herbicide use halves the numbers of the preferred insects by destroying their fod plants. Where aphicides are used on winter wheat, a predominant practice since about 1985, they can halve chick survival, bringing it to a level far below that necessary to maintain partridge numbers. Insect numbers are also affected by other aspects of modern farm management, particularly the reduction in the practice of undersowing cereals with clover. Chick survival is much improved in fields where the field edges are left unsprayed, as "conservation headlands" (Rands 1985, Aebischer & Potts 1989). Furthermore, field edges and headlands are the best feeding areas, since it is there that the insect faunas which overwinter in hedges can encroach upon the crop. Hence, conditions for Grey Partridge chicks can be improved on farms where a practical interest in game-bird stocks still remains. However, partridge conservation is expensive on a typical cereal farm. The costs can usually be met only from the income derived from shooting, though grants for using traditional farming methods are currently available in two Environmentally Sensitive Areas.

Regional variation

No variations in trends are apparent from the CBC. However, the Game Conservancy Trust data indicate that those aspects of recent declines which are not attributable to increased predation have been most severe in the south and east (G.R. Potts). In 1988 density rankings, the lowest were the western regions and Scotland, where much of the habitat has always been suboptimal for Grey Partridges.

Trends elsewhere in Europe

Severe declines this century have been reported from most European countries, despite large-scale restocking attempts in some, notably France and Italy. Agricultural changes and reduced protection from predators after the break-up of large estates are the main reasons (Potts 1986). Grey Partridges are now seriously reduced and perhaps endangered in Ireland (Lack 1986). Hutchinson (1989) reports that the species has recently become extinct in Norway.

Quail *Coturnix coturnix*

Present population trend: unknown, owing to huge year-to-year fluctuations.
Percentages of plots occupied 1968/78/88: all CBC habitats 0/0/1.
Latest estimate of breeding population: over 600 calling birds in Britain in 1964 influx (Parslow 1973); many fewer in normal years. See below.

The Quail is our only migratory game bird, wintering in Africa south of the Sahara, and the very variable numbers reaching Britain depend on the scale of spring migration into northwest Europe as a whole. This is an enigmatic bird, far more often heard than seen, and there remain many gaps in our knowledge of its movements and biology. Status assessments are usually made on the basis of calling males. Calling may become infrequent after pairing has occurred, so that persistent callers (which are more readily detected) are more likely to be unmated individuals that may move considerable distances and so lead to duplication of reports (Sharrock 1976). However, paired males sing throughout the summer in localities where other males are holding territories close by, and groups such as these do not disperse until the crop they are in has been harvested (S.P. Dudley, pers. comm.).

Historically, there is reason to believe that Quails were formerly more numerous here; certainly up to the 17th century they figured in banquet menus and poultry price lists to such an extent that they must have been common enough to be worth the attention of birdcatchers (Moreau 1951). A marked and progressive decline then set in, and by 1865 there were few counties in which Quails were considered to breed annually (More 1865). Numbers remained very low up to about 1940, but from 1942 there was a discernible improvement leading to higher recent averages (Moreau 1951, 1956; Parslow 1973). However, allowance needs to be made for the ever-increasing numbers of birdwatchers over the post-war period. Occasionally, spring arrivals in Britain, and in northwest Europe generally, are on a larger scale. There were particularly good years in 1870, 1893, 1947, 1952-1953, 1964, 1970, 1983 and 1989; the temporal distribution of these peaks accords with the notion of a general upward trend since the 1940s. The record number of 600 birds in 1964 (Parslow 1973) was certainly well exceeded in the exceptional summer of 1989, for which a final total is not yet available.

The recent peak years show up well in the farmland CBC ubiquity figures (see graph). These also demonstrate a further point: numbers do not subside as quickly as they build up, for peak years are followed by a second or even a third year during which Quail numbers are above average. Perhaps this arises from a tendency for Quail hatched in Britain to return to their natal area the following year.

There is no good evidence that the 19th-century decline, which was paralleled to some extent in other parts of Europe, was associated with agricultural change. Moreau (1956) noted a preference for cereal crops, and CBC farmland registrations have been 36% in long grass (including leys), 30% in barley, and 16% in other cereals. Moreau (1951) believed that the most important factor in the earlier decline was the huge scale of hunting, including commercial netting, in the Mediterranean countries. Spring hunting had been particularly harmful, and its curtailment by regulations in 1937 and then by the Second World War fits the pattern of improvement noted in Britain after 1942. Zuckerbrot et al (1980) concluded that fluctuations in Quail abundance are now associated with long-term climatic trends in Europe and the Sahel wintering area; but

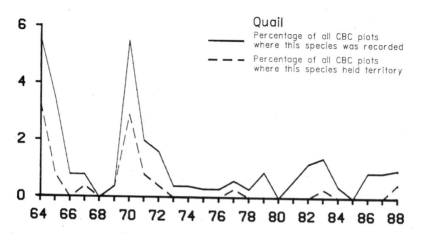

Quail

——— Percentage of all CBC plots where this species was recorded

— — — Percentage of all CBC plots where this species held territory

their assessment of the impact of hunting was limited to autumn data, and many birds trapped then are in poor condition and perhaps would not have survived anyway.

Some of the larger-than-normal arrivals in northwest Europe in spring have been associated with dry conditions in France and persistent southeast winds. Yet no such correlation existed in 1953 (Moreau 1956), nor in 1964 when the species was unusually numerous throughout western Europe including Mediterranean France (Davis *et al* 1966). Main arrivals in Britain are often as late as June or even July, and are believed to represent intra-season (summer) movements, with birds assumed to have shifted their breeding grounds in response to deteriorated conditions further south or east (Moreau 1951). Clutches laid in August and later could belong to late arrivals, or be replacement or true second clutches of pairs which arrived in spring.

Regional variation

In normal years the distribution corresponds reasonably well to that of chalk and greensand in southern and eastern England; in general, the pattern of occurrence is influenced partly by adherence to traditional sites, and partly by a tendency for several birds to settle within earshot (Moreau 1956). In their occasional peak years Quails occur almost anywhere in agricultural habitats, as far north as Shetland.

Trends elsewhere in Europe

Numbers fluctuate everywhere in western Europe, but recent downward trends have been reported from the Netherlands and some parts of France (Cramp & Simmons 1980).

Pheasant *Phasianus colchicus*

Present population trend: stable or increasing where releases continue, but the wild population has fallen recently.
Percentages of plots occupied 1968/78/88: farmland 57/64/78; woodland 47/53/60.
Latest estimate of breeding population: 3 million territorial males and 4½ million females in Britain and Ireland (see below); 73% of occupied squares during 1968-1972 were in Britain (Sharrock 1976).
Regional density rankings 1988: farmland EE>SE>S> NI>W>NE>WE; woodland EE>WE>SE>NE>S.

Of the dozen introduced species on the British list, the Pheasant was the earliest to be brought here – probably in the 14th century (Yapp 1983). By the 16th century it was known from Wales and Scotland also, though there was no evidence for widespread feral existence until later (Hill & Robertson 1988). It was the expanded popularity of shooting during the 19th century, with large-scale artificial rearing of game birds and gamekeeping to control predators, which led to the Pheasant becoming the common species we know today.

Long-term records of the numbers of Pheasants shot annually in Britain are available from the National Game Census, which is organised by the Game Conservancy Trust. These indicate a steady overall increase during the course of this century, apart from temporary declines during the two World Wars when releasing was banned and game shooting was restricted. On shooting estates which release artificially reared birds, the numbers shot have doubled since 1961 from an average of 95 per sq.km then to 190 per sq.km now, while the corresponding figures for numbers released have risen from 92 to 336 birds per sq.km. On estates where none are released and only wild birds are shot, numbers remained stable at around 70 birds per sq.km until 1982, since when there has been a decline to 40 birds per sq.km (P.A.Robertson, *in litt.*).

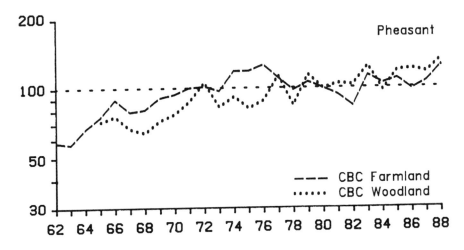

The CBC documented increases from its beginning. On farmland this increase lasted until the mid-1970s; since then, high levels have been maintained though the upward trend has been replaced by fluctuations at around the 1973-1975 levels. In contrast, the woodland increase has continued through to the present.

Whether the Pheasant population is currently declining except where sporting releases continue (NGC), or remains high after earlier increase (CBC), is a matter which cannot be resolved without knowing the proximity of CBC plots to release sites. Also, both data sources present problems: CBC fieldwork does not identify male status, so the index measures total numbers of males rather than numbers of breeding males (see below), while the emphasis of the NGC on returns submitted by sporting estates raises the question of how representative these are of farmland and woodland in general. Also, the NGC figures for numbers shot per year reflect not only the size of the breeding population, but also its productivity. The Pheasant's polygynous mating system certainly raises problems in interpreting census data. Not all males succeed in establishing a territory; the rest remain non-territorial. Of the territorial males, many fail to attract any females, others attract only one or two, while a few practise harem polygyny with ten or more hens. Variation occurs from area to area, depending on the extent to which the spring sex ratio has been skewed by discriminate shooting of males in winter.

It is clear that large-scale but localised releases of artificially reared birds are no longer raising the overall population level. The implication is that Pheasants have reached optimum densities in those habitats and areas where artificial stocking methods are not practised. Yet it seems from recent Game Conservancy Trust studies that the British population as a whole could not sustain present hunting levels without regular releases to supplement the stocks (Hill & Robertson 1988).

A conservative estimate of the numbers of Pheasants released and shot per year would be in the range of 10-15 million in each case. Around 45% of released birds are shot during their first winter and a further 25-30% are lost through other causes, such as predation. Those released birds which survive the winter then augment the feral stock, though their sedentary disposition must ensure that they filter only gradually into surrounding districts. Some 61% of released birds are shot within 400 metres of the release point and under 1% disperse further than two kilometres (Lack 1986).

In 1988-1989, the Game Conservancy Trust made a national survey of Pheasant breeding season densities, obtaining data from 156 sites (P.A. Robertson, pers. comm.). They found average densities per sq.km of 10 territorial males, 7 non-territorial males, and 16 females. All of the sites visited during this survey contained surplus males. From longer-term studies, it appears that the numbers of territorial males remains virtually constant between years, though the numbers of females and non-territorial males fluctuate widely as a response to the level of releasing of artificially reared birds. Applying the 1988-1989 densities to the number of 10-km squares with confirmed breeding during the BTO Breeding Atlas, it is estimated that national totals are in the order of 3 million territorial males, 2 million non-territorial birds, and 4½ million hens.

Regional variation

On the basis of CBC data, there are east-to-west and south-to-north gradients of declining density, plus some decrease with rising altitude. Yet as far north as Scotland there are local distortions due to the presence of game-rearing estates. National Game Census figures allow predictions of the size of the wild Pheasant bag in different regions, in the absence of rearing (Robertson 1988). Much the highest figure per sq.km is 105 birds in East Anglia, followed by 44 in southern England and 38 in the east Midlands. The Welsh figure is 19, and the lowest figures of all are 2 in northwest England and 1 in west Scotland.

Trends elsewhere in Europe
As in Britain, the picture is distorted by artificial stocking all over western Europe.

Moorhen *Gallinula chloropus*

Present population trend: probably stable overall.
Percentages of plots occupied 1968/78/88: farmland 64/68/64; woodland 15/37/26; all WBS plots -/93/86.
Latest estimate of breeding population: 300,000 pairs in Britain and Ireland (Sharrock 1976); 71% of occupied squares were then in Britain.
Regional density rankings 1988: farmland S>EE>WE>NE>SE>NI>W.

This is a familiar bird of virtually all freshwater habitats from large lakes to small ponds, and from rivers to wet ditches. Though at times shy and skulking, the Moorhen can be highly conspicuous and vocal where accustomed to man. Its success can be attributed primarily to its adaptability and to its highly territorial nature; the latter results in a mobile "floating" stock of non-breeding birds, which can take advantage of any new or temporary sites that become available. The British population is mostly sedentary, and is subject to temporary declines following winters severe enough to freeze the larger fresh water-bodies; but due to a high breeding potential, with up to three broods being reared in a year (Wood 1974, Gibbons 1987), it usually recovers quickly from such setbacks.

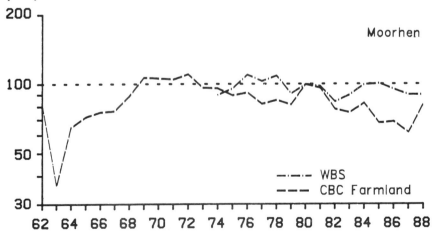

Following the severe winter of 1962/63, which reduced Moorhens seriously, recovery was rapid: half the losses were made good in one year. Thereafter, the farmland CBC index continued to rise, reaching a peak in 1972. After that the index values fell gradually, continuing to do so almost through to the present, though there was a large increase in 1988. One must be cautious about interpreting this as long-term population decline. In reality, levels were high in the early 1970s after a run of mild winters, and low by the mid-1980s when winters averaged colder, while the 1988 index returned to the intermediate level of the late 1960s and of the late 1970s. The effects of the coldest recent winters (1978/79, 1981/82 and 1986/87) are visible on the CBC graph, though these are small compared to the major decline which followed 1962/63; nevertheless there does seem to have been a cumulative effect in the 1980s. WBS data, available since 1974, also show these same small troughs after cold winters. Otherwise the WBS picture is one of stability; and this is probably the more reliable indication of current trends in the Moorhen.

Over the past two decades, farmland has probably deteriorated in terms of the Moorhen's requirements, especially in the most intensively arable regions. There has been increased emphasis on improving the drainage of low-lying land, including piping ditches and the more regular clearance of dykes and streams to hasten rainwater run-off, and the filling in of farm ponds. The effects of such changes might have been more apparent in farmland CBC results, were it not for the fact that some farmland CBC plots include canal or river habitats which allow the continued presence of Moorhens.

WBS data show that Moorhen density is greater on canals than on rivers, with a mean canal value of 2.9 territories per km (Marchant & Hyde 1980b). On rivers, densities decline as river gradient increases and the water flow becomes faster (Taylor 1984). This author also showed that Moorhens present on newly managed sections of the River Ouzel and Grand Union Canal in Buckinghamshire bred later, nested further from the channel and produced fewer second broods than did pairs on unmanaged sections. Population changes between years become more pronounced on managed sections of waterways (Taylor 1984, Campbell 1988). As a species which depends for nest sites largely upon emergent vegetation and bankside bushes which overhang the water, the Moorhen is one of the species worst affected when waterways are dredged and banks regraded; the continued presence of non-breeding birds at such sites further indicates that it is nest-site availability rather than feeding potential which suffers (Campbell 1988). The practice of working from one bank only during management operations, and the retention of patches of emergent vegetation, both benefit Moorhen populations. A particularly sympathetic form of river management is to reduce dredging and, instead, construct berms – broad but shallow margins to the watercourse which accommodate extra flow during flood conditions (Raven 1986).

Regional variation

A marked increase was noted in Scotland in the early half of this century (Alexander & Lack 1944), but numbers have probably decreased slightly since then (Sharrock 1976). Scotland's prominence in 1988 density rankings may be an artefact of small plot samples there.

Trends elsewhere in Europe

A general northward extension of range into Fenno-Scandia has been noted since the mid-19th century. Breeding was first noted in Finland in 1842 (Pulliainen 1980), Norway in 1860 and Denmark in 1865. Many birds there, and elsewhere in northern Europe, are migratory but remain susceptible to severe weather in their European wintering areas (Cramp & Simmons 1977).

Coot *Fulica atra*

Present population trend: increasing, in England at least.
Percentages of plots occupied 1968/78/88: all CBC habitats
9/19/14; all WBS plots -/44/50.
Latest estimate of breeding population: 50,000-100,000
pairs in Britain and Ireland (Sharrock 1976); 75% of
occupied squares were then in Britain. See also below.

A widespread and familiar bird of shallow lakes and other bodies of standing water,
the Coot occurs also on quiet stretches of canal and on slow-moving lowland rivers
where these possess rich growths of emergent and submerged aquatic vegetation.
Nutrient-poor waters are generally avoided, such as upland lochs which are often deep
and unvegetated; hence there are few breeding sites for Coot above 250 m altitude.

Both the Great Crested Grebe and the Tufted Duck are known to owe a large part
of their modern success to reservoir construction and to sand and gravel extraction
since the 1930s. The Coot must also have benefited from the creation of this new
habitat, though the species has never been the subject of national surveys to assess the
trend of the breeding population over time. Yet the fact that colonisation by Coots of
newly flooded sites has not been at the expense of other waters nearby suggests
strongly that an overall increase has taken place (Sharrock 1976). Dobbs (1975)
considered that breeding numbers had doubled in Nottinghamshire since the 1950s
due to flooding of new gravel pits. Gladwin & Sage (1986) reported an increase in
Hertfordshire of over 30% between county censuses in 1965 and 1973, and in the
London Area Coots were breeding at only 160 sites in a 1957 survey though in 236
tetrads during 1968-1972 atlas fieldwork (Montier 1977). Such increases may have
been general over the eastern half of England, where the species has become
increasingly tolerant of human presence and breeds even on urban park lakes if these
hold suitable nest sites.

BTO monitoring of the Coot is mainly on linear waterways, though rivers and
canals are known to be only a minor habitat for the species. Regional Coot surveys in
Hertfordshire (Sage 1959) and the London Area (Homes *et al* 1960) both estimated
that 3% of all pairs bred on rivers, compared to 75-80% on lakes and gravel pits and
15-20% on reservoirs. According to WBS data, Coots hold territories mainly on rivers
and canals that are below 50 m altitude, and such territories are largely within
southern and eastern England (Marchant & Hyde 1980*b*). The WBS index dates from
1974, and has recorded a sustained increase over the years. It is uncertain whether this
scale of increase reflects a wider trend, for it is possible that the use of rivers and
canals, mainly in the eastern half of England, is essentially overflow from the
preferred standing-water habitats. Some CBC plots are flanked by rivers or lakes, and
a CBC index for Coot can be given for the years since 1971. This shows a fairly
constant population level over these 18 years, and therefore differs from the WBS
trend. This difference may owe something to the inclusion of lakes as well as linear
waterways in the CBC samples.

Though Coot mortality rises during severe winter weather, harsh conditions seem
to have little effect on breeding population levels. Probably this is due to buffering by
a regular non-breeding segment of the population, such birds being available to
replace cold weather losses among the breeding pairs (J.A. Horsfall, in Lack 1986).
One consequence of the modern creation of large reservoirs, less liable to freeze over
completely during periods of low temperature, has been a tendency for Coot to occur
less often on tidal waters in winter (Cox 1984).

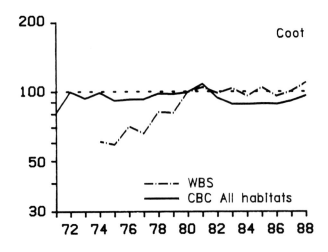

There is considerable uncertainty about the size of the British population. Sharrock (1976) implied 50,000-100,000 pairs for Britain and Ireland together; but the British portion would be below 50,000 pairs if Salmon *et al* (1988) are correct in assessing the British autumn population (including juveniles) at 100,000 individuals. However, not all Coots are then concentrated on the larger waters, which are those covered by the WWT organised counts.

Regional variation

Increases may have been more pronounced in the eastern half of England than elsewhere, for the reasons discussed above: otherwise no clear trends are apparent. There has been some expansion in the southwest, with breeding in Gwent since 1939 and a spread in Cornwall since the 1950s (Parslow 1973). In contrast, there has been some contraction in Scotland: Coots no longer breed in Shetland, numbers in Orkney and the Hebrides are reduced, and it is everywhere scarce and local in the western Highlands where in any case there are few suitable sites (Thom 1986).

Trends elsewhere in Europe

During the course of this century the Coot has expanded northwards, and range extensions have also been noted in Switzerland and West Germany (Cramp & Simmons 1980). The Finnish population has been greatly reduced from a peak in the mid-1970s by severe winters in the mid-1980s (Hildén 1989). On a European scale, the population size is now thought to be stable (Rüger *et al* 1986).

Oystercatcher *Haematopus ostralegus*

Present population trend: long-term increase.
Percentages of plots occupied 1968/78/88: all CBC habitats 7/8/10; all WBS plots -/30/29.
Latest estimate of breeding population: 33,000-43,000 pairs in Britain (Piersma 1986).

Within Wales and southern England (and also Ireland) the Oystercatcher is essentially a coastal species, though inland breeding has become commonplace in northern England and throughout Scotland. The use of inland habitats has been widespread in eastern Scotland since at least the 18th century, but elsewhere the colonisation of river corridors has occurred "within living memory" (Buxton 1962). This expansion is still continuing. In northwest England there was a 50% increase between 1968 and 1978-1980, most of it inland, and further increase is still occurring there (Briggs 1984; K.B. Briggs, pers. comm.). During the 1980s, a few pairs have held territory regularly in Nottinghamshire and Staffordshire and at one site in Leicestershire; in Norfolk there has been an extensive inland spread along the River Yare, and breeding has become regular on the riverine washes of Cambridgeshire and west Norfolk (Smith 1983). The WBS has monitored the Oystercatcher from 1974, since when a steady increase has been maintained. This scheme has good representation of plots in northern England.

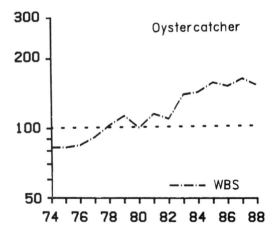

Breeding numbers declined throughout eastern and southern England during the 19th and early 20th centuries, due it was thought to persecution (Alexander & Lack 1944). Relaxation of this pressure was followed by population recovery; but this cannot have caused the subsequent national increase which has been most conspicuous in the northern half of the country. Clearly, British Oystercatchers have broadened their range of breeding habitats. Safriel (1985) suggested that increases since the

Second World War of shore-breeding gulls, which are predators of nests and chicks, have triggered a genetically based behavioural change in Oystercatchers towards breeding inland. Improved breeding success there has consequently promoted population increase. Even in some coastal areas, birds have been forced to breed on adjacent farmland or wasteland due to greater recreational and other disturbance of the foreshore; but, in these cases, intertidal feeding remains an option.

Nowadays, breeding Oystercatchers utilise three broad types of habitat: the ancestral coastal sites, typically on shingle, sand or saltmarsh; the gravel margins of slow-moving rivers and reservoirs, through which the spread inland first manifested itself; and, latterly, agricultural land along river valleys but away from water (Briggs 1984). Where riverbank management has modified gravel beds, Oystercatcher pairs are especially liable to move into smaller river valleys and onto pasture. Inland breeders have advanced their timing of breeding by up to one month in order to meet the peak abundances of soil invertebrates such as earthworms and leatherjackets (Briggs 1984). Pairs which nest on gravel or cultivated land lead their chicks to grassland and fallows where these are available (Heppleston 1972, Wilson 1978). However, the way that parent birds are able to feed some distance away, and fly back with food items for their dependent young, enables this species to breed in sites which would be unsuitable for chick-rearing in other waders (K.B. Briggs, pers. comm.). Extreme manifestations of this are nesting on the flat roofs of buildings (Munro 1984), on cliffs and in quarries.

In winter Oystercatchers are almost exclusively coastal and are usually faithful to particular wintering grounds (Lack 1986). Changes in populations of cockles and mussels, their preferred prey species, can affect this dramatically, however. Periodic food shortages on particular estuaries force many birds to move to other wintering sites then. Such changes are believed to cause additional mortality, especially when supplementary feeding on terrestrial invertebrates becomes difficult as fields freeze over in severe winter weather (Evans & Pienkowski 1984, Davidson & Clark 1985).

Regional variation

Outside eastern Scotland, inland breeding was first noted along the rivers feeding into the Solway Firth, from where the habit spread into northern England (Buxton 1962). In the latter area, initial colonisation has tended to occur in the central parts of river systems, with subsequent spreads upstream and downstream (K.B. Briggs, pers. comm.). As densities stabilise on the preferred river gravels, so these develop substantial non-breeding populations inland in summer. If the present trends continue, population increases are likely to be most pronounced in inland areas, shifting further south with time. Recent records from the English east Midlands are quoted above.

Trends elsewhere in Europe

A marked expansion in Iceland in the decades following 1920 was attributed to climatic warming (Gudmundsson 1951). Across much of northwest Europe there has been a general increase, particularly in inland areas, aided by legislative protection (Cramp & Simmons 1982).

Ringed Plover *Charadrius hiaticula*

Present population trend: apparently increasing.
Percentages of plots occupied 1968/78/88: all CBC habitats 2/4/2; all WBS plots -/8/9.
Latest estimate of breeding population: 8600 pairs in the United Kingdom in 1984 (Prater 1989).

Historically, the Ringed Plover is a coastal bird in the British Isles, breeding on sand and shingle beaches. Particularly since the 1930s, such sites have come increasingly under pressure from various categories of human disturbance but especially that related to the development of holiday resorts. This caused the abandonment of many former breeding sites around the coasts of England, Wales and southern Scotland. An inland concentration on stony parts of the East Anglian Brecks numbered some 400 pairs at the turn of the century, though this has since almost disappeared due to farming and afforestation (Parslow 1973). In the northern half of Britain, however, some Ringed Plovers have long nested inland on river shingle. Numbers there have been increasing since the 1950s, in parallel with those of Oystercatchers (Parslow 1973, Briggs 1983). Over the last fifteen years there has been a growing incidence of pairs nesting inland in central and southern England. Often these birds occupy sites more typical of Little Ringed Plover, and there are documented cases of the latter species being driven away by its more aggressive congener.

The Ringed Plover is not indexed by any BTO monitoring scheme, but it has been the subject of national surveys in 1973-1974 and again, using similar methodology, in 1984 (Prater 1976, 1989). A comparison of the results from these provides an indication of recent national trends. The basic figures on breeding numbers are given in the following table, in which the Isle of Man is included with England, and Northern Ireland is excluded.

	1973-74 totals	1984 totals	% increase to 1984	Distribution (%) of 1984 population
England:				
coastal	1910	2054	+8	24
inland	181	405	+124	5
combined	2091	2459	+18	29
Wales	185	224	+21	3
Scotland	3568	5796	?	68
TOTALS	5844	8479	?	

Coverage of Scotland was much improved in 1984, and the apparent increase there between surveys can be accounted for almost entirely by upward revisions of population totals for the northern and western isles. Indeed, in 15 counties of eastern and southern Scotland which received comparable coverage in both surveys, there was actually an 8% decrease overall (Prater 1989). Ringed Plovers are still under pressure on public access beaches there, as in England and Wales. The 8% coastal increase in

England and 21% increase in Wales must owe much to the protection afforded by the expanding network of national and local reserves. In Hampshire and Sussex, for example, about 70% of breeding Ringed Plovers are now in wardened reserves (Steventon 1985, Prater 1989). The species is also able to find acceptable nest sites on privately owned coastal land, as in power-station complexes where breeding success on gravel-covered compounds is often higher than in natural sites; Pienkowski (1984) argued that nest camouflage is far more effective on gravel than on sand.

The increase of over 124% in pairs using English inland sites during the 10-year period was spectacular, though absolute numbers remain small on a national scale. Briggs (1983) found that breeding success was higher inland since, there, a longer season allowed more time for replacement clutches, and feeding conditions were more constant when independent of a tidal cycle. In Wales, only 3 of the 224 pairs in 1984 were inland. Much the most important Scottish concentration was that of the Western Isles, where over 2300 pairs were accounted for in 1984, more than one-quarter of the entire United Kingdom population, and over 70% of these were on *machair* (Fuller *et al* 1986, Prater 1989). Elsewhere in Scotland, detailed habitat data were forthcoming for 2500 pairs, of which 26% were inland, especially on lakes, reservoirs, river gravels and industrial sites.

In summary, the 1984 survey provided a more realistic estimate for Scotland, where there have been declines in a few counties, and provided evidence of some small increases in England and Wales. However, it remains uncertain how typical 1984 was for breeding Ringed Plovers in Britain. There is evidence from Hampshire and Sussex that it was a particularly good year, in those counties at least (Prater 1989).

Regional variation

Most mainland counties along the east coast of Scotland showed stability or decrease between 1974 and 1984, though this was overshadowed by the larger numbers located that year in the west and north. In contrast, increases were reported from most English east and southeast coastal counties, from Durham round to Hampshire; but breeding Ringed Plovers remain scarce or absent on the Southwest Peninsula. In Wales, the biggest changes detected in 1984 had occurred in the south, though Gwynedd in the north retains much the largest nesting concentrations (Prater 1989).

Trends elsewhere in Europe

Cramp & Simmons (1982) reported that there had been some decrease in Finland and East Germany, and increase in West Germany, France and the Netherlands.

Lapwing *Vanellus vanellus*

Present population trend: marked downward trend in the south; probably downward overall.
Percentages of plots occupied 1968/78/88: farmland 62/62/70; woodland 5/14/13; all WBS plots -/30/57.
Latest estimate of breeding population: 200,000-225,000 pairs in Britain in 1987, with 123,000 pairs in England and Wales and 75,000-100,000 pairs in Scotland (Shrubb & Lack, in press).
Regional density rankings 1988: farmland S>NE>WE>EE>SE>W.

A widespread and familiar species throughout the country, the Lapwing is absent as a nesting bird only from some parts of the far west and from the most exposed of uplands. Agricultural land has long been the main breeding habitat (Nicholson 1938, Lister 1964), and a BTO survey in England and Wales in 1987 found only 4% of pairs on habitats other than farmland (Shrubb & Lack, in press). In recent decades, regional variations in the patterns of agricultural change have led to a marked north-south divide in Lapwing population trends.

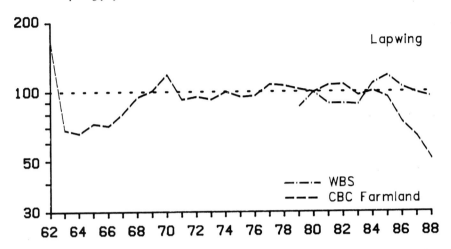

Data from farmland CBC plots indicate that the national population fell sharply in 1963, following the severe winter; but the more recent hard winters of 1978/79 and 1981/82, and others since, had little effect. With its capacity for partial migration and its readiness to undertake cold-weather movements, it is likely that our breeding population is much less affected by harsh winter weather (except when this extends to southern Europe also) than by changes in conditions for breeding. Recovery in the late 1960s fell short of the 1962 index level. Since then the trend has been towards a fluctuating but generally declining index that has fallen away noticeably since 1985. Decreases on CBC plots have been greatest in southern and central England, where agricultural changes deleterious to Lapwings have been most pronounced (see below). The Breeding Wader Monitoring Scheme has recorded a one-third decline of Lapwings between 1984 and 1988; this scheme concentrates on lowland grasslands, and therefore deals mainly with southern sites. In contrast, the WBS index shows little overall change between 1979 and 1988, perhaps because this monitoring scheme has better representation in northern England where Lapwing numbers have been more stable over the last decade.

In lowland areas, breeding Lapwings favour a mosaic of arable and pasture, with ploughed land (tillage) for nesting and grassland for rearing their chicks, these being led by their parents from the nest site to suitable pasture (Redfern 1982, O'Connor & Shrubb 1986a, Galbraith 1988). A satisfactory mosaic of habitats used to be common on farmland, as a consequence of the rotational farming techniques which were practised until the post-1945 agricultural revolution. However, that revolution has had three main impacts on the tillage:grassland balance preferred by Lapwings. First, in England and Wales (outside East Anglia and parts of the east Midlands) tilled land has become dominated by cereal crops, which now comprise 80-90% of tillage compared to 60% or less in the 1930s (MAFF statistics). Second, since 1969 there has been a general change to sowing cereals in autumn instead of spring, together with a big increase in acreage of oil-seed rape which also is primarily autumn-sown. As a result, autumn tillage now accounts for 70% of all tilled land in England and Wales, compared to only about 22% in 1962, and the current figure is even higher in many cereal-growing areas in central and southern England. An analysis of nest record cards shows that, of all land-use types, spring tillage provides the most successful nesting sites (Shrubb, in prep.). Autumn-sown crops are often too tall by the following spring to be used by nesting Lapwings. Third, the trend in England and Wales away from rotational farming, and towards more specialised enterprises, has itself reduced the land-use diversity favoured by Lapwings. As extremes of this pattern, only 7% of Welsh farmland is now tilled, while in East Anglia only 15% of farmland remains as pasture.

Superimposed onto these events have been important changes in grassland management. In England and Wales, there has been an increase of 37% in stocking rates since 1962, and an increase from 2% to 26% in the area of grassland which is cut for silage. High stocking rates have a serious effect on Lapwing breeding success, because of the increased incidence of nest trampling by livestock. Further, silage grassland receives earlier and multiple mowings, and larger applications of inorganic fertilisers, which result in a denser and faster-growing sward that is less suitable for foraging by chicks; the increase in silage acreages may be pushing more grassland Lapwings into nesting in stock fields (Lister 1964; Shrubb & Lack, in press). Faster growth of nesting cover in spring has led to an earlier start to the breeding season (Beintema *et al* 1985).

Regional variation

A very marked decrease in the south has been only partly counterbalanced through increase up to about 1977 in northern England. No overall change has been determined in Scotland (Thom 1986); but Galbraith (1988) has shown that Lapwings nesting in arable areas of Scotland are being affected by factors similar to those operating in the south. Yet the impact may be less serious there than in southern England, because Scottish farming still retains a higher proportion of spring tillage: the trend towards autumn ploughing did not begin until the 1980s. Galbraith *et al* (1984) found an overall average density of 3 pairs per sq. km on Scottish farmland, three times that found in England and Wales in a 1987 BTO survey (Shrubb & Lack, in press).

In predominantly grassland areas, such as Wales, the absence of any significant areas of tillage, in combination with unfavourable changes in grassland management, have probably seriously undermined the Lapwing's ability to breed successfully enough to maintain its numbers (Shrubb, in prep.). In Scotland, however, stocking rates are very much lower (O'Connor & Shrubb 1986a), particularly in areas of marginal and upland grass. Therefore grassland pairs may well be more successful there than further south.

In contrast, in the north and northwest of England a satisfactory balance between spring tillage and grassland remains even on improved farmland. The BTO survey of 1987 recorded very high densities on spring tillage there: an average of 7 pairs per sq. km compared to an average of 2 on spring tillage elsewhere in England and Wales (Shrubb & Lack, in press). It seems possible that this large and successful population is regularly exporting a surplus to maintain numbers in adjacent areas of upland grass, but this possibility requires more detailed investigation.

Trends elsewhere in Europe

A marked northward expansion occurred in northwest Europe from the late 19th century, during a period of climatic warming. This was followed in the first part of this century by a decline in many parts of Europe which has been generally attributed to habitat changes and egg-collecting. Widespread increases have been noted in many countries since 1940, but not in Denmark or Finland (Cramp & Simmons 1982). Finnish and Swedish populations have shown a steep downward trend since the early 1970s (Hildén 1989), as have Danish index values since 1976 (DOFF 1989).

Snipe *Gallinago gallinago*

Present population trend: downward on lowland farmland; trends in other habitats are unknown.
Percentages of plots occupied 1968/78/88: all CBC habitats 19/24/15; all WBS plots -/24/23.
Latest estimate of breeding population: 30,000 pairs in Britain (Reed 1985, Piersma 1986).

The Snipe breeds locally throughout the country, but only where there is suitable wet ground – be it flood meadow, rough grazing or upland bog. Fields of uniformly short grass are avoided: 89% of grassland nests (in nest record cards) are described as being in a tussock, and probably such features are important for concealment (Mason & Macdonald 1976). The effects of drainage and pasture improvement, resulting in loss of rough, damp grazing land, and a widespread switch to arable farming, are probably the major causes of the widespread decline of breeding Snipe in lowland Britain, with nest losses as a secondary factor.

Local decreases have been reported since the early 19th century, following extensive drainage projects. However, lowland Snipe had a temporary respite in the late 19th century and up to the 1930s, when agricultural recession led to there being more neglected pastures and uncleared ditches which gave rise to winter flooding. At that time the Snipe was able to colonise a large area of the south Midlands as well as many districts in southern England where it had previously been absent as a breeding species (Alexander & Lack 1944). Since the Second World War, however, agricultural conditions have changed to the Snipe's disadvantage. By the 1960s, declines had occurred in practically all counties south of a line from Cheshire to Norfolk (Parslow 1973).

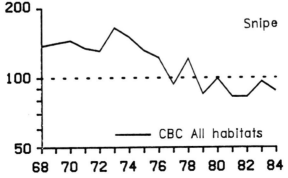

93

Some CBC data are available, mainly from lowland farmland plots. Samples are small, but are adequate for indexing between 1968 and 1984. The graph shows progressive decrease over this period, until by 1985 too few territories were involved for monitoring to continue.

A survey of English lowland grasslands in 1982 located under 2000 drumming Snipe, and over 70% of these were in just four regions: the Norfolk/Cambridgeshire washes, the Somerset Levels, the Derwent Ings in Yorkshire, and the Avon valley in Dorset and Hampshire (Smith 1983). Elsewhere, birds were few and far between. More recent work has shown that counts of drumming Snipe underestimate population size, due to the brevity of the dawn and dusk drumming peaks, and to a great variability between males and between days in the amount of time spent drumming (Green 1985): on this basis, the 1982 counts probably represented closer to 3400 pairs. Decline in the English lowlands is still continuing: the Breeding Wader Monitoring Scheme found an overall drop of 30% on its survey sites between 1984 and 1988.

In nest record cards from lowland sites, only 36% of eggs hatched – this being due to high levels of nest predation and trampling by livestock (Morgan 1982). With nest success so poor, the frequency of repeat layings becomes very important. Recent field studies of Snipe breeding biology (Green 1988) have shown that both length and timing of the breeding season are dependent on the level of soil moisture. The onset of breeding may be delayed by up to 70 days when there is excess surface water, and the season will continue for just so long as the local soil remains moist enough for the birds to probe effectively for food. Hence one important consequence of improved land drainage is to shorten the Snipe's breeding season, allowing less time for replacement clutches, while at the same time permitting more and earlier grazing by livestock which increases nest losses through trampling. Given this background, it is hardly surprising that in the English lowlands the Snipe's range has contracted to give increased importance to a few large tracts of wet grassland that are owned or managed by conservation bodies (Green 1988).

Appropriate management of reserves can enhance their suitability as Snipe habitat. For example, the cutting of reed beds and rushes opens up areas of shallow muddy water which are ideal for feeding. At a Danish fjord, an increase in Snipe numbers was stimulated by river management which made the area muddier (Meltofte 1987). Reducing densities of cattle, and delaying their release onto grazing pasture, also lead to increased breeding success by Snipe (Beintema et al 1985, Green 1988).

Regional variation

Local declines have been noted throughout lowland Britain, in Scotland (Thom 1986) as well as in England (see above). However, no detailed studies have yet been made of Snipe trends in the uplands and other non-agricultural habitats, which hold important numbers particularly in Scotland and northern England.

Trends elsewhere in Europe

Declines have occurred in many countries, due to habitat change and especially drainage. Reductions seem to have been most marked in the zone of temperate farmland eastward from Denmark and the Netherlands (Cramp & Simmons 1983). Swedish index values, fluctuating during 1975-1980, have since been reduced by more than half (Hustings 1988).

Woodcock *Scolopax rusticola*

Present population trend: some decline is suspected, perhaps in southern counties only.
Percentages of plots occupied 1968/78/88: farmland 10/7/4; woodland 34/37/31.
Latest estimate of breeding population: tentatively 18,000-46,000 pairs in Britain and Ireland (Sharrock 1976); 77% of occupied squares were then in Britain. But existing estimates are unreliable, in part because "pair" is an inappropriate unit in this species.

Woodcock are unusual waders in being crepuscular in behaviour and adapted for a woodland existence. Their optimum habitat is dry deciduous woodland with damp areas for feeding. They also occupy mixed deciduous and conifer woodlands, and young conifer plantations up to the thicket stage. Breeding sites typically have a ground cover of bracken, dead leaves or brambles, so that incubating females are well camouflaged (Morgan & Shorten 1974).

Until the 1820s the species was known as a locally distributed breeding bird, but only in England. However, little systematic fieldwork was being done in Wales or Scotland in that early period. Even so, the pattern of records does indicate that genuine increase and spread occurred subsequently, so that by 1930 Woodcock were breeding (or had bred) in every mainland British county. This increase may have been assisted by a cessation of shooting in the breeding season and by the indirect protection afforded on sporting estates and in other preserves established for Pheasant (Alexander & Lack 1944, Alexander 1945-1947).

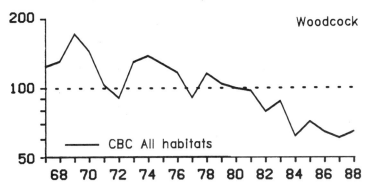

The trend shown by the CBC index is one of progressive decline, becoming somewhat steeper after about 1980. However, this species has an unique non-territorial breeding behaviour, apart from being crepuscular and difficult to observe, and it is not certain how reliably the CBC monitors its population. In any case, the CBC data are biased towards the south, where there has been a net loss of woodland and covert since the 1930s, and takes little account of the new habitat created by afforestation in the north. In addition to possible effects on the index of habitat loss, the decline steepened at a time when winters began to average colder.

Only in recent years has the breeding strategy of the Woodcock been clarified through the use of radio telemetry (Hirons 1980, 1982). It is now known that

Woodcock have a successively polygynous mating system. During roding, displaying males are not holding territory as such, but searching actively for a receptive female. When one is found, the male stays with her for a brief courtship and egg-laying period, usually less than ten days, then resumes roding and the search for another short-term mate. In this way, some males may fertilise four or more females in a season; females alone incubate and tend the chicks. Roding males do not defend an exclusive territory and may display over a number of separate woodlands, often over an area of 100 ha. Where there are several males in the vicinity these have overlapping home ranges, though some individuals, perhaps those less successful at finding mates, rode much more than others. A male's success rate may prove to be related to a dominance hierarchy, perhaps age-related, in that area. As a consequence of this complicated system, density estimation is difficult and there is as yet no reliable figure for the size of the British population. Hunting statistics are of little help, since our winter population is augmented by many migrants from northern Europe. Game Conservancy Trust figures show an increasing national bag size for Woodcock since the mid-1960s, but this may be due to coincidentally increased hunting pressure as Pheasant shoots grow in numbers (Rands & Tapper 1986).

Regional variation

In the present century, Woodcock have continued to increase locally in southwest Scotland, northern England, the East Anglian Brecks and in North Wales where new conifer plantations have extended the area of habitat available (Parslow 1973). However, these gains have been balanced to some extent by net losses in southern England, caused by the felling and fragmentation of old woodlands and the dissolution of former sporting estates, though there are still southern woodlands where the species remains relatively common. There can be little doubt that Woodcock are now more numerous overall in the northern half of Britain than in the south, and there are certainly fewer gaps there within the breeding distribution (Sharrock 1976).

Trends elsewhere in Europe

Past trends claimed from analyses of hunting statistics are conflicting. There has certainly been an overall increase and spread in Denmark and the Netherlands during the present century; while in East and West Germany, Woodcock are increasing in the north but declining, or now stable after earlier decline, in the south (Cramp & Simmons 1983). Dutch breeding census index values for 1984-1987 were halved over that period (Hustings 1988); this may have been an effect of cold winters, to which this species is known to be susceptible.

Curlew *Numenius arquata*

Present population trend: uncertain; expansion of breeding range suggests an overall increase.
Percentages of plots occupied 1968/78/88: all CBC habitats 13/18/19; all WBS plots -/27/33.
Latest estimate of breeding population: 33,000-38,000 pairs in Britain (Reed 1985).

During the present century there have been large changes in both the numbers and the distribution of breeding Curlews in Britain.

Alexander & Lack (1944) noted an increase in several parts of Scotland and England associated with an expansion of the population from traditional damp upland breeding haunts to river valleys and low heather moors. The trend began with confirmed nesting in Wiltshire in 1916 (Stanford 1955), and continued so that Parslow (1973) was able to comment that breeding occurred widely in lowland areas, and that there were only a few counties, mainly in the south and east, where this species did not breed. This was reflected in the data collected from Breeding Atlas fieldwork during 1968-1972, which showed the Curlew to be widespread in all regions to the west of a line from the Humber to the Isle of Wight (Sharrock 1976). The reasons for these major distributional changes are unknown.

In their new habitats, rough or overgrown damp pasture, clover and cereal crops all appear to be attractive as nesting sites (Nethersole-Thompson & Nethersole-Thompson 1986), and these authors have suggested that more pairs now breed in the lowlands than in upland habitats. Nevertheless, Curlews are probably most numerous on submontane grasslands and lower moorland (Ratcliffe 1977).

Since 1950 the rate of expansion appears to have slowed, perhaps because of a decline in suitable habitat due to drainage and urbanisation (Sharrock 1976). These factors may also be responsible for the local decreases reported in southwest England and the western Midlands since the 1960s. In the four west Midland counties, the earlier cutting and grazing of traditional hay meadows and an overall improvement of pasture have also contributed to population declines (Harrison *et al* 1982). In the CBC index, derived from the few plots (mainly farmland) on which Curlews were present, these having a wide geographical scatter, there has been little overall change since 1974. Recent fluctuations may have been artefacts of small sample sizes.

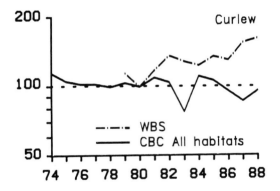

Breeding populations of Curlew have also been monitored by the WBS since 1979, but the plots on which the species occurs are again rather few. The WBS trend has been one of overall increase, the data on which it is based being biased towards northern England. In the results of the Breeding Wader Monitoring Scheme (1984-1988), there was a progressive decline after 1985, the index falling from 125 to 78; but the significance of this was uncertain since Curlews were present on rather few of the plots which were sampled.

It is possible that overwinter survival and spring conditions, in addition to habitat quality, are influencing population trends. The species is known to be susceptible to severe winter conditions: there were widespread reductions following the hard winter of 1962/63 (Dobinson & Richards 1964). In Devon at least, although numbers have subsequently increased, the population has been prevented from full recovery by habitat loss (Sitters 1988).

Regional variation
No quantified data are available on regional differences.

Trends elsewhere in Europe
A general expansion of range has occurred throughout northern Europe over the course of this century, particularly in Scandinavia (Parslow 1973). There is evidence of decline in many countries since the 1950s (Cramp & Simmons 1982). In the Netherlands this is due to habitat destruction (Braaksma 1960). In some regions Curlew decreases due to habitat loss are offset by shifts to cultivated land.

Redshank *Tringa totanus*

Present population trend: probably downward, certainly so in the south.
Percentages of plots occupied 1968/78/88: all CBC habitats 8/14/12; all WBS plots -/31/33.
Latest estimate of breeding population: 30,000-33,000 pairs in Britain (Reed 1985, Piersma 1986).

A vociferous and conspicuous breeding wader, the Redshank occupies a wide variety of wetland habitats from marginal land in the uplands to low-lying country, notably wet meadows, coastal grazing marshes and saltmarshes. Small isolated pockets of suitable breeding habitat are often occupied by one or two pairs, and this results in a complex pattern of local distribution which changes as sites dry out and are deserted, or become damp enough after spring flooding to be utilised. Such local changes complicate the assessment of overall population trends.

Historically, the British Redshank population has experienced mixed fortunes. There was decline and range contraction during the first half of the 19th century (except perhaps in northern Scotland, although early information is sparse), and the species then became virtually restricted to eastern coastal counties; this range contraction has been linked with extensive land drainage during that period. Recovery began in about 1865, with increases in numbers and a westward expansion that included a resurgence of inland breeding. This phase of increase was at its height during 1893-1915, when 26 counties in southern England and Wales were colonised or recolonised, and it lasted until about 1940 (Thomas 1942). It may not be coincidental that the main period of this spread was one of deepening agricultural recession, in which arable farming declined and pastures often became neglected and invaded by rushes. It was also one of marked climatic warming, which may have aided the species through promoting overwinter survival.

Although no clear national trend has been identified since 1940, a downward trend is strongly suspected, with major losses from inland and some coastal sites. Nevertheless, Redshanks are probably still more numerous now than they were at the beginning of this century. It is in the southern half of England that Redshanks have declined most obviously, as a direct consequence of land-use changes. Land drainage, more-intensive management of grasslands and conversions of pasture to arable have all been widespread both on coastal marshes and at inland sites. One ray of hope for the future comes from the payments now being made to farmers in Environmentally Sensitive Areas to manage their grasslands in a manner sympathetic to breeding waders, although more attention needs to be paid to raising of water-tables than is presently given in these schemes.

A survey of breeding waders on lowland grasslands in England and Wales in 1982 confirmed that Redshanks are now spread very thinly indeed, with pairs found on only one-third of the sites checked and those occupied having a decidedly coastal bias (Smith 1983). Inland, there are notable concentrations on the Cambridgeshire washes and the Derwent Ings in North Yorkshire and Humberside, but elsewhere the scattered pairs are often associated with sewage farms, gravel pits, reservoirs and waste ground. In Scotland also, the preferred marginal farmland (damp pasture and rough grazing) is under pressure from drainage and subsequent improvement (Galbraith *et al* 1984).

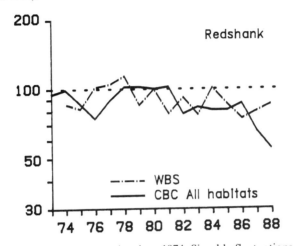

The WBS has monitored this species since 1974. Sizeable fluctuations are apparent in these data, but the peaks have tended to be smaller of late. Only small numbers of CBC plots are occupied by Redshanks, and these include both coastal and inland farms; since 1973, when samples became large enough for index purposes, the population trend has been steadily downwards. The BTO/Wader Study Group Breeding Wader Monitoring Scheme has also found a definite downward pattern. This project has monitored Redshanks on a sample of lowland grassland sites since 1984, and has found a fall in numbers of one-third over the five breeding seasons up to 1988. It is likely that the more optimistic position indicated by the WBS is actually due to better representation of northern and especially northwestern England in its sampling. Unfortunately, there is no national monitoring of the important saltmarsh population. However, a study on part of the Ribble Marshes, Lancashire, where Redshank nesting densities averaged 115 pairs per sq. km during 1975-1985, found an overall decline of 31% in numbers of breeding males over that period. Annual survival was lowest following the hard winters of 1981/82 and 1984/85 (P.S. Thompson, pers. comm.).

Regional variation
The agricultural changes described above have affected particularly the southern half of England, and resulted in Redshanks there withdrawing towards coasts. In 1982 the largest farmland concentrations were on the coastal grazing marshes of East Anglia, the Cambridgeshire washes and the North Kent marshes; other notable areas were the Derwent Ings and the coastal marshes around Morecambe Bay (Smith 1983). Northwestern and eastern England also hold the largest saltmarsh concentrations. Scotland holds perhaps one-sixth of British Redshanks, and there also agricultural

99

changes have had an impact. Much the most important numbers – 40% of the Scottish population – are on the *machair* of the Western Isles (Galbraith *et al* 1984).

Trends elsewhere in Europe

Declines affecting many parts of Europe are typically associated with land drainage and other agricultural improvements (Cramp & Simmons 1983).

Common Sandpiper *Actitis hypoleucos*

Present population trend: stable.
Percentages of plots occupied 1968/78/88: all CBC habitats 6/9/4; all WBS plots -/49/53.
Latest estimate of breeding population: 17,100-20,100 pairs in Britain (Piersma 1986).

The fast-flowing rocky upper courses of streams and rivers, with gravel shores or banks maintained by scouring, are important breeding grounds for this species. However, lake shores are also utilised at a wide range of altitudes; and in the Peak District well over half the local population is to be found on high-altitude reservoirs where extensive shingle shorelines are exposed as water levels fall in summer (Holland *et al* 1982b). Even the margins of lowland rivers are used occasionally.

About half of WBS plots hold Common Sandpipers, notably those in Scotland, northern England and Wales. Hardly any territories have been recorded on plots south of a line from the Severn to the Humber. Marchant & Hyde (1980b) showed that, although territory densities were more or less equal on rivers in four altitude classes between sea-level and 300 m, Common Sandpiper density was greatest on plots of shallow gradient, less than 5 m/km. However, WBS plots are probably sampling low density populations, compared to those which occur on upland lakes and reservoirs (D.W. Yalden, *in litt.*).

Following their arrival on the breeding grounds in mid-April, pairs establish discrete territories in suitable habitat. These areas are occupied only until the young have fledged, typically in mid-July (Holland *et al* 1982a). On rivers in the Peak District, Yalden (1986) found that the range of territory lengths was 100-300 m, with the density over a 2.7-km section of the River Ashop reaching a maximum of 4.7 pairs per km. He also found that occupied river stretches were wider than unoccupied reaches and had twice the width of shingle. Observations suggested that the shingle was defended as the important resource within the territory, not for the benefit of the adult pair, but for their chicks which were dependent on it during their main period of growth. However, associated factors may also be important. Yalden (1986) pointed out for instance that wider shingle banks were less likely to be completely inundated by flash floods than narrower deposits, and that wide areas of shingle were typically associated with meanders, and with broad and open treeless valleys with particular flow characteristics. Thus selection for wide shingle banks within territories could be an artefact, at least in part, of selection for one or other of these additional features. More recent observations (D.W.Yalden, *in litt.*) suggest that the shingle shores of reservoirs are especially important in providing secure hiding places for the chicks.

There have been no national quantitative studies of Common Sandpiper distribution, and thus it is difficult to evaluate population trends accurately. WBS index values, available from 1974, show a fairly stable population level on the sampled plots. This is consistent with the view of Glutz von Blotzheim *et al* (1977) that in stable

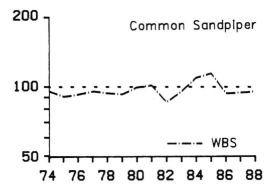

200 ┤

Common Sandpiper

100 ┤ ·⁻·⁻·⁻·⁻·⁻·⁻⁻·⁻·⁻·⁻⁻⁻·⁻⁻·

─·─·─ WBS

50 ┤
74 76 78 80 82 84 86 88

habitats there is little annual change in Common Sandpiper numbers. Indeed, with an annual adult survival rate of 75-80% (Holland *et al* 1982*a*), rather little fluctuation would be expected. There is, however, some evidence that mortality rises when bad snow storms occur in late April, as happened in the Peak District in 1981 and 1989 (D.W. Yalden, *in litt.*).

Although the Common Sandpiper is mostly a summer visitor which winters in trans-Saharan Africa, the incidence of overwintering birds here, most commonly in estuarine areas, has increased since the 1950s (Prater 1981). The winter population is now probably about 100 birds, but this is of course tiny compared with British breeding numbers.

Regional variation

Sharrock (1976) reported that no marked change in distribution is known to have occurred in Britain this century, but cited several instances of local declines throughout the range from the 1930s to 1950s, some of which, especially on the edge of the breeding range, may still be continuing. For example, in the four west Midland counties the Common Sandpiper has shown a gradual decline over the last half-century due to disturbance and other human pressures (Harrison *et al* 1982), as also around Manchester (Holland *et al* 1982*b*). Though common on Dartmoor in the 1930s, the species has now virtually disappeared as a breeding bird in Devon (Sitters 1988). By contrast, Mather (1986) reported that a slight eastward extension of breeding range had occurred in North Yorkshire since the 1950s. The Common Sandpiper has occasionally nested outside its normal breeding range, for example in Norfolk and Surrey, but this has never resulted in colonisation of the lowlands.

Trends elsewhere in Europe

Glutz von Blotzheim *et al* (1977) and Sharrock & Hildén (1983) report a general decrease over central continental Europe but commented that populations appeared to be stable elsewhere. In Ireland a general contraction in the breeding distribution has taken place since the 1950s (Hutchinson 1989).

Stock Dove *Columba oenas*

Present population trend: now stabilising after partial recovery from earlier large decline.
Percentages of plots occupied 1968/78/88: farmland 33/48/68; woodland 27/42/54.
Latest estimate of breeding population: 100,000 pairs in Britain and Ireland (Sharrock 1976); following increase in the 1970s, this figure may now apply to Britain alone (Hudson & Marchant 1984).
Regional density rankings 1988: farmland W>WE> SE>EE>NE; woodland SE>EE>S>W>WE.

It seems likely that the Stock Dove was originally a woodland-edge and parkland bird in Britain. At the beginning of the 19th century it was confined to eastern and southern counties, but then began expanding rapidly and colonised Scotland and Ireland in the 1860s and 1870s. This major spread doubtless owed much to the 19th-century expansion of arable farming, though Stock Doves may also have benefited from the contemporary decline of maintained dovecote pigeons which were potential food competitors. It is not known when this expansion petered out, though it is thought that population levels by 1950 were as high as at any time this century (Parslow 1973).

Subsequent changes in the fortunes of British Stock Doves were investigated by O'Connor & Mead (1981, 1984) and O'Connor & Shrubb (1986*a*). Population levels fell steeply in the period 1951-1961, with a tenfold drop indicated by indices based on annual ringing totals and intakes of nest record cards, and recovered thereafter at a

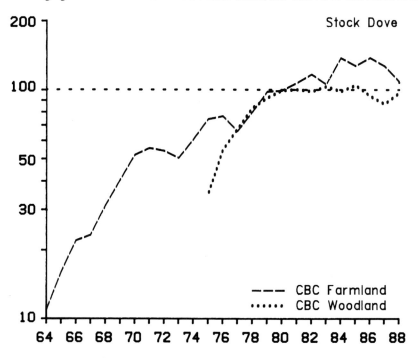

slower rate. This corresponded well with the widespread use of organochlorines as seed dressings in the 1950s and the subsequent restrictions placed on their use in the early 1960s. Breeding success, measured as the percentage of nests fledging young, was halved in the period 1950-1959 from its value during 1942-1949, and did not return to the previous level until 1980. At the height of the pesticide-induced decline, Stock Doves withdrew into coastal areas and away from intensively arable farmland, and virtually disappeared from some regions.

The CBC began early in the Stock Dove's recovery period, which lasted at least until 1980 before the population curve started to smooth out. The ringing and nest record card indices suggest that by 1980 the species was halfway to recovery from the post-1950 crash (O'Connor & Mead 1984), though biases inherent in these two sources of data may have affected this estimate. Nevertheless, it is likely that the national population level has stabilised below the former level, due to recent farming and environmental changes. For a species which depends upon weed seeds when grain is unavailable, the now-widespread use of herbicides for farmland weed control is clearly disadvantageous, and has been especially so since chemicals effective against *Polygonum* species were introduced. With the modern switch to autumn sowing of cereals, fallows and old stubbles are no longer left over winter; these used to be seasonally important feeding sites. Modern techniques of sowing cereals result in a more even density of the crop, which has eliminated the thinly vegetated patches which Stock Doves preferred. Moreover, potential nest sites have become fewer following Dutch elm disease and a more general removal of hedgerow trees and dilapidated farm buildings. It is probable that Stock Doves are now most common in areas of mixed farming, with numbers lower where either arable or pasture dominates the agricultural scene (Lack 1986).

Regional variation

All regions experienced the population crash of the 1950s, though this seems to have been more severe in the cereal-dominated areas of eastern and midland England. Regional recovery curves showed signs of reaching a plateau first (in the late 1970s) in southern and western England. Thom (1986) reported that recovery in Scotland remains incomplete. Some recent decline has occurred in northern England in both farmland and woodland.

Trends elsewhere in Europe

Numbers have declined in recent decades in Scandinavia and Finland; this may have some bearing on the recent trend in northern Britain (see above). At temperate latitudes in western Europe, the overall picture is one of long-term spread with expansion of arable farming, which has had a more lasting effect than the temporary pesticide-induced declines (Yeatman 1971, Cramp & Simmons 1985). In central Europe there are widespread reports of population decline, though not of range fragmentation.

Woodpigeon *Columba palumbus*

Present population trend: some decline during 1970s; partial recovery since.
Percentages of plots occupied 1968/78/88: farmland ?/52/92; woodland ?/47/75.
Latest estimate of breeding population: perhaps 2½ million pairs in Britain in 1983 (see below).
Regional density rankings 1988: farmland W>EE>NI> SE>WE>NE>S; woodland NE>NI>S>W>EE> SE>WE.

The Woodpigeon is too abundant on many CBC plots for accurate assessment by the mapping method; territories are difficult to define in a species in which birds can sing and nests can be built very close together. A compounding problem is that its breeding season extends well beyond the period of census fieldwork. Thus the CBC data are incomplete in respect of each plot and biased towards plots where density is manageably low.

There was a major increase in the 19th century of this economically important agricultural pest; this was in line with the expansion then of arable farming, which included green crops such as clover to provide overwinter foods for livestock. It was then that the species began colonising suburban and urban areas. Parslow (1973) considered that, by 1960, Woodpigeon numbers had been stable for many years in traditional arable farming regions, though local increases were still occurring where marginal land was brought under cultivation. There was no evidence of a decline during the organochlorine pesticide period in the 1950s, such as occurred in the Stock Dove. However, a nest record card analysis (O'Connor & Pearman 1987) found evidence of deteriorating breeding success in the early 1960s coupled with a reduced use of arable habitats; these observations are compatible with there being sublethal organochlorine effects prior to the 1966 ban.

Potts (1981) reviewed subsequent Woodpigeon trends, as indicated by figures from the Game Conservancy Trust's National Game Census: there was severe mortality in the cold winter of 1962/63, when pesticides may also have been involved, followed by a slow recovery during 1966-1969 and a plateau in 1970-1972, but a steady decline thereafter. However, it is likely that population trends differ in detail between farm cropping regimes. For example, a rather different pattern was shown by regular winter censuses of a 1000 ha study site in Cambridgeshire (Inglis *et al*, in press). There, partial recovery from the cold winters of the early 1960s occurred only up to 1966, after which the population level began falling again as farm cropping changed (see below). A low point was reached in early 1977, following a poor breeding season and reduced food supplies in the hot, dry summer of 1976. Since then, numbers have risen again, as local acreages of oil-seed rape increased; by 1986 the population level was equal to that of the late 1960s. Murton (1965) estimated a July population in Britain of 5.8 million birds (equivalent to nearly three million pairs), based on densities in this Cambridgeshire study area. I.R. Inglis (in Lack 1986) used densities from the same area to extrapolate to a national figure of 4.8 million birds (equivalent to about 2½ million pairs) at the lowest point in the annual cycle in 1983. This indicated a fall of about one-sixth over 20 years.

In the limited CBC data available, samples have been large enough since 1976 to construct separate indices for farmland and woodland. These indicate a progressive upward trend through to the present, with a doubling of values over the 13 years.

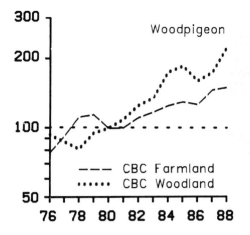

300 ┐

200

100

50

76 78 80 82 84 86 88

Woodpigeon

——— CBC Farmland
•••••• CBC Woodland

However, CBC data cannot be accepted without qualification. O'Connor & Shrubb (1986*a*) showed that the breeding season, which used to be at its height in July-September, has advanced in response to the switch towards autumn sowing, and thus earlier ripening, of cereals; more pairs now nest in May and June, and relatively fewer in late summer. Hence CBC index values are strongly influenced by the increased proportion of birds now nesting during the CBC fieldwork season.

Woodpigeons feed upon weeds (including weed seeds) in the early summer, before cereal crops ripen, and to a large extent upon green foods (especially clover and brassicas) in late autumn and winter after the stubbles have been burnt off or ploughed in. The quicker clearance of stubbles nowadays, with the switch to autumn sowing, means that the birds have to resort earlier to green foods, and this has extended their period of potential winter hardship. In Cambridgeshire, the population decline from the late 1960s to the mid-1970s occurred as autumn sowings were increased at the expense of clover ley acreages (Inglis *et al*, in press). With conditions being harshest for Woodpigeons in winter, most mortality occurred then, among first-winter birds in particular. Against this background, Murton *et al* (1974) suggested that winter shooting was ineffective as a pest-control method, merely substituting shooting for starvation as a cause of death: fewer birds starved when there were fewer to share the available food. However, others questioned whether a relationship between Woodpigeon survival and food supply had been established. Potts (1981) related the slowness of the recovery from the 1963 fall to pest-control shooting pressure, and the higher numbers of birds by 1970-1972 to the withdrawal of cartridge subsidies in 1965. More recently, Inglis *et al* (in press) have found that oil-seed rape, a relatively new crop, aids overwinter survival to the extent that winter starvation has virtually ceased in areas where this crop is grown. These authors suggest that, depending on the degree of local immigration, winter shooting may now be a valid control measure where these new conditions apply.

Regional variation
O'Connor & Shrubb (1986*a*) noted that breeding success was highest in cereal-dominated regions, particularly in eastern England. The population may still be increasing in Scotland, aided by planting of conifers, which provide nest sites, close to arable farmland (Thom 1986).

Trends elsewhere in Europe
There has been a marked northward expansion this century in Fenno-Scandia. The Faeroes were colonised in 1969, and there have been occasional nesting records from Iceland since 1964. Some regional increases have been reported from elsewhere in Europe, and these may be a prerequisite of spread into urban areas (Tomiałojć 1976, Cramp & Simmons 1985). There is believed to be a slow increase in population sizes in northern Europe, due to improved breeding success in recent decades (Purroy *et al* 1984). Index trends in Sweden and Denmark since the mid-1970s have been generally upward (Hustings 1988, DOFF 1989).

Collared Dove *Streptopelia decaocto*

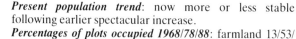

Present population trend: now more or less stable following earlier spectacular increase.
Percentages of plots occupied 1968/78/88: farmland 13/53/68; woodland 6/41/35.
Latest estimate of breeding population: over 100,000 pairs in Britain (see below).
Regional density rankings 1988: farmland EE>SE> WE>W>NI>NE>S.

The spectacular 20th-century spread of the Collared Dove across Europe is well known (Cramp & Simmons 1985). It took no more than 25 years for the species to colonise the Continent from the Balkans to the North Sea. In Britain, the first breeding records came from Norfolk in 1955 and 1956, and in 1957 birds that were probably fresh immigrants settled and bred in Kent, Lincolnshire and Morayshire. From these centres, and with the aid of additional immigration, the species spread and by 1964 was nesting in 34 English counties, together with eight in Wales and 20 in Scotland. Initial population growth was extremely fast, from four birds in 1955 to an estimated 18,855 by autumn 1964, and by 1970 the breeding population was put conservatively at 15,000-25,000 pairs (Hudson 1965, 1972).

Collared Dove presence on CBC plots has been adequate for indexing since 1971 (farmland) and 1975 (woodland) and the early years documented continuing steep increase. The rate of growth began to level out during 1977-1979, and the population peaked in 1982. Since then the index values seem to have stabilised at around the 1977 level. However, the CBC does not measure population changes in villages and suburbia, which appear to be primary Collared Dove habitat. Rather, it measures overspill into open countryside and the colonisation of farmsteads and farm buildings as, presumably, maximum densities are reached elsewhere. Recent index trends suggest that even rural habitats are now fully occupied. Ringing data show that the amount of long-distance movement declined as Collared Dove densities levelled off. Cramp & Simmons (1985) suggest that the balance of selective advantage has altered: individuals now have more chance of entering the breeding population by staying close to their natal area, where resources will be familiar to them, rather than by dispersing to distant areas which, almost inevitably, are already fully occupied.

The current population size is hard to assess because there are few estimates of urban densities. Recent regional assessments in Staffordshire, West Midlands, Warwickshire and Worcestershire (Harrison *et al* 1982), Gwent (Tyler *et al* 1987) and

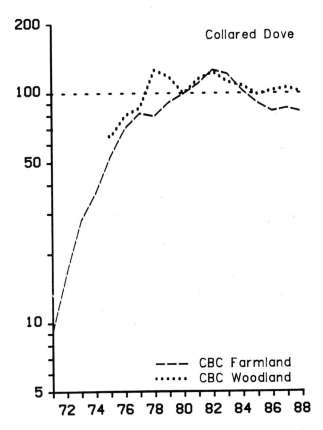

200

Collared Dove

100

50

10

——— CBC Farmland
•••••• CBC Woodland

5

72 74 76 78 80 82 84 86 88

Devon (Sitters 1988) suggest that densities greater than 100 pairs per 10-km square are not unusual. Applying this figure to just the 1035 squares in the two higher abundance categories of the Winter Atlas (Lack 1986) suggests a British population now in excess of 100,000 pairs.

There have been reports in recent years of local decline, as also on the Continent (see below). Some of these may have been the result of changed patterns of dispersion, for example of roosts or feeding concentrations, but CBC index values have fallen a little from their 1982 peak. This may be population adjustment after rapid colonisation or, as suggested by Thompson (1988), an effect of recent cold winters. Better protection of grain delivered to flour mills and of livestock food stores might also be involved, since there is a clear financial incentive for people to prevent Collared Doves taking grain; a flock of 800 on one Sussex dairy farm was estimated to take 50 kg of grain daily, equivalent to about 18.25 tonnes in a year (O'Connor & Shrubb 1986a). Surprisingly, perhaps, Collared Doves seem to make little use of grain stubbles; they prefer to feed around buildings where grain is stored or used.

Regional variation

Regional indices show that the slight decline after 1982 has not occurred in eastern England, the region where grain production is highest, and perhaps not in Wales or Scotland where, however, the CBC samples are small.

Trends elsewhere in Europe

The post-1930 spread across central Europe was analysed by Stresemann & Nowak (1958), by which time all regions north to southern Scandinavia had been colonised. Expansion in Fenno-Scandia continued until the 1970s, and since the early 1970s the species has bred in the Faeroes and irregularly in Iceland; Spain and Portugal were reached in 1974 and the spread continues there, while Egypt was colonised in 1979 (Cramp & Simmons 1985). More recently, a decrease has been reported from Sweden (Kjellen 1986), and there have been large post-1980 falls in census indices for Denmark (DOFF 1989) and the Netherlands (Hustings 1988), the scale of which suggests the effects of cold weather. Decreases in Finland since 1980 are attributed to the effects of the 1984/85 and 1986/87 winters, which were exceptionally severe there (Hildén 1989).

Turtle Dove *Streptopelia turtur*

Present population trend: recent decline, following earlier increase.
Percentages of plots occupied 1968/78/88: farmland 37/47/ 36; woodland 42/48/26.
Latest estimate of breeding population: at least 125,000 pairs in Britain (Sharrock 1976), before recent decrease.
Regional density rankings 1988: all CBC habitats SE> EE>WE>NE.

The Turtle Dove is known to have increased in numbers and range around the middle of the 19th century, for reasons we do not understand. During this period its breeding distribution expanded westwards and northwards into Wales, Cheshire and Yorkshire (More 1865). Another upsurge in the early decades of the present century coincided with agricultural recession, which must have resulted in weedy conditions much to this species' liking. At this time there was further expansion in Wales and the breeding range extended to Lancashire (from 1904) and Northumberland (from 1919). Though nesting occurred in southeast Scotland in 1946 and on several occasions thereafter, the species has not become established there (Thom 1986). Then in the 1950s regular breeding ceased in Gwynedd and Dyfed, and subjective reports of decrease around that time came also from other counties, especially those along the English/Welsh border (Parslow 1973).

From 1963, the CBC population trend was one of slow but consistent increase, which lasted to about 1978-1979. Since then, the index values have fallen steadily and are now well below the level of the early 1960s. Goodwin (1987) thought that Turtle Doves had declined greatly over the previous 25 years or so, to become scarce or even absent from some areas where they were formerly abundant. This generalisation is not wholly consistent with CBC results, though it is of interest to note that several of Goodwin's correspondents dated the decline from the early to middle 1980s, with which the CBC results agree. Since the CBC receives its best support in central and southern England, where most Turtle Doves occur, its results should provide a particularly accurate reflection of this species' population trends.

Turtle Doves winter in the Sahel and adjacent savanna zones of West Africa from Senegal and the Gambia eastwards. With this the winter range, one might have expected the effects of African droughts to be apparent in British population levels;

108

but index values for Turtle Doves continued to rise during the 1970s at the time when, for example, Sand Martins and Redstarts were in decline. There is some evidence that winter flocks of Turtle Doves have become more mobile in West Africa in response to drought (Cramp & Simmons 1985), a behaviour which may mitigate drought-induced mortality. Also, there is large-scale hunting of Turtle Doves on their migrations through France and the Mediterranean region; but the impact (if any) of this on our breeding population is not known.

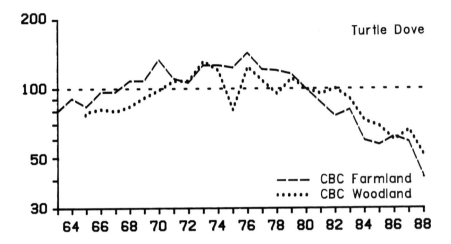

In Britain, the species feeds especially on weed seeds; Murton *et al* (1964) found a close correspondence between the distribution of the Turtle Dove and that of the common fumitory. It is unknown whether this remains a major food plant, since farmland has changed so much over the last quarter-century. In any case, the CBC results are inconsistent with the theory that adverse changes to arable crop management, such as increased herbicide use, caused the Turtle Dove decline, for these changes were well under way on arable land during the 1970s, when Turtle Doves were still increasing (M. Shrubb, pers. comm.). Similarly, hedgerow removals, which presumably reduce nest-site availability, began long before the present decline.

Murton (1965) noted in his Cambridgeshire study area that 93% of all feeding by Turtle Doves in May and June was on grassland, mainly weedy hayfields. Here, three subsequent general changes may be relevant. First, the switch in England and Wales from hay crop to silage (the latter 2% in 1962, 26% now) involves earlier and multiple mowings, which limit seeding by grassland herbs. Second, there has been a major increase since the mid-1970s in the acreage of permanent grassland that is treated with herbicides. Third, the much increased use of fertilisers on grassland results in loss of plant diversity as only the dominant grasses benefit from the chemical treatment. It is possible that these changes have reduced food supplies for Turtle Doves during the early part of their summer season, and so acted as limiting factors; any reduction of grassland food resources could not be made up by alternatives, such as cereal grains or the seeds of oil-seed rape, since these do not become readily available until mid-July (M. Shrubb). If farming practices are implicated in the present decline of Turtle Doves, then changes in grassland management provide a more consistent background than those related to arable crop management.

Regional variation

The pre-1978 increase is not apparent in the index for western England, which is consistent with Parslow's (1973) suggestion of range contraction then in western counties. There were temporary falls in the early to middle 1970s in southern England (farmland only) and eastern England (woodland only); these indices rose again in the late 1970s, prior to the decrease in the 1980s which appears to have been general.

Trends elsewhere in Europe

Some expansion of range has occurred in northern Europe. There has been an increase, especially since the 1960s, in the Soviet Baltic States; and more recently Turtle Doves have been seen increasingly in Sweden, where breeding has not yet been proved, and in Denmark, where breeding may now be regular. A severe decline in the Netherlands has been attributed in part to habitat changes (Cramp & Simmons 1985).

Cuckoo *Cuculus canorus*

Present population trend: uncertain; information is conflicting.
Percentages of plots occupied 1968/78/88: farmland 68/71/74; woodland 60/64/62.
Latest estimate of breeding population: 20,000-30,000 laying females in Britain and Ireland (see below); 73% of occupied Breeding Atlas squares were in Britain (Sharrock 1976). The typically promiscuous mating system makes it unwise to refer to "pairs".
Regional density rankings 1988: farmland WE>EE>SE>W>NE>S; woodland WE>SE>EE>S>W.

Although the carrying distance of the male Cuckoo's calls may create the impression of abundance, this species, although widespread, normally occurs at low densities. Moreover, it has been suggested that these densities are being lowered further by population decline.

In the 1940s there were statements of Cuckoo decreases in Wales and Cornwall, and also in Ireland, and such reports subsequently became more widespread in regional bird literature, especially during 1953-1964. The almost complete lack of numerical data made it impossible to assess the significance and severity of the reported trend (Parslow 1973), though the reports were so widespread that the claimed decrease was almost certainly real. British springs averaged colder and summers wetter by the 1950s, as the climate became cooler after the earlier long period of amelioration (Williamson 1975).

Brooke & Davies (1987) attempted to quantify the Cuckoo's population by assessing the proportions of parasitised nests over different time periods in the BTO nest record cards. By multiplying these figures by the estimated population sizes of the host species (from Sharrock 1976), and allowing an annual output of eight eggs by each female Cuckoo (Wyllie 1981), they produced average population figures of 34,500 females laying annually in the period 1939-1961, 30,600 during 1962-1971 and 20,900 during 1972-1982. This implied an overall decline of 40% over the study period. All three figures fell within Sharrock's range of 17,500-35,000 "pairs" of Cuckoos in Britain and Ireland. Brooke & Davies also found that the proportion of Reed Warbler nests parasitised had doubled since 1939, while the proportions for all other hosts had

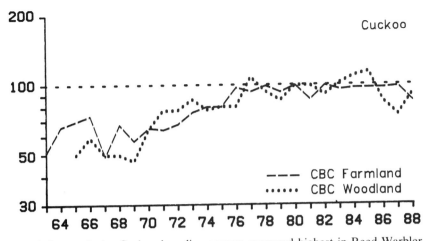

200 ┤
100 ┤
50 ┤
30 ┤

Cuckoo

CBC Farmland
CBC Woodland

64 66 68 70 72 74 76 78 80 82 84 86 88

declined. Interestingly, Cuckoo breeding success appeared highest in Reed Warbler nests.

The Cuckoo population trend cited above is at variance with the picture which emerges from the CBC. This indicates increases during the 1970s, of similar magnitude in woodland and on farmland; since 1977, both Cuckoo indices have been relatively stable around the new, higher levels. However, it is suspected that the standard CBC territory-mapping method is less reliable for species with large territories and, in any case, the CBC does not cover the full range of habitats utilised by Cuckoos. Moreover, the Cuckoo's territorial system is peculiar in that both sexes defend territory but either may mate with intruders of the opposite sex. Riddiford (1986) found that subordinate females are tolerated at the periphery of dominant birds' territories. Possibly these subordinates are (or include) first-summer birds. Seel et al (1981) found that first-years mostly return to the vicinity of their natal area, though arriving later than older birds, and that some at least are physiologically capable of breeding.

In summary, the available evidence on Cuckoo trends is inconclusive and partly conflicting, two independent assessments having used different methods applied to different sexes. Brooke & Davies (1987) reported a decline in laying females, of a magnitude that ought to show in any set of data; but their calculations included certain assumptions on population sizes and trends of host species and extensions of these to before the CBC period. On the other hand, CBC data for Cuckoo indicate stable or increasing numbers of territorial males; but CBC mapping on plots which are small relative to a Cuckoo's territory may be poor at detecting population change.

Regional variation

No differences in trends between regions are apparent in the CBC data. The 1988 regional rankings indicate that densities were lowest in Wales and the north, but these are the regions from which there are fewest CBC data. Densities were highest in western England in both habitat divisions.

Trends elsewhere in Europe

Mapping census or point-count schemes in Estonia, Sweden, Denmark and the Netherlands have found short-term fluctuations but no long-term trends. Von Haartman (1981) found that Cuckoo fluctuations in Finland were linked to those of a local host species, the Redstart.

Barn Owl *Tyto alba*

Present population trend: declining since the 1930s; not necessarily a continuous trend.
Percentages of plots occupied 1968/78/88: all CBC habitats 5/2/1.
Latest estimate of breeding population: 4400 pairs in Britain (Shawyer 1987), but see below.

Though the Barn Owl still has a wide distribution across Britain, densities are now very low almost everywhere. It has never been common enough on CBC plots to allow the calculation of an index, though ubiquity figures are available and help to illustrate the later stages of the decline (see graph). Moreover, this species is one of the most difficult to census because it is so elusive; the most robust method is to check individual nest sites.

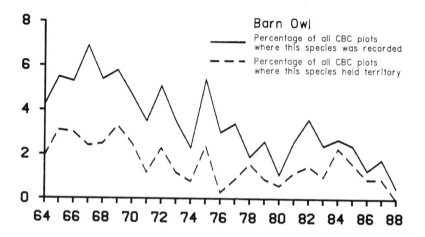

In recent years the Barn Owl has been the subject of a monograph (Bunn *et al* 1982), while Shawyer (1987) has investigated British distribution and densities. It has been shown that there are short-term fluctuations in population size, primarily on three- to four-year cycles, and most markedly in northern Britain, related to the cycles of abundance of the short-tailed vole which is the main prey species.

The Barn Owl was once a common British bird, having benefited from land enclosures and farmstead building during the 18th and early 19th centuries. But a decline set in after about 1820, with the development of breech-loading firearms, game preservation, and a Victorian attraction to the taxidermist's art. This downward trend, relative to Tawny Owl, continued almost to the end of the 19th century, perhaps exacerbated by a high frequency of severe winters during 1860-1900 (Shawyer 1987). The first protective legislation was enacted in 1880, and soon after 1900 there were reports of increased numbers in northern counties at least. Then, coincident with a resumption of gamekeeping after the First World War, further decline was noticed in several southern and eastern counties. Blaker (1934) estimated the population of England and Wales at 12,000 pairs in 1932 (25,000 birds including non-breeders), and considered that there had been a fall of one-third during the previous ten years. Because Blaker's pioneer survey used a questionnaire approach, his figures must be treated with reservation.

Though figures are lacking, it is thought that a slow decrease continued through the 1940s, when there were some cold winters, and that the decline became steeper and more general after 1955. This was coincident with the increased use of organochlorine pesticides on farmland and other more lasting agricultural changes (Parslow 1973). By the Breeding Atlas period, 1968-1972, there were possibly only 4500-9000 pairs in Britain and Ireland (Sharrock 1976), although this estimate was based on an untested assumption of 2-4 pairs per occupied 10-km square. By the mid-1980s there were considered to be about 3750 pairs in England and Wales plus 650 pairs in Scotland, or about 10,000 birds in all with the inclusion of unmated individuals (Shawyer 1987). However, there remains considerable doubt over the reliability of published population estimates, especially since Taylor et al (1988) showed that numbers of Barn Owl breeding pairs within a Scottish region can more than double across a single vole cycle. A further complication is that vole cycles are not necessarily synchronised between regions, and often clearly are not.

Several factors have been involved in this long-term decline, though at present there is little information by which to rank them. Barn Owls are sensitive to extremes of weather, with survival and breeding success being affected by severe frost, persistent deep snow and heavy rainfall. Britain is, of course, at the northern edge of the species' range. Hence the increased frequency of severe winters since the 1940s may be implicated. Yet agricultural changes are likely to have been more damaging in the long term. Modern farming methods are unsympathetic to the voles and other rodents which are the main prey of Barn Owls. Combine harvesters have eliminated stackyard threshing, and the replacement of horses by tractors has much reduced the availability of hay lofts; modern barns are far less suitable for nesting. Vole populations have also suffered from losses of unimproved grasslands, the elimination of rough grass strips along field boundaries, and large-scale hedgerow removals. Farmland Barn Owls are now most numerous in areas of mixed farming, especially in river valleys where there are damp grassland margins and in areas where, for conservation or for sporting reasons, there is sensitive management of habitats (Shawyer 1987). Another major hunting habitat for them is young forestry plantation, where voles can sometimes achieve high densities.

It is uncertain to what extent the availability of nest sites has become critical, though there are fewer dilapidated outbuildings nowadays and many large hedgerow trees have been felled. The loss of elms through Dutch elm disease is believed to have been detrimental (Burton & Osborne 1980). Barn Owls use buildings and tree holes, with regional variations in their relative importance. The proportion of tree-hole sites is highest (70%) in East Anglia, their importance declining towards the west and north where up to 90% of pairs nest in buildings. Shawyer (1987) sought to relate this to regional rainfall patterns, but the gradient of nest-site preferences across regions also reflects farming productivity. In the prosperous arable regions of the south and east there has been more demolition or conversion of unwanted farm buildings, so that Barn Owls there may have become more dependent on tree sites. Conversely, in the west and north, old farm cottages and other buildings are more often left empty and become derelict, especially where afforestation leads to the abandonment of farmsteads (I.R. Taylor, pers. comm.).

113

Regional variation

The species is now very sparsely distributed over much of the country, though with higher densities in a few favoured areas. Reported densities in excess of 5 pairs per 10-km square were found in the mid-1980s in Cornwall, south Hampshire and the Isle of Wight, east Suffolk, Anglesey and Wigtownshire (Shawyer 1987). The highest figure was from the Isle of Wight, where there were 13.4 pairs per 10-km square, followed by west Cornwall with 10.0. The population of southwest Scotland varies between 140 pairs in poor vole years and 320 pairs in good ones (Taylor *et al* 1988); this study highlights the problems of attempting to produce gross estimates of numbers or densities in this species.

Trends elsewhere in Europe

A widespread decrease has affected much of the Barn Owl's European range. It is now almost extinct in Sweden, and in the Netherlands it has declined by over 80% since 1960. National and regional declines have variously been ascribed to human persecution, habitat loss, and rodenticides and other pesticides, plus the temporary effects of severe winters (Cramp & Simmons 1985).

Little Owl *Athene noctua*

Present population trend: fluctuates; no clear recent trend but possibly increasing.
Percentages of plots occupied 1968/78/88: farmland 27/34/39; woodland 6/6/1.
Latest estimate of breeding population: 7000-14,000 pairs in Britain (Sharrock 1976).
Regional density rankings 1988: all CBC habitats WE> W>EE>NE>SE.

Previously a rare vagrant to the British Isles from the near Continent, the Little Owl was introduced into England in the 1870s and 1880s and established a feral breeding population. Initial releases were made in Kent and Northamptonshire, and by the close of the century there were two separate breeding groups, in southeast England and the east Midlands. The spread subsequently was very rapid, aided by further releases, and soon Little Owls were present west to the River Severn and north to the River Trent (Witherby & Ticehurst 1908). By 1925 they had colonised much of Wales and expanded northwards to central parts of Lancashire and Yorkshire. Durham and Northumberland were reached in the 1930s, the Lake District in the 1940s, southeast Scotland (Borders and Lothian) from 1958, then Dumfries & Galloway from the 1970s (Fitter 1959; Lever 1977, 1984; Thom 1986). However, the Little Owl remains extremely rare in Scotland, and has not successfully penetrated north of the Edinburgh-Glasgow line.

Though peripheral expansion continues, the initial explosive phase had slowed by the mid-1930s and was followed by reports of decreases in density over large parts of central and southern England. There is some evidence that this was accompanied by a reduction in average clutch size (F.C.R. Jourdain, in Hibbert-Ware 1937), a feature which, in birds of prey, usually denotes problems with prey availability. A run of severe winters in the 1940s may also have affected Little Owls adversely. Some improvement occurred in the early 1950s, but there was further decline during 1955-1963, which coincided with the organochlorine pesticide era and then the cold winters of 1961/62 and 1962/63 (Parslow 1973, Sharrock 1976).

114

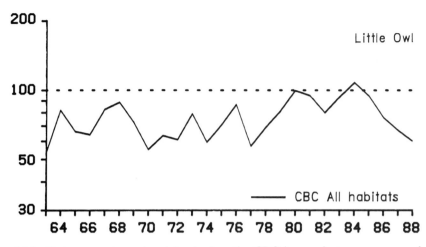

200

Little Owl

100 ·

50

━━━ CBC All habitats

30

64 66 68 70 72 74 76 78 80 82 84 86 88

Little Owls were at a reduced level when the CBC began, but soon recovered somewhat. The subsequent pattern has been an unusual one, with its fairly regular spacing of peaks and troughs. The peak years (1964, 1968, 1973, 1976, 1980, 1984) have been at intervals of three to five years and average four years apart. This has all the appearance of being cyclical – a pattern known to occur in some birds of prey but which has not previously been indicated for British Little Owls. Comparisons with the CBC graphs for two other rodent predators, Kestrel and Tawny Owl, show some coincidences of timing, though not complete agreement. Thus Kestrels also peaked in 1968 and 1973, while Tawny Owls increased in 1968 but continued to do so until reaching a peak in 1972. In 1976, Tawny Owls peaked simultaneously with Little Owls, though Kestrels not until the following year; neither of these other species peaked in 1980, though both did so in 1981; but all three species reached peak levels in 1984. The discrepancies may be due to the fact that small mammal cycles are not necessarily synchronised across the country, which factor introduces a certain amount of variation into national data pools; CBC data for Little Owl are drawn from a more restricted area of the country than those for the other predators, which are distributed more widely.

Such predator cycles lag behind those of small rodent prey: predator clutches are larger, and more pairs attempt to breed, in those years when rodent densities are high than when they are low. Although British Little Owls eat insects, earthworms and other invertebrates all year round, field-mice and voles dominate the diet in years when these are abundant (Hibbert-Ware 1937). It seems possible that reports of Little Owl decline after the mid-1930s (referred to above) included such cyclical oscillation; and such natural variation in population levels may have contributed to other low points mentioned in the literature.

Superimposed onto this cyclical pattern has been some longer-term variation in Little Owl densities, though it cannot yet be said that an overall trend has been confirmed. After recovery in the early 1960s the average population level varied little up to 1975, but this increased in the late 1970s and early 1980s to produce a highest-ever index figure in 1984. This overall increase occurred despite two very cold winters, 1978/79 and 1981/82, which seemed to have had little effect; 1982 was a natural low point in a cycle. There has been a steady fall over the last four years, so that another peak year is due in 1989 if the previous pattern is to be maintained. Yet

115

even the index figure for 1988 is no lower than the trough-year index values of the 1960s and 1970s.

In nest record cards submitted between 1939 and 1975, only 13% of Little Owls used elm trees for breeding sites (Glue & Scott 1980). Hence the impact on the species of tree loss through Dutch elm disease should be small and localised.

Regional variation

Population changes are not known to vary regionally. The western regions came highest in the 1988 density rankings.

Trends elsewhere in Europe

Widespread declines occur after severe winters, especially in the north of the range and at higher altitudes. Populations are declining in many parts of northwestern and central Europe (*e.g.* Juillard 1989), with decreases attributed locally to habitat changes and the use of pesticides.

Tawny Owl *Strix aluco*

Present population trend: higher levels reached during the early 1970s have not been sustained.
Percentages of plots occupied 1968/78/88: farmland 26/33/38; woodland 39/46/66.
Latest estimate of breeding population: 50,000-100,000 pairs in Britain (Sharrock 1976).
Regional density rankings 1988: all CBC habitats S> SE>W>NE>WE>EE.

This is Britain's commonest owl and probably our most numerous bird of prey. Though it declined somewhat in the 19th century as a result mainly of zealous gamekeeping, it recovered and increased further in the period 1900-1930. Local increases continued up to about 1950, especially in southern Scotland. Some expansion is still occurring in the uplands where conifer forests are providing new habitat (Petty 1985), but over much of the country the species has not shown any marked change during the last three decades.

There were only slight or local indications of Tawny Owls being affected by organochlorine pesticides in the late 1950s and early 1960s (Prestt 1965). Moreover,

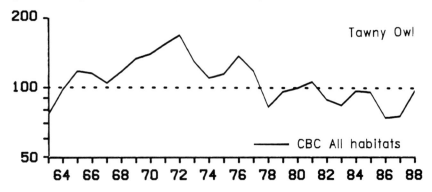

the severe winter weather of 1962/63 affected this species less than other owls (Dobinson & Richards 1964). Hence the scale of increase recorded during the early years of the CBC is surprising. The index increased through the late 1960s to reach a peak in 1972; since then it has fluctuated around a distinctly lower level, with peaks not so large now as they were in the early to middle 1970s. The Tawny Owl has been predicted to be affected in the long term by reduced nest-site availability following Dutch elm disease (Osborne 1982). In recent years there were noticeable dips in population in 1978, 1982-1983 and 1986-1987. These may have been due, at least in part, to bad winter weather or to low points of small mammal cycles. The latter are not always synchronised nationally, however, which may help to account for instances where peaks and troughs do not coincide exactly between Tawny Owl, Little Owl and Kestrel (see further under Little Owl).

A general problem in censusing birds of prey is that their territories are often very large compared with the size of the CBC plots on which their numbers are being assessed, and this is likely to reduce the accuracy of CBC monitoring. Attention must also be drawn to the fact that the Tawny Owl index is an amalgam of woodland and farmland data, whereas the species is dispersed differently in these habitats. The highest densities are in woodland, where territories are smaller and usually contiguous but on farmland the territories are often linear, so that there is normally less interaction between birds at these lower densities (S.M. Percival, pers. comm.). It is well known that many rural Tawny Owl pairs refrain from breeding in years when prey density is low (e.g. Southern 1970): it is uncertain how this affects CBC censusing, which records territoriality.

Tawny Owl populations are regulated through the mechanism of territorial behaviour (Southern 1970, Hirons et al 1979). Juvenile Tawny Owls have a protracted period of 11-13 weeks under parental care, and disperse from their natal territory during July-November. Those unable to find a territorial vacancy of their own often starve rapidly (Hirons et al 1979). There are, however, cases where birds have been recruited into the breeding population at three and four years old (S.J. Petty, pers. comm.). The apparent stability of Tawny Owl populations in comparison with other British owls can be attributed to the Tawny's longer lifespan, its ability to cope with severe winter weather, and its broader diet (e.g. Yalden 1985). Indeed, urban and suburban pairs rely on avian and invertebrate rather than mammalian prey. It is likely that this wider prey spectrum has prevented the species from being affected so severely on farmland as has the Barn Owl through reductions in rodent populations brought about by changes in agricultural management. Nevertheless, the Tawny Owl is one of several birds for which density on farmland is correlated with the density of farmsteads (O'Connor & Shrubb 1986a). Presumably this arises through small woods and hedgerows close to farmsteads being less likely to be removed, and the presence of mature trees in farmhouse gardens.

In woodland, there appears to be an area threshold influencing selection as breeding sites. Tawny Owls are absent from only 18% of woods greater than 100 ha in size, though they are missing from over 90% of woods that are smaller than that (Moore & Hooper 1975). It has sometimes been assumed that a substantial overlap exists between Tawny and Long-eared Owls in planted spruce forests, but a recent study (Petty 1985) has found this not to be so. Long-eared Owls occur in the early stages of plantation growth but seldom persist when the forest matures. Tawny Owls arrive when the canopy has closed and openings begin to appear from windblow, thinning and clear felling. This is consistent with the dietary separation between them reported by Yalden (1985).

Regional variation

The recent small decline in index values has been more pronounced on farmland in eastern England than elsewhere, and barely detectable in western England and Wales. This may be related to the higher incidence of cereal monocultures, which encourage hedgerow removal, and the greater impact of Dutch elm disease in eastern counties.

Trends elsewhere in Europe

Finland was colonised from 1878 onwards, especially in the period of climatic amelioration in the 1920s and 1930s when there was also northward expansion elsewhere in Scandinavia and in northwest Russia. In the Netherlands there has been considerable increase and spread since the 1920s, involving expansion into coastal regions, aided by afforestation.

Kingfisher *Alcedo atthis*

Present population trend: decline since the mid-1970s.
Percentages of plots occupied 1968/78/88: all CBC habitats 8/13/10; all WBS plots -/61/51.
Latest estimate of breeding population: 5000-9000 pairs in Britain and Ireland (Sharrock 1976); 72% of occupied squares were then in Britain.

The Kingfisher has its strongholds in slow-flowing lowland rivers, particularly in England and Wales. Other flowing and standing waters, such as canals, lakes and reservoirs with natural margins, are also occupied, but only where suitable, undisturbed, steep or vertical banks are available for nesting.

It has long been known that Kingfishers are especially vulnerable to the effects of severe winter weather. Jourdain & Witherby (1918) reported a considerable decrease after the hard winter of 1916/17, and a disappearance from the less-favoured upper reaches of rivers; it was presumed that survivors of this cold winter had moved preferentially to the lower reaches. The species was affected even more seriously in the winter of 1939/40, when decreases exceeded 75% in some districts (Ticehurst & Witherby 1940). Similar mortality occurred again in 1946/47, but survival was better on some faster streams in western counties which did not freeze over (Ticehurst & Hartley 1948). Of all British birds the Kingfisher was the worst affected by the winter of 1962/63 (Dobinson & Richards 1964). Not only were inland feeding sites frozen but the foreshore, a last refuge, was also widely ice-bound. The species was exterminated in some areas and in many others the population was reduced by up to 90%. Yet, with a clutch size of six or seven and up to four broods in a year, the Kingfisher is capable of making good such losses quite quickly, given a run of mild winters (Morgan & Glue 1977).

A ringing index for the period since 1960, based on the annual ringing total divided by the number of ringing permits issued for that year, shows that numbers were reduced by the cold winter of 1961/62, before the even greater consequences of 1962/63; the 1963 index was only one-fifth that of 1961. Subsequent recovery took four years to achieve, and this upward trend then continued until 1976 which was the peak year. This pattern can be seen in other British resident species, and is thought to have owed much to a run of mild winters between 1965 and 1975. WBS monitoring began in 1974. This also showed 1976 to have been a peak year for Kingfishers. Subsequent decline steepened after the cold winters of 1978/79 and 1981/82. There was some recovery after both of those seasons, but densities have remained well below those of the mid-1970s despite a substantial rise in the WBS index in 1988. WBS ubiquity fell from 61% to 51% between 1978 and 1988.

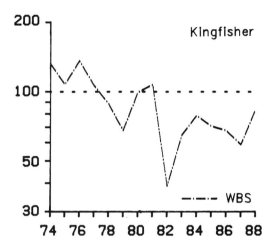

The more gradual and longer-term decline in index values is likely to have had several causes. Stream pollution is one factor. Meadows (1972a, b) showed that, after the 1962/63 crash, the Kingfisher's recovery rate and population density were correlated negatively with general levels of river pollution. Pollution may poison birds directly, especially as Kingfishers accumulate heavy metals and pesticides from their prey, or act indirectly by reducing the food supply. Also relevant are disturbance levels and losses of suitable breeding and feeding sites, caused by human leisure activities and by waterway regulation through flood-prevention schemes and water abstractions. Moreover, cold winters have been more frequent during the 1980s, with less time for recovery from one before the onset of the next.

Although persecution was an important cause of mortality in the 19th century, this is not now the case (Parslow 1973).

Regional variation

Sharrock (1976) commented on a marked decrease in Scotland since 1947, which he attributed to hard winters and pollution. However, Thom (1986) considered that too few regular surveys of Kingfisher haunts had been carried out in Scotland to permit assessment of the extent to which birds there might be more seriously and lastingly affected by hard winters than those further south.

Trends elsewhere in Europe

Marked fluctuations in northern and central Europe are attributable to hard winters. Cramp & Simmons (1985) reported a general decline in many countries, citing pollution, river management and persecution as the causes. The Irish population is not subject to such striking fluctuations as that in Britain, since winters are generally less severe and coastal feeding sites remain ice-free (Ruttledge 1968).

Green Woodpecker *Picus viridis*

Present population trend: small decline in the 1980s, after earlier stability.
Percentages of plots occupied 1968/78/88: farmland 24/40/43; woodland 43/64/66.
Latest estimate of breeding population: 10,000-15,000 pairs in Britain (Hudson & Marchant 1984).
Regional density rankings 1988: farmland W>SE>EE>NE; woodland SE>EE>W>NE>WE.

The largest and most brightly coloured of our woodpeckers, the Green Woodpecker is typically a bird of wooded areas with open ground, the latter providing important feeding sites. Well-timbered parkland and deciduous woods adjacent to pasture are characteristic habitats. Its diet consists principally of ants and their pupae, and it may be considered to have the most specialised feeding ecology of all the European woodpeckers (Cramp & Simmons 1985).

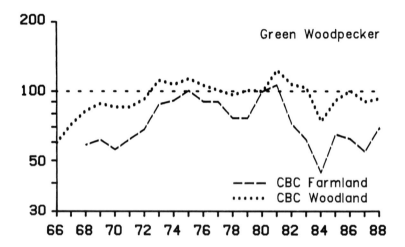

The Green Woodpecker is known to be sensitive to cold-weather extremes, especially when a thick ground cover of snow makes feeding conditions difficult. The 1962/63 hard winter caused locally severe losses, and this was then the worst affected of British woodpeckers (Dobinson & Richards 1964). The CBC indices, beginning in woodland in 1966, showed an initial increase which may have included late stages of recovery from the 1962/63 winter; the phase of increase lasted until the early 1970s, and included overflow onto farmland plots. This was followed by a period of general stability which lasted until the early 1980s, but since then there has been a slight decline, more marked in the farmland index.

Sharrock (1976) noted that, in the early 19th century, Northumberland was the northern limit of this species in Britain but that its abundance then declined. This was ascribed by Hutchinson (1840) to the scarcity of decaying trees and to persecution. However, by the early 1900s recovery was well under way and by 1941 the range had extended to the Scottish border at Berwick (Temperley & Blezard 1951). By contrast, the advance into northwest England (north Lancashire and Cumbria) did not begin until the 1940s.

The first confirmed breeding record in Scotland was in 1951 in Selkirkshire, and the species is now well established in lowland districts north to the Great Glen. Thom (1986) commented on continuing gradual spread in Scotland, checked sporadically by hard winters.

Temperley & Blezard (1951) considered that widespread coniferous afforestation may be indirectly implicated in this spread, since such new habitats have allowed the wood ant, a favoured prey, to increase in abundance. However, managed commercial plantations do not normally last to the overmature stage when there are likely to be nest sites available for Green Woodpeckers.

Population changes are probably related to two factors. First, as a resident ground-feeding species, the Green Woodpecker is sensitive to severe weather conditions which render prey unavailable. There are reports in the literature, however, of anthills being located by Green Woodpeckers under snow, and Glutz von Blotzheim (1980) records one tunnelling 85 cm through snow to reach an active mound. Yet it must be noted that the CBC graphs for the last ten years do not show a pattern of sudden falls after severe winters, except for one in 1984 that followed a winter which was cold but not exceptionally so. Nevertheless, vulnerability to cold may account in part for the failure to colonise northern and western Scotland, although habitat and overall food availability may also be important in this respect.

Second, there has been a decline in sheep husbandry in England, especially in the east where tillage now predominates, plus a decrease in the extent and intensity of grazing by rabbits following deliberate introduction of the myxomatosis virus. The feeding activities of both sheep and rabbits produce a short, dense turf which, with a high exposure to direct sunlight, is capable of supporting larger and more diverse ant populations than the longer swards which otherwise develop. Also, the conversion of pasture to arable, and grassland improvement generally may have been contributory factors. Since the 1970s especially, an increased acreage of old pasture has been modernised, with much fertilising and reseeding. Yet grassland changes cannot be the whole answer, since these trends began well before the recent decline by Green Woodpeckers.

Regional variation

The national index has shown a small downward trend recently, but higher numbers and range expansion are documented for the north of the country. Presumably this anomaly is related to the bias in CBC fieldwork towards central and southern regions. Within CBC data, the largest recent declines have been in eastern England.

Trends elsewhere in Europe

No systematic population trends are evident across Europe. Cramp & Simmons (1985) noted recent range extensions in Denmark and Sweden, but declines in northern Italy and (since the 1930s) in the Netherlands, mainly due to habitat change.

Great Spotted Woodpecker *Dendrocopos major*

Present population trend: perhaps now beginning to fall from high levels of the late 1970s and early 1980s.
Percentages of plots occupied 1968/78/88: farmland 21/49/57; woodland 55/79/86.
Latest estimate of breeding population: 30,000-40,000 pairs in Britain (Sharrock 1976); perhaps too high then but applicable by 1982 (Hudson & Marchant 1984).
Regional density rankings 1988: farmland SE>W>EE>WE>NE; woodland W>EE>NE>SE>WE>S.

The last two centuries have seen some marked changes in the fortunes of this woodpecker. Originally widespread in Britain, it underwent enormous decrease and range contraction in Scotland during the first half of the 19th century and became virtually extinct there by 1860. Moreover, this decline affected large areas of northern England also. The change was attributed by Thom (1986) primarily to the large-scale felling of native woodlands, but probably it also had a climatic basis. Around 1890, coincidental with the onset of a long period of climatic amelioration, Great Spotted Woodpeckers began to spread northwards again and soon recolonised much of southern and central Scotland (Harvie-Brown 1908). Such a climatic warming could be expected to benefit the arboreal invertebrates on which *Dendrocopos* woodpeckers feed. This phase of increase continued into the 1950s, slowing latterly, and was marked not only by further spread in Scotland but also by increases within the established range. As a consequence, more birds entered suburban environments including parks and gardens (Upton 1962, Parslow 1973).

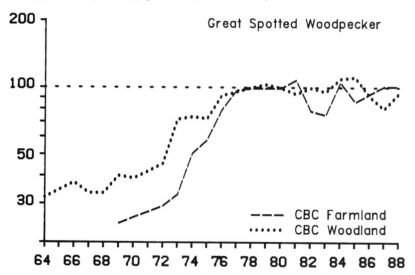

Unlike the largely ground-feeding Green Woodpecker, the present species can apparently cope well with occasional severe winters. The effects of 1962/63 were small (Dobinson & Richards 1964), and no subsequent cold-winter falls have been detected by the woodland CBC. The graph indicates a stable population over the early years of monitoring, with signs of an increase around 1970 which subsequently became very pronounced, and was sustained throughout the decade. This trend was almost certainly related to the disastrous outbreak of Dutch elm disease, which began in the late 1960s and was rampant for fifteen years before subsiding in the 1980s: the English distribution of the elm corresponded well with the principal regions of CBC fieldwork. The larvae of scolytid beetles, the vectors of DED, were abundant in the trunks of infected elms and were still to be found for up to two years after the trees had died, until bark began to fall; these provided an abundant source of food for woodpeckers (Osborne 1982, 1983). It should be noted, however, that comparison of the Breeding Atlas map for 1968-1972 (Sharrock 1976) and the Winter Atlas map for 1981-1984 (Lack 1986) shows no sign of significant geographical spread accompanying the higher population levels of the 1970s and early 1980s. It is unlikely that these high levels can be maintained much longer now that DED has subsided. Indeed, CBC index values for woodland have fallen a little since 1985.

It has been suggested that Great Spotted Woodpeckers will benefit from the expansion of conifer afforestation in the north and west of Britain, but this is by no means certain. A German study (Rutschke 1983) found that densities in pine woods were only 10-20% of those in broad-leaved woodland. While densities will depend upon the structure and age of the woodland, the German figure is nevertheless likely to be a reliable guide. Moreover, for commercial reasons, most trees in British plantations are felled before they reach an age best suited to the feeding and breeding requirements of woodpeckers. Indeed, in any kind of woodland, active management often involves removal of the dead, dying and overmature trees which woodpeckers require. Rotting wood provides better conditions for both feeding and nest-hole excavation. At the height of the DED-related population increase, Great Spotted Woodpeckers occurred increasingly on farmland: the farmland index values quadrupled between 1969 and 1979. There was then a correlation between woodpeckers and the presence of lines of trees, especially those without a hedgerow at the base, presumably because such features were likely to contain dead or dying trees (O'Connor & Shrubb 1986a).

There has been no change over the last seventeen years in the numbers of this woodpecker visiting suburban gardens (Thompson 1988), but there has been an increase in rural gardens, matching the CBC population trend.

Regional variation
The increase in the 1970s and early 1980s was more pronounced in eastern and southern England than elsewhere. This was perhaps to be expected, since those regions contained particularly high densities of infected elm trees.

Trends elsewhere in Europe
Increase and expansion during the present century has been reported from Belgium, the Netherlands, Denmark and Fenno-Scandia, owing to increased afforestation and possibly also to climatic changes. In northern Europe, numbers are believed to fluctuate with food supply and the species is eruptive when conditions dictate. Swedish index values increased from 1970 to reach a peak in 1980-1981, and have since declined markedly (Hustings 1988); no such decline is evident in Denmark (DOFF 1989).

Lesser Spotted Woodpecker *Dendrocopos minor*

Present population trend: declining from 1970s peak.
Percentages of plots occupied 1968/78/88: farmland 7/24/11; woodland 19/33/20.
Latest estimate of breeding population: 3000-6000 pairs in Britain (Cramp & Simmons 1985).

In addition to being the smallest of the woodpecker group in Britain, the Lesser Spotted Woodpecker has always been the scarcest and the most easily overlooked, except for the Wryneck which is now nearly extinct here as a breeding species. Compared to the Great Spotted Woodpecker, it has a much more restricted range, being absent from Scotland and very local in northern England and western Wales. Generally it avoids conifers, though in other respects the Lesser Spotted has a broader spectrum of breeding habitat than its larger cousin, being more likely to occur in small patches of woodland (such as farmland spinneys), in avenues of mature trees, orchards, cemeteries, parks and similar habitats. It is especially associated in Britain with lowland river valleys and other highly fertile land.

Between 1900 and 1960 there was no evidence for any widespread change in this bird's distribution or status. By the 1970s, however, it was clear that it was increasing considerably and that this was due to an abundance of invertebrate foods during the spread of Dutch elm disease (Sharrock 1976). For example, in one Kent woodland of 52 ha, mainly of oaks and elms, there were one to three pairs annually in the decade up to 1968, rising to about 15 pairs in the early 1970s as the elms succumbed to DED (Flegg & Bennett 1974). At that time also, overspill occurred onto farmland as growing numbers of infected and moribund hedgerow elms provided good feeding opportunities (Osborne 1982).

Too few Lesser Spotted Woodpecker territories were defined on CBC plots prior to 1971 for the species to be indexed then. However, supplementary details for the 1960s can be gleaned from two sources: annual CBC ubiquity, defined as the percentage of plots on which the species was encountered, and annual ringing totals. These sources agree that an increase was detectable in 1964-1965, before the DED outbreak started in 1968. The most likely explanation for this is that the species was then recovering from some degree of setback caused by the 1962/63 severe winter. Cold-weather recovery will have merged in the late 1960s into DED-related population growth.

The CBC all-habitats index was rising from its outset, and its annual values more than doubled to reach a peak in 1979. The rate of increase in the CBC index was very similar to that of Great Spotted, but ringing data suggest a steeper rise for Lesser Spotted than for Great Spotted; in *Dendrocopos* ringing totals the proportion of Lesser Spotteds continued to rise up to 1982, even though Great Spotted was itself increasing substantially. The CBC ubiquity data showed clearly the overspill onto farmland during the 1970s, with values quadrupling from 6% in 1967 to 24% in 1978 which proved to be the peak year in that habitat. The CBC graph shows the beginnings of a decrease in the early 1980s, which steepened after 1985; by 1988, the gains of the 1970s had almost entirely disappeared. As the DED outbreak died away, the present species declined rapidly while Great Spotted numbers remained high, and its proportion of *Dendrocopos* ringing totals halved between 1982 and 1987. By 1987 the

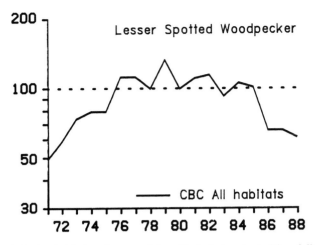

Lesser Spotted Woodpecker

CBC All habitats

DED epidemic had subsided and most of the affected elms had either fallen or been felled.

Regional variation

During the period of greatly increased numbers, the distribution remained virtually unchanged. In Northumberland, however, the species was recorded almost annually during the 1980s; no nests were found, though sightings included a juvenile in August 1984 and an adult carrying food in June 1985. No regional variation is known in the CBC data, which are too few for meaningful subdivision.

Trends elsewhere in Europe

There is no consistent trend. Local fluctuations are not uncommon, and are attributed to habitat changes and temporal variations in food abundance. There has been a marked recent decline in Finland and some decrease is suspected in the Netherlands; but the species has colonised Denmark since 1964 (Cramp & Simmons 1985).

Skylark *Alauda arvensis*

Present population trend: recent decline, following a long period of relative stability.
Percentages of plots occupied 1968/78/88: farmland 94/92/94; woodland 22/27/14.
Latest estimate of breeding population: around 2 million pairs in Britain (Hudson & Marchant 1984).
Regional density rankings 1988: farmland S>EE>NE>SE>W>WE>NI.

Though only ranking the twelfth most numerous British breeding bird, the Skylark is the most widely distributed, being found in 98% of 10-km squares during the Breeding Atlas (Sharrock 1976). Historically, there is no evidence for any marked widespread change in numbers or distribution, although local losses have occurred through habitat changes such as urbanisation (Parslow 1973). However, Nethersole-Thompson &

125

Watson (1974) considered that the incidence of breeding on higher ground in Scotland had increased since the 1940s.

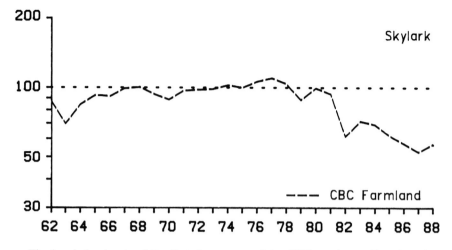

The low index levels of the first three years of the CBC can be attributed to the hard winters of 1961/62 and 1962/63, though the use of organochlorine pesticides may also have contributed; recovery was apparently complete by 1965. Thereafter the annual index values fluctuated between rather narrow limits up to 1981, but since then they have fallen noticeably and are now at half the level of the 1970s. A temporary decrease in 1979 and a larger one in 1982 both followed particularly severe winters, and it could be that the fall in average winter temperatures since then is inhibiting recovery. However, changes in farming practice are also implicated, and these are likely to have been more important. O'Connor & Shrubb (1986a) reported that Skylarks had begun declining about 1975 under certain agricultural regimes. By the late 1970s this could be detected in some regional indices (see below).

On grassland, nest record cards show a single egg-laying peak in early May; the birds are then able to exploit the flush of insects exposed where grass is cut for silage in mid-May. Where the grass is not cut, it is likely to become too long for use by Skylarks later in the season. In contrast, there are multiple egg-laying peaks on arable land, the second being the largest, suggesting that grassland pairs may change habitat for their second brood (O'Connor & Shrubb 1986a). On any one farm Skylarks prefer some crops to others, though the preference depends on what is available.

A detailed ecological study in Switzerland (Schläpfer 1988) showed that optimal conditions for Skylarks were to be found on small-scale farming enterprises where crop diversity was high. The presence of two or more crop types within a territory was important all through the breeding season, and territory sizes increased (and density fell) as crop diversity declined. In this study, the presence of specific crops was less important than crop diversity. Spring-sown cereals and mown grasslands were preferred. Autumn-sown cereals and oil-seed rape (also autumn-sown) were included within territories only in April, after which these crops became too tall: Skylarks shifted their territories when ground vegetation became too thick for the birds to walk through.

Similar factors seem to be operating in Britain also. Cereals are important for Skylarks, since grain and weed seeds are major seasonal foods, and the birds graze upon the leaves of winter wheat as a last resort during the winter hardship period (Green 1978). In cereal-growing regions there has been a major loss of overwinter stubbles and spring plough, which used to be important feeding areas, with the modern change towards autumn sowing. Weed abundance on arable farms has also been reduced by herbicides. The latter are certainly implicated in the Skylark being considered a pest locally in sugar-beet fields, because the primary reason that the birds graze on seedlings of sugar-beet and other crops is the modern scarcity of formerly abundant weeds (Green 1980, Jepson & Green 1983). O'Connor & Shrubb (1986a) noted a preference by Skylarks for nesting in young leys, where their breeding success is higher; but the national acreage of leys has been declining for 25 years. Moreover, major changes under the post-1950 agricultural revolution have included a phasing-out of rotational farming and its replacement by regional specialisation. Thus we now have a situation where only 7% of Welsh farmland is tilled and only 15% of East Anglian farmland remains as pasture. Evidently, the impacts of these various farming changes have now come together, to upset the land-use conditions that were best for Skylarks, and the species has declined as a consequence.

Regional variation

There are several regional deviations from the national trend of stability up to 1981 but subsequent decline. The decline began earlier, in the late 1970s, in northern and eastern England. The latter region in particular is notable for its high rate of conversion of grassland to arable land. In Scotland, Skylarks continued to increase through the 1970s; the index values stayed high through the early 1980s and did not fall until 1986. Scotland was top of the 1988 regional density ranking.

Trends elsewhere in Europe

Census and other studies have revealed declines during the 1980s in Sweden, Denmark and the Netherlands (Sharrock & Hildén 1983, Hustings 1988, DOFF 1989). The species is also reported as having decreased in Switzerland and France (Cramp & Simmons 1988). Declines are now affecting large parts of western and central Europe, due to changes in farming methods (Schläpfer 1988).

Sand Martin *Riparia riparia*

Present population trend: major decline beginning in late 1960s; recent partial recovery.
Percentages of plots occupied 1968/78/88: all CBC habitats 11/9/7; all WBS plots -/55/42.
Latest estimate of breeding population: 100,000-500,000 pairs in Britain during 1984-1988 (see below).

Sand Martins breed on a small number of WBS and CBC plots, but the species is not indexed because these are too few. Most data are approximate estimates of occupied nest-holes, and it is known that there are considerable problems associated with censusing the species in this way (Mead 1979a, Cowley 1983). CBC ubiquity figures are available, however, and are shown in the graph.

Natural Sand Martin nest sites comprise river banks and sea cliffs, but the majority of British pairs now nest in the artificial cliffs of the sand and gravel pits which proliferated with the post-1945 construction boom. This new habitat led to considerable increases of Sand Martins in the southern half of Britain, where such man-made sites became most abundant, during the 1950s and 1960s. Yet it was unclear whether these increases were real or due to a redistribution of birds, as there were reports of contemporary reductions in Sand Martins using the less attractive natural sites in the north and extreme west of the country (Parslow 1973). In all probability the population did expand then, for the extensive faces of excavated pits allowed colonies to reach sizes seldom possible along natural riparian sites.

The situation was to change quite suddenly, with a serious population crash between the 1968 and 1969 breeding seasons, as also occurred in Redstart and Whitethroat. One feature these species have in common is their winter distribution in the Sahel and adjacent savanna zones of Africa, and it is now accepted that the declines were due to drought in the Sahel region of West Africa (Winstanley et al 1974, Mead 1979b). In the 1950s, Sahel rainfall was above the 1951-1982 mean, but it has been well below that level since 1968 (Lamb 1982).

The most precise information on the scale of the Sand Martin decline came from Nottinghamshire (Cowley 1979). The population there fell by 45% during 1968-1969 and by a further 29% the following year, thereafter fluctuating at around the 1970 level. Colony counts from other counties in England and Wales were less precise, but indicated decreases of similar magnitude. Cowley was also able to relate fluctuations in the 1970s to breeding success the previous year. Temporary increases in four seasons each followed a summer of fine weather in which breeding began earlier and more second broods were reared. He expressed the view that the drought-related decreases had, in most years, been exacerbated by cool, late springs in Britain which had delayed breeding and affected overall productivity (Cowley 1979). In the CBC ubiquity graph, the lower line shows the reduced levels of site occupancy since the early 1970s, following the population crash.

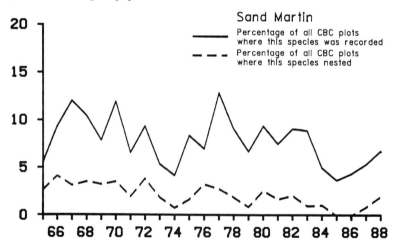

Sahel rainfall has remained below the long-term average, and was particularly poor in 1983. Sand Martins returned to Britain in even lower numbers in 1984, and Mead (1984) expressed the view that the population was then less than 10% of that in the mid-1960s. The 1984 Nottinghamshire figure was 9% of Cowley's 1968 total. If Sharrock's (1976) estimate of 1 million pairs in the 1960s was in the right order of abundance, then there may have been only 100,000 pairs by 1984. There were marked improvements in 1986 and subsequently, with annual ringing totals rising by 1988 to 4½ times the 1984 figure. On this basis it seems possible that the British population has varied between 100,000 and 500,000 pairs in recent years. Continuing recovery is expected to follow the modest improvement to Sahel rainfall since 1986.

Jones (1987) has presented evidence that the Sahel drought has brought about selection in favour of smaller body size in Sand Martins. Dramatic selection episodes of this kind are rarely recorded among birds.

Regional variation

The post-1968 decline affected all regions. In central Scotland, however, there was appreciable recovery by the early 1980s, while recovery from the further crash of 1983/84 was almost complete by 1989 (D.M. Bryant, *in litt.*).

Trends elsewhere in Europe

Substantial declines between 1968 and 1969 were noted widely in western Europe, especially in the more northerly countries. Recovery in Sweden has apparently been faster than in Britain (Persson 1987). In Denmark, index values for 1978-1988 show deep troughs in 1980 and 1985-1986, with subsequent partial recoveries (DOFF 1989). East European populations winter in East Africa where they will have experienced less severe drought conditions.

Swallow *Hirundo rustica*

Present population trend: considerable decline since 1980.
Percentages of plots occupied 1968/78/88: farmland 69/85/ 92; woodland 21/25/26.
Latest estimate of breeding population: at least 500,000 pairs in Britain in 1982 (Hudson & Marchant 1984).
Regional density rankings 1988: farmland NI>WE>S> NE>W>SE>EE.

Reviewing county and regional literature and other status reports since the early 1940s, Parslow (1973) noted that most claims of change in the status of the Swallow referred to decreases. Yet because Swallows can fluctuate markedly from year to year, and because few quantified data were available, he was uncertain of how seriously to treat these reports of lower numbers. The only significant changes in distribution recently have been in the western and northern isles of Scotland, where breeding was formerly intermittent but has become regular since the early 1970s (Thom 1986).

The CBC revealed a stable population level, with some fluctuation, between 1962 and 1973. There was a large fall in 1974, the cause of which is unknown, and these losses were made good over the following three or four years. Since 1980, however, the index values have fallen steadily. That for 1987 was only half the level which applied in the late 1960s; there was a notable improvement in 1988, however.

Swallows have long been commensal with man, and natural nest sites are now rarely used in Britain or elsewhere in western Europe. Most pairs nest in barns and outhouses, with others in, for example, garages, workshops, sheds and porches. Farmland is the most important habitat, and breeding densities there increase with the area of farm buildings (Møller 1983). Voous (1960) suggested that a general decline believed to be occurring in European towns and villages was due to improved farm hygiene and consequent reductions in fly numbers, and Parslow (1973) noted that British reports of local decrease were mostly attributed to renovations of farm

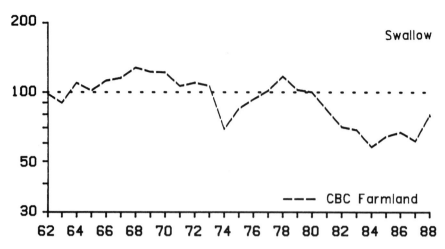

```
200 ┐                                          Swallow


100 ┤


 50 ┤

                                     ─ ─ ─  CBC Farmland
 30 ┴┬──┬──┬──┬──┬──┬──┬──┬──┬──┬──┬──┬──┬──┬─
    62  64  66  68  70  72  74  76  78  80  82  84  86  88
```

buildings. Old farm buildings are gradually being modernised or replaced. Whether their new equivalents are steel-framed Dutch barns, hygienic milking parlours or intensive-rearing units, they are likely to offer fewer, if any, nest sites to Swallows. Yet the gradual replacement of traditional farm buildings hardly seems compatible with the sudden onset and scale of the recent Swallow decline, as indicated by CBC data. On the other hand, studies in central Scotland suggest a pattern there of progressive decline since around 1970, with the 1974 fall being part of this; such a gradual decline over two decades is more consistent with the influence of agricultural changes on the availability of nest sites and the abundance of insect food (D.M. Bryant, *in litt.*).

British Swallows spend half the year in Africa, crossing the Sahara on each passage. Moreau (1961) noted that desert mortality is reported more often for this species than for any other European migrant. Swallows have not obviously been affected by the Sahel drought, though the recent effective broadening of the Sahara may have increased the hazards associated with crossing it. Our population winters in South Africa. Prior to the 1960s, recoveries of ringed birds came almost entirely from the eastern half of that country, where the rainfall season is the northern winter; but since about 1962 the winter distribution of ringing recoveries has extended into southwestern Cape Province, where the rain falls in the northern summer (Mead 1970). This distributional change probably has a climatic basis, for South Africa has been experiencing periods of drought which have affected particularly the Transvaal, Orange Free State and north-central Cape Province. There have been large variations in the patterns of rainfall deficit (Zucchini & Adamson 1984, Tyson 1986). However, the overall trends were towards (a) dry conditions, locally severe, in the 1960s, when Swallow winter quarters began to change, (b) better rainfall in the 1970s, and (c) a return to drought conditions since the 1978/79 season, which matches the onset of the recent Swallow decline.

Even though it is likely that British farming changes are implicated in the decline, nevertheless it seems probable that events in Africa have had the greater influence. This is consistent with a study in Denmark (Møller 1989), where Swallows have been decreasing since the late 1970s. Møller found a positive correlation between Swallow mortality and South African rainfall, and he further demonstrated that egg production has fallen during the years of decline. It seems likely that the breeding condition of returning birds is impaired, thus reducing their reproductive performance.

Regional variation
The decline since the late 1970s has been most pronounced in eastern and southern England, the regions where agricultural modernisation has been most intense. In 1988, these were the regions where mean density was lowest.

Trends elsewhere in Europe
Recent decreases have been reported from the Soviet Baltic States, West Germany, Denmark, the Netherlands, and Sweden. These populations have winter distributions which overlap only partly with that of British Swallows, but it should be noted that below-average rainfall has periodically affected large parts of Africa during the last three decades.

House Martin *Delichon urbica*

Present population trend: no major change is known.
Percentages of plots occupied 1968/78/88: all CBC habitats 25/35/37.
Latest estimate of breeding population: 300,000-600,000 pairs in Britain and Ireland (Sharrock 1976); 73% of occupied squares were then in Britain.
Regional density rankings 1988: all CBC habitats NI> NE>WE>EE>S>SE>W.

The ancestral breeding habitat of the House Martin comprised cliffs and caves, both maritime and inland (Clark & McNeil 1980). Since all but a tiny proportion of birds now nest on man-made structures, it can be inferred that the species is now much more widespread than was the case prehistorically. Within modern times, however, the evidence for population change is sparse and conflicting.

Reviewing regional bird literature for the 20th century, Parslow (1973) noted that most expressions of opinion on House Martin status favoured an overall decrease. Yet it was evident that marked local deviations occurred, both upwards and downwards, and of a magnitude that did not allow confidence in other subjective reports alleging general decline. Parslow considered the evidence unsatisfactory and, instead, expressed the opinion that if an overall diminution of numbers had occurred then this had been slight. Part of the evidence related to undoubted decreases in the 19th and early 20th centuries in the numbers of cliff and cave colonies in Scotland. However, Clark & McNeil (1980) showed that there has been temporal variation in the use of natural sites, with fewer such colonies in cold climatic periods than in warm ones. Recently, further reductions in cliff-nesters in Caithness have been balanced by increased numbers breeding on buildings (Thom 1986).

Counts at individual colonies are an unreliable guide to population trends over a wider area. This is especially true of large colonies, with over a hundred nests, which are atypical anyway. Small nesting groups are more usual, commonly one to three pairs at a site, and the species has a social tendency rather than being strictly colonial (Bouldin 1968, Mawson & Crabtree 1981). In a ten-year study in east Lancashire, in an area of 1370 sq. km holding on average 570 nesting sites (colonies or single pairs), the sizes of individual nesting groups fluctuated considerably from one year to the

131

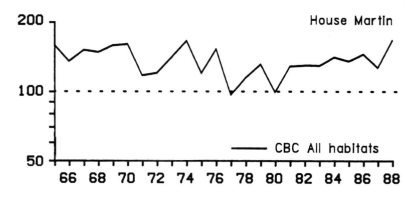

200   House Martin

100

                               CBC All habitats

50

66 68 70 72 74 76 78 80 82 84 86 88

next, though the total population of the study area remained more or less constant (Bouldin 1968).

Some CBC data are available from 1965 onwards in the form of an index based on nest counts, mainly on farmland plots. This index has been fairly stable overall, but with fluctuations including low points in 1977 and 1980. These fluctuations are not thought to be significant, however, because annual variations in the sizes of individual colonies are normal (see above); none of the CBC percentage changes is based on data from more than 26 plots (average 21).

It is certain that there have, in the past, been withdrawals by House Martins from the polluted regions of industrial cities (e.g. Mather 1986). This trend is now being reversed, for the most obvious change in the last three decades has been deeper penetration by breeding birds into suburban and urban areas. Documented examples of this include studies in London (Cramp & Gooders 1967, Montier 1977), Manchester (Tatner 1978) and Birmingham (Harrison et al 1982). This followed the 1956 Clean Air Act, which led to reductions in aerial pollution, while modern greening of urban environments has further encouraged increases in insect numbers (Turner 1982). House Martins have also been opportunistic in taking advantage of new housing estates, leading to local increases, but in Hertfordshire at least this seems to have been at the expense of rural densities (Gladwin & Sage 1986). Individual housing estate nesting sites are sometimes temporary, since not all householders are tolerant of the mess made by nesting birds, and this results in pairs being thinly scattered through such estates on houses where they are not discouraged.

On the available evidence, it seems that the House Martin has a somewhat mobile nesting population, often changing or fluctuating locally, but without there being convincing evidence of a national upward or downward trend. Conceivably, its aerial and highly itinerant mode of life in the African winter quarters (like that of the Swift) has mitigated the effects of the droughts which have affected the other two British hirundines.

Tatner (1978) showed that sample survey areas need to be of at least 30 sq.km to produce reliable density values. He re-assessed previous local studies which met this criterion and concluded that their average density was 2 nests per sq.km. On that basis the overall population level would be towards the top end of Sharrock's (1976) estimate of 300,000-600,000 pairs in Britain and Ireland.

Regional variation

There is no evidence of any differences in trends between regions.

Census indices for Sweden and Czechoslovakia indicate considerable fluctuations between years but no overall trend (Hustings 1988). A sharp decline has been reported from the Netherlands (Wammes *et al* 1983, Veenhuizen 1984), and Danish index values have been in overall decline since they began in 1976 (DOFF 1989).

Tree Pipit *Anthus trivialis*

Present population trend: fluctuates; some downward drift since 1970.
Percentages of plots occupied 1968/78/88: farmland 15/10/10; woodland 43/30/38.
Latest estimate of breeding population: 100,000 pairs in Britain (Hudson & Marchant 1984).
Regional density rankings 1988: all CBC habitats S> W>WE>SE>NE>EE.

By the 1950s and 1960s there was a general consensus in county avifaunas that the Tree Pipit was becoming less common and less widespread in the lowlands of the southeastern quarter of Britain, despite benefiting locally from new conifer plantings (Parslow 1973). Further west and north, the species was maintaining its status. Indeed, it had increased and spread this century in the Scottish Highlands north of the Great Glen; it had become one of the commonest breeding birds of Sutherland birch woods, where it had been almost unknown a century earlier (Pennie 1962), and Caithness was colonised in the 1960s. In all probability the declines in English sites, possibly since the 1930s, were only slight, though they are hard to evaluate because of undoubted fluctuations in population levels (Sharrock 1976).

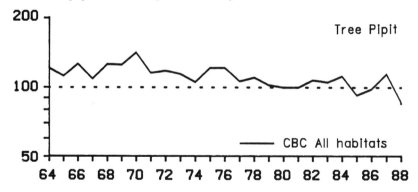

CBC monitoring of the Tree Pipit is through an all-habitats index. Results up to 1970 showed well the fluctuations to which Tree Pipits are prone, but especially during the second half of the CBC's span there has been a gradual downward drift, concealed only partly by such fluctuations. The 1988 index value was the lowest yet recorded.

Tree Pipits require both open ground for feeding and trees as song perches, and are typically birds of parkland, heath, hillside scrub and open woodland. In an analysis of nest record cards, Rose (1982) found that 94% of nests were at altitudes below 300 m, with the principal habitats comprising open woodland or wood edge (30%), lowland heath (25%), waste land (13%) and young or felled conifers (12%). Only on lowland heath did this species overlap with the Meadow Pipit, the latter preferring rough grazing and moorland. Fuller (1982) noted that Tree Pipits were present in 70-80% of woodlands larger than 80 ha, though in only 30-40% of woodlands smaller than 10 ha. Larger woods are more likely to have a diverse habitat structure, including glades, wide rides and low shrubby areas, for example from replanting. Conifer plantations are attractive only in their early stages of growth (Hughes 1972).

No factors are known which might cause national decline, unless these lie in the unstudied African winter quarters. It is clear that Tree Pipits have not been affected by West African drought to any important degree. Although they must cross the Sahel in spring and autumn, they winter in more wooded country to the south. Within Britain, eastern and southern England have probably been affected most by local factors, such as scrub removal, woodland felling, and conversions of downland and heath to farmland. Moreover, major expansions of human conurbations have been most pronounced in the southeast.

Regional variation
The decline since the mid-1970s has been most pronounced in southern England, and occurred to a lesser extent in northern and eastern England also. These came lowest in the 1988 regional density rankings. In Scotland, Wales and western England, population levels have been fairly steady through the 1970s and up to the present time.

Trends elsewhere in Europe
Short-term fluctuations characteristic of this species have been noted in most European countries. Major changes have only been reported from the Netherlands, with a marked decline since about 1900, and Denmark, with a considerable increase since 1976 (DOFF 1989).

Meadow Pipit *Anthus pratensis*

Present population trend: decline since the early 1980s.
Percentages of plots occupied 1968/78/88: farmland 46/46/58; woodland 22/14/12.
Latest estimate of breeding population: 1-1½ million pairs in Britain (Hudson & Marchant 1984).
Regional density rankings 1988: all CBC habitats NE> S>WE>W>NI>EE>SE.

There is no historical evidence for any marked change in the status of the Meadow Pipit. It has long been a widely distributed species, breeding in every British county, and was found in 94% of 10-km squares during the survey period for the Breeding Atlas. However, such a general statement masks major regional variations in densities. It has always been distributed thinly in the English lowlands, especially on the heavier clay soils of central and southern England, and is suspected to have become scarcer in the face of agricultural changes there (Parslow 1973, Sharrock 1976). Densities are higher in the north and west, where most occur on hill farmland and moorland. It is our commonest passerine at altitudes above 500 m.

This is not an easy species to census, for there is little intraspecific aggression at territory boundaries, while some males sing and display much less than others, or even not at all (Seel & Walton 1979). The Meadow Pipit is monitored by the CBC, though the concentration of CBC plots in central and southern England means that the resulting index is biased towards lowland farmland and under-represents the upland habitats where the bulk of the population breeds. This index recorded an initial increase in the 1960s and fluctuating levels through the 1970s, but the beginnings of a decline in the early 1980s which became steep in 1985 and 1986, and from which there has been only a small improvement since.

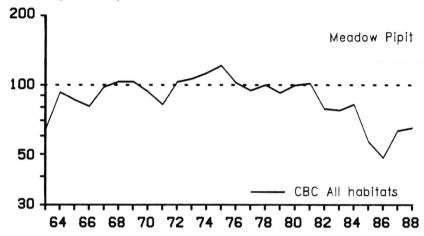

It has been suggested that the population of the English lowlands is declining in the face of the conversion of grassland to arable (Williamson 1967) and the loss of marginal land to cultivation and afforestation (Parslow 1973). This may be so locally, but nationally the CBC index offers no evidence of this. The fall in the 1980s was too sudden and too late to be attributed to land-use trends which had been apparent for at least two decades. While it is tempting to attribute the index low points (1963, 1982, 1985-86) to cold winters, the ringing and observational evidence suggests that most British Meadow Pipits leave the country in winter – perhaps 80% of them (Lack 1986). It seems that immigrants form the bulk of our winter population. However, the winter of 1984/85 was unusually severe in southern Europe also, while the British summers of 1986-1988 were cool and wet. Hence climate may be the main influence on British Meadow Pipit population levels.

The CBC mean farmland density is about 1.6 pairs per sq. km (Hudson & Marchant 1984), which is low compared to densities commonly of 25-50 pairs per sq. km on moorland, upland sheepwalk, young conifer plantation, chalk downland and saltmarsh (Sharrock 1976, Moss et al 1979, Newton 1983). In a four-year study, 1972-1975, on sheep walk in Snowdonia, Seel & Walton (1979) found densities varying annually from 33-74 pairs per sq.km, averaging 48 pairs per sq. km. The home range of a pair averaged 2.18 ha, and this varied little between years. An analysis of nest record cards (Rose 1982) found that the main breeding habitats for Meadow Pipits are moorland (35%), rough grazing (25%), lowland heath (13%), and coastal dunes/saltmarsh (13%).

In the Breeding Atlas, Sharrock (1976) offered a figure of over 3 million pairs as the likely size of the British and Irish population. With two-thirds of occupied 10-km squares then being in Britain, around 2 million of these pairs may be apportioned to Britain alone. Subsequently, Hudson & Marchant (1984) estimated 1-1½ million British pairs in 1982, based on CBC densities but making allowance for the fact that CBC data under-represent the higher densities of upland breeding areas.

Regional variation
    Regional index values follow the national trend, with only minor variations. Low levels in 1963 were barely apparent in Scotland and northern England, perhaps because northern birds are more migratory. Population growth through the 1970s was apparently steepest in northern England, while the index for western England showed a fall in 1976-1977 from which no recovery is yet apparent. The 1988 regional density rankings show eastern and southern England to have the lowest mean densities.

Trends elsewhere in Europe
    No consistent trend is apparent. There are some unquantified regional reports of decrease due to habitat changes, while in France there has been considerable southward expansion of the breeding range (Isenmann 1987).

Yellow Wagtail *Motacilla flava*

Present population trend: some decline during the 1980s, after an earlier peak.
Percentages of plots occupied 1968/78/88: all CBC habitats 19/19/21; all WBS plots -/43/30.
Latest estimate of breeding population: at least 100,000 pairs in Britain in 1982 (see below).
Regional density rankings 1988: all CBC habitats EE> SE>NE>W>WE.

During the first half of the present century the Yellow Wagtail's range contracted sharply in Scotland, so that it became virtually restricted to the Clyde area. Decreases were claimed from many parts of southern England and Wales between 1900 and 1950, but, in contrast, reports from northern England referred to stability or increase (Smith 1950, Parslow 1973). The causes of these different regional trends are obscure. English farming was in a depressed state for a long period prior to the Second World War; pasture quality declined and there was major disturbance to grassland:arable ratios. However, such land-use changes were much less marked in Scotland, where Yellow Wagtail declines were most severe.

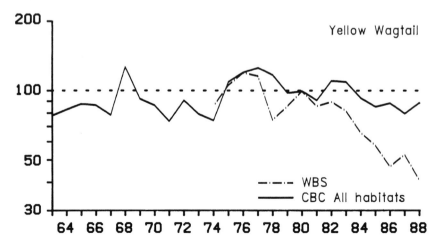

136

The Yellow Wagtail has been monitored by the CBC since 1963 and by the WBS since 1974, but the results from the two are not wholly in agreement. Both reveal the existence of large, probably natural fluctuations, which included big peaks in 1968 (CBC) and the mid-1970s (both schemes). However, a large fall in the WBS index for 1978 was not matched in the CBC returns. Since 1980 or earlier there has been a major decline in the WBS index levels (the index for 1988 being under half that of 1980); but decrease was only apparent in the CBC through comparison with the mid-1970s peak. The CBC population level has returned to that which applied in the years around 1970.

Typically, Yellow Wagtails are birds of lowland flood meadows, damp grazing and coastal marshes, though they are also common on some submontane grasslands and upland river valleys (Ratcliffe 1977, Mather 1986). It is not essentially a riparian species (thus differing from the Grey Wagtail), and so is affected little by river management. On farmland this is a field species which declines where there is large-scale conversion of grassland to arable (Møller 1980), especially now that autumn sowing has largely replaced spring tillage (O'Connor & Shrubb 1986a). It is unclear why the WBS has recorded much larger recent decreases than has the CBC, but the difference may be an artefact of sample plot distribution (see below). Unlike some other summer migrants, there is no good evidence that the Yellow Wagtail has suffered from the effects of drought in its African winter quarters.

The British population was estimated at 25,000 pairs by Sharrock (1976). Hudson & Marchant (1984) considered this figure to be too low compared with the scale of passage in coastal counties. Using 1982 mean densities, they arrived at a figure of 175,000 pairs, but were uncertain whether sufficient allowance had been made for the patchiness of the distribution. However, it seems likely that the population was then at least 100,000 pairs. This will have fallen since, though it is difficult to assess by how much.

Regional variation
Welsh and Scottish CBC samples are too small to be analysed separately. In eastern, western and southern England, CBC population levels have been relatively stable through the 1980s. In northern England, the 1970s increase was especially pronounced; but since 1977 there has been a progressive decline so that the latest index values there are the lowest since the CBC began. This is a reversal of the trend reported by Parslow (1973) and, in conjunction with the Scottish and Irish histories, suggests peripheral decline and associated range contraction. The better representation of the WBS in northern England may help to explain the steeper population decrease recorded by that scheme.

Trends elsewhere in Europe
Over the last hundred years the British race *flavissima* has been showing an increasing tendency to breed along the eastern side of the North Sea. Populations are now established in southwest Norway, the Netherlands and in north and northwest France, with irregular nesting between these areas (Glutz von Blotzheim 1985). In the Netherlands the Yellow and Blue-headed Wagtails breed side by side and appear to behave as separate species (van Dijk 1975). Regular breeding ceased in Ireland in the 1940s. The several dark-headed races of continental Europe are reported to have decreased in the Netherlands, West Germany, southern Sweden, Austria and Czechoslovakia, with habitat change being most frequently cited as the reason, but to have increased in Denmark and in northern parts of Sweden and Finland.

Grey Wagtail *Motacilla cinerea*

Present population trend: downward since the mid-1970s.
Percentages of plots occupied 1968/78/88: all CBC habitats
11/16/18; all WBS plots -/79/69.
Latest estimate of breeding population: 25,000-50,000 pairs
in Britain and Ireland (Sharrock 1976); 67% of occupied
squares were then in Britain.

Unlike its two British congeners, the Grey Wagtail is generally a bird of upland and hilly country. Hence its centres of abundance lie in the north and west, and there is considerable similarity with the distribution of the Dipper. Grey Wagtails occur on both hard-water and soft-water streams, with some preference for the former, and the birds further select sites where there is fast flowing water with riffles and where banks are lined with deciduous trees (Marchant & Hyde 1980*b*, Ormerod & Tyler 1987*a*). The latter authors consider that tree-lined banks are important for providing additional foods such as spiders, caterpillars and dipterans of non-aquatic origin, to supplement the diet of aquatic invertebrates, and for their leaf input into rivers which enhances productivity generally. During the present century, and especially since about 1950, there has been a gradual expansion of breeding range into southern and eastern England, with breeding becoming regular in several lowland counties where it had previously been erratic (Parslow 1973). In such lowland sites the birds continue to show a preference for running water, their territories often including weirs, mills, locks, lake overflows or other features resembling natural waterfalls.

Sharrock (1969) presented a population index for Grey Wagtails over the period 1956-1967, based on nest record card intakes, annual ringing totals and numbers of passage birds counted at coastal migration stations. This index showed a pronounced upward trend initially, in line with the lowland expansion mentioned above, which peaked in 1961. Serious decline then followed the cold winters of 1961/62 and 1962/63. Recovery from this setback was still proceeding in 1967, and subsequent BTO ringing data show that increase was still continuing in the early 1970s when the WBS and CBC indices began.

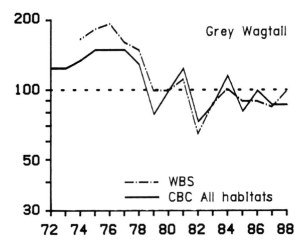

In common with a range of other British resident passerines, Grey Wagtail densities seem to have reached high levels by the mid-1970s following a run of mild winters, but to have fallen thereafter with a return to colder winters. Such falls were particularly sharp in 1978/79, 1981/82 and 1984/85, and the population indices remain low relative to 1975. There is an interesting contrast here with the Dipper, which is resident and generally remains all year on upland streams that in the main run too swiftly to freeze in winter, and has actually increased during the 1980s. Grey Wagtails move much more, descending into lowlands for the winter, dispersing southwards, and some emigrating; yet they are at risk in the occasional severe winters when lowland fresh waters and terrestrial feeding sites freeze completely. Whereas Dippers exploit the larval stages of aquatic invertebrates, Grey Wagtails are more dependent upon the aerial stages of insects and these are in short supply in freezing conditions. Presumably Grey Wagtails find it consistently more difficult to survive winters at higher altitudes, where insects are even scarcer at that season.

The downward trend of British Grey Wagtails since the mid-1970s is emphasised by the 1970s population levels apparently being unusually high (as in Pied Wagtail). It is also possible that the WBS and CBC exaggerate the scale of decline through the extent of their coverage of the species' suboptimal, lowland, habitats. WBS ubiquity values fell from 79% to 69% between 1978 and 1988. On the evidence available, winter climate seems to be the major influence on Grey Wagtail population levels. Contemporaneous declines of other waterway species also may have a climatic basis. However, taking these species in combination, there is a suspicion that general habitat degradation may also be a secondary factor. This might act directly, for instance by destruction of potential nest sites, or indirectly through its effects on food supply. Recent work has confirmed that the Grey Wagtail is much less affected than the Dipper by stream acidification, due to the former's broader and more opportunistic diet (Ormerod & Tyler 1987b).

Regional variation

The southerly and easterly spread into the English lowlands became very marked in the 1950s, but faltered during the 1960s when in a few counties breeding ceased temporarily. This was attributed to population reductions after two cold winters having more effect in suboptimal areas. The peripheral spread was resumed around 1970, after population recovery (Lack 1986). Subsequently, overall increases have been reported from Essex (Cox 1984) and the London area (Palmer 1983).

Trends elsewhere in Europe

Grey Wagtails expanded their range in central Europe from the 1850s onwards, and have spread northwards. They have been breeding in the Netherlands and Sweden since 1915-1916, Denmark since 1923, and Finland since 1976. Numbers fluctuate with winter severity, and recent reductions have been reported from the Netherlands and Poland (Cramp & Simmons 1988).

Pied Wagtail *Motacilla alba*

Present population trend: fluctuates somewhat according to winter weather conditions.
Percentages of plots occupied 1968/78/88: farmland 56/85/77; woodland 16/26/16; all WBS plots -/93/84.
Latest estimate of breeding population: 300,000 pairs in Britain (Hudson & Marchant 1984).
Regional density rankings 1988: farmland S>W>NE>NI>WE>SE>EE.

The Pied Wagtail is a particularly widely distributed British breeding bird, having been found in 94% of all 10-km squares during the Breeding Atlas. Its range of breeding habitats extends from upland streams to sea-coasts and city centres. Normally it is absent only from woodland, heather moorland and bare mountains. Thus the CBC monitors only one of the habitats (farmland) in which Pied Wagtails nest, although since 1974 the species has also been indexed by the WBS. The good agreement between the two indices gives encouragement that the longer-running CBC is representative of the broader pattern in the United Kingdom as a whole.

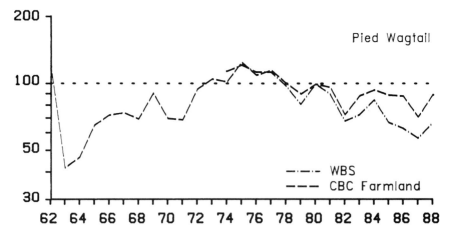

The initial years of the CBC were influenced by the cold winter of 1962/63, in which Pied Wagtails declined seriously and from which they took several breeding seasons to recover, and even then not returning to the high level recorded for 1962. It is possible that the 1962 index was too high an estimate, however, owing to initial problems in CBC methodology. Population levels rose during the 1970s, a decade of mainly mild winters; and in that period the species spread into agricultural land further away from water, in response to rising population pressures (Williamson & Batten 1977). Index values fell after the winters of 1978/79 and 1981/82, both of which were marked by periods of severe weather. The steeper fall in 1981/82 was perhaps due to there being a more continuous freeze (as in 1962/63), without the interruptions by brief thaws which occurred in 1978/79 (Marchant 1983a). Since then population levels have remained fairly stable, but below those achieved in the 1970s. Winters have averaged colder in the 1980s, with intervals between severe ones too short to allow full recovery. Despite British Pied Wagtails being partially migratory, winter weather appears to be the strongest influence on population size. In the severest winters, the effects of low temperatures also extend to British emigrants in southern Europe. Winter mortality is related especially to the duration of unbroken periods of frost, which deny the birds access to the soft substrates from which their food is obtained.

Hudson & Marchant (1984) assessed the British population at 300,000 pairs, using sample densities for 1982, when the species was at a low level after a hard winter.

Regional variation

O'Connor & Shrubb (1986a) noted that Pied Wagtail densities are correlated positively with several different farmland features, which in their view explained why the species is best represented on mixed farmland. Earlier, Sharrock (1976) noted that Breeding Atlas fieldworkers had found the species to have become scarcer in eastern England, especially in comparison with Scotland and Ireland. This trend was attributed to a regional concentration on cereal farming having reduced livestock levels, as well as other wagtail feeding opportunities such as farm ponds.

CBC regional density rankings confirm that population levels are highest in the north and west. This picture may be partly a result of recent cold winters, which have affected particularly the southern half of the country. In Scotland, high densities have been maintained from the late 1960s through to the present, without major fluctuations. Western England seems not to have experienced the high population levels achieved elsewhere in the 1970s and has, instead, been affected by a shallow but persistent decline since about 1973.

Trends elsewhere in Europe

The British and Irish subspecies *yarrellii* has long bred irregularly on the eastern side of the North Sea, from south Norway to north France and the Channel Islands. The incidence of this may be increasing, since small numbers now nest annually in the Netherlands (SOVON 1987). Otherwise this race is replaced on the Continent by the White Wagtail (nominate *alba*), which is migratory in northern Europe. It has declined in Sweden during the 1980s but has increased in Denmark (Hustings 1988, DOFF 1989), these being the only countries for which long-running census data are available.

Dipper *Cinclus cinclus*

Present population trend: stable or increasing.
Percentages of plots occupied 1968/78/88: all CBC habitats 7/5/6; all WBS plots -/50/52.
Latest estimate of breeding population: 30,000 pairs in Britain and Ireland (Sharrock 1976); 70% of occupied squares were then in Britain.

The Dipper is a characteristic bird of rocky, fast-flowing streams and rivers, and although some do occur on lowland streams, for example associated with weirs, it is usually regarded as an upland species. Nevertheless, there are many pairs in Wales that are near the sea or otherwise below 100 m, where stream gradient is suitable. In Ireland it is much more commonly found on lowland waters (Perry 1986).

Dippers use such a wide variety of nest sites that their availability is unlikely to be a significant factor in the suitability of a given waterway. On the other hand, food availability plays an important role in determining territory size and hence population density. Marchant & Hyde (1980b) showed that densities of Dippers were lower on sites with a gradient less than 10 m/km, and on those with a steep gradient (greater than 25 m/km), compared to sites of intermediate gradient. Intermediate gradients provide a high proportion of the important riffle areas of the stream, in which caddis larvae and mayfly nymphs are abundant. In slow-moving rivers, although prey abundance may be high, its availability is likely to be low due to deeper water and a sandy or silty substrate, while in fast-flowing upland sites prey is likely to be scarce (Shooter 1970). Round & Moss (1984) found Dippers to be absent from the upper River Wye, where Brooker & Morris (1980) had previously shown invertebrate abundance to be low. In subsequent detailed studies in the Wye catchment, Ormerod et al (1985a) confirmed that the abundance of breeding Dippers showed strong correlations with the abundance and availability of large stream invertebrates, chiefly caddis larvae. Thus, any factors affecting the numbers, distribution and availability of these prey items are likely also to affect the numbers and distribution of breeding Dippers. These include severe or prolonged freezing, drought and spate conditions, pollution and, of current and widespread concern, stream acidification.

Ormerod et al (1985b) noted that Welsh rivers which had suitable gradient, but where Dippers were scarce, were acidic. Their studies showed a highly significant positive relationship between pH and the density of Dipper pairs, which was considered to be an indirect effect of acidity on prey abundance. Additionally, on the upper River Irfon and two tributaries of the River Wye, a long-term increase in acidity from 1963 to 1984 was associated with declining Dipper abundance. A West German study (Kaiser 1985) showed that acidification led to desertion by Dippers of some streams and to reduced clutch sizes on others. In Britain there is a clear trend for Dippers to be scarce or absent and to have impaired reproductive performance on the most acidic streams, those with high levels of aluminium and those with heavily afforested catchments (Ormerod et al 1986, Ormerod & Tyler 1987b).

The effects of severe winter weather on Dippers, which are highly sedentary, is little known. Dobinson & Richards (1964) considered that Dipper populations suffered only a small national decrease following the winter of 1962/63. However, this overall trend masked marked regional differences which ranged from areas where the population had been eliminated, or severely reduced, to a single area where there was an increase. This is in strong contrast to Grey Wagtail, which occupies similar habitat and whose populations are badly affected by severe weather (Lack 1986).

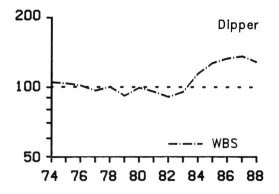

In a study of the Dipper population of Derbyshire during 1958-1968, Shooter (1970) concluded that on gritstone the major influence on the size of the breeding population was the severity of the previous winter. On limestone rivers, which were typically warmer by up to 4°C, and where invertebrate abundance was typically higher, freezing was less likely to occur, and the population was considered to be regulated by reduced breeding success due to "excessive territorial competition". Recent work in Wales has found that first-year dispersal is notable there, and many young females move across watersheds. Perhaps due to such mobility, there have been no marked changes in population sizes from year to year in these Welsh study areas, regardless of winter weather (S.J. Tyler, *in litt.*).

WBS index values for Dipper, available from 1974, show a generally stable population initially, though a small and sustained increase since 1983. Certainly no widespread decline is shown coincident with the trends noted above in parts of Wales and also on some waters in southwest Scotland (Harriman & Morrison 1982). Unfortunately most WBS data derive from plots outside those areas, and samples are too small to allow regional analysis.

Regional variation

Stream acidification has been implicated in local declines in parts of Wales (Ormerod *et al* 1985*a*, *b*) and in southwest Scotland (Harriman & Morrison 1982). However, increases have occurred in south Wales (Rivers Taff and Rhymney and their tributaries) where, due to mine closures and industrial decline, the rivers are now cleaner than they were a decade or two ago (S.J. Tyler, *in litt.*).

Trends elsewhere in Europe

Cramp & Simmons (1988) presented estimates of the population size of Dippers for various countries, but the only trends reported were for Czechoslovakia (no change), East Germany (decline) and Poland (decline). A decline has also been reported from Hungary where only 10-15 pairs remain (Horváth 1988).

Wren *Troglodytes troglodytes*

Present population trend: fluctuates according to winter weather conditions.
Percentages of plots occupied 1968/78/88: farmland 96/97/99; woodland 96/99/99.
Latest estimate of breeding population: 3-3½ million pairs in Britain in 1982 (Hudson & Marchant 1984).
Regional density rankings 1988: farmland NI>W>SE>WE>EE>NE>S; woodland W>EE>NE>NI>SE>WE>S.

The Breeding Atlas (Sharrock 1976) found Wren to be the third most widespread species in Britain and Ireland (following Skylark and Carrion Crow), having been located in 97% of 10-km squares. Moreover, it was then thought to be the most abundant breeding bird of all, with an estimated 10 million pairs (perhaps 7-7½ million in Britain alone). It is now evident that there was a peak in the Wren population in the early to middle 1970s.

Winter weather is the major determinant of population changes in British Wrens. Being one of the very smallest of European birds, the Wren is subject to the twin

143

difficulties of a high rate of heat loss, owing to a high surface:volume ratio, and a relatively poor capacity to store winter fat. Even a short spell of winter weather that is severe enough to prevent efficient feeding results in high mortality.

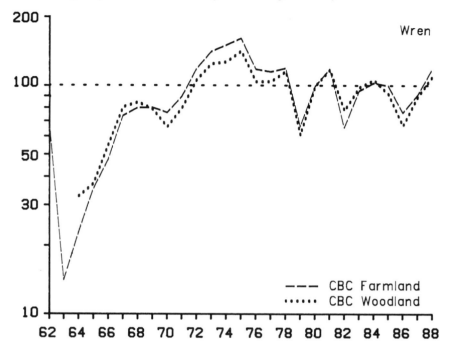

In retrospect it is clear that the recovery of the national population, following severe depletion in the cold winters of 1961/62 and especially 1962/63, took until 1967 or 1968. In common with a variety of other resident species, Wren population levels surged higher during the 1970s. It is thought that this owed much to the run of mainly mild winters which characterised that period. In the case of the Wren, this upward surge was checked by a spell of hard weather in the 1975/76 winter, which affected mainly eastern and southeastern England. The first severe winter of the recent series was that of 1978/79, which caused a sharp drop in Wren index values. After two years of recovery from that, there was a further decrease caused by the hard winter of 1981/82. On the basis of 1982 densities, Hudson & Marchant (1984) estimated the British population at 3-3½ million pairs, or half the level of ten years earlier, but the difference was due in part to a more conservative extrapolation of sample densities. The Wren then ranked as only seventh in the league table of abundance of British breeding birds. Throughout the 1980s the picture has been one of recovery from a cold winter until reduction again in the next hard spell. Despite winters being cooler on average during the 1980s, none has depressed index values to levels anywhere near as low as those reached in the early 1960s.

The pattern of recovery from the crash in the early 1960s established that woodland and waterside vegetation are the preferred Wren habitats, for it was in those that the few surviving Wrens bred (Williamson 1969, Benson & Williamson 1972). Gardens and orchards were reoccupied next, with farmland and lane-side hedgerows last of all.

144

Since then, however, the woodland and farmland index trends have paralleled each other remarkably closely, suggesting no marked habitat preference at the level of the census plot and over the ranges of densities experienced during the last two decades.

Regional variation

Recent cold winters show regional variations in their effects, depending on the prevailing distribution of harsh conditions. Thus Wrens decreased most in eastern and southern England in 1975/76, but in eastern and northern England and in Scotland in 1978/79 when there was also a good correlation with altitude (Cawthorne & Marchant 1980). Harsh conditions were more general in 1981/82, and in that season the biggest losses occurred in western England. In 1986/87 the severe weather was concentrated in southeastern England; elsewhere Wren index values actually rose in 1987. However, regional indices have broadly followed the national pattern over the long term.

Analysing CBC farmland data on a regional basis, O'Connor & Shrubb (1986a) found north-to-south and east-to-west gradients of increasing density. Their highest values were in southwest England, where farmland structure was particularly diverse. These trends are confirmed by the 1988 regional density rankings, but the pattern in woodland is less clear-cut.

Trends elsewhere in Europe

In continental Europe also, the key features of Wren population changes are severe dips and subsequent recoveries following hard winters. Inevitably, these affect northern regions more than southerly and maritime ones. The Swedish index trend, of increase from 1970 to a peak in 1974-1975, then a fall and subsequent fluctuation around cold winters, is very similar to the British one; but the largest recent falls were in 1979 and 1985 (Hustings 1988). Population changes in Denmark since 1976 have been similar but of smaller magnitude (DOFF 1989).

Dunnock *Prunella modularis*

Present population trend: shallow but progressive decline since the mid-1970s.
Percentages of plots occupied 1968/78/88: farmland 95/98/96; woodland 86/94/85.
Latest estimate of breeding population: 2 million territories in Britain (Hudson & Marchant 1984).
Regional density rankings 1988: farmland W>EE>NI> SE>WE>S>NE; woodland S>NE>EE>NI>SE> W>WE.

The Dunnock is a common but unobtrusive bird of scrub and woodland edge, largely avoiding closed-canopy woodland. It has successfully exploited linear scrub in the form of farmland hedgerows, and indeed these are now a major habitat for it: hedges paralleled by ditches are especially favoured (Arnold 1983). The Dunnock is also numerous in urban and suburban situations, where it frequents parks, gardens, churchyards and similar habitats. In the decades prior to the CBC there was no good evidence for any marked or widespread change having taken place in Dunnock distribution or status, other than suggestions of increase in some urban areas (Parslow 1973). More recently, however, it has declined, for reasons which remain obscure.

The CBC began when populations of the Dunnock were at a low ebb after two hard winters, 1961/62 and 1962/63. Following rapid recovery in 1964 and 1965 and then a

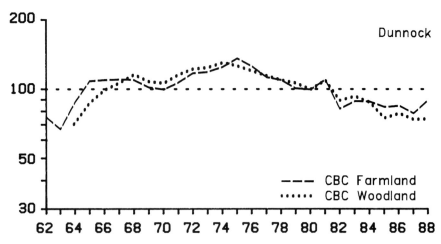

200

Dunnock

100

50

—— CBC Farmland
······ CBC Woodland

30

62 64 66 68 70 72 74 76 78 80 82 84 86 88

short plateau period, there was further increase during the early to middle 1970s. This was reversed after 1975 by a short, very cold spell of winter weather, and since then populations have been in slow decline almost through to the present. Considerable decrease has also been detected by the Garden Bird Feeding Survey in urban and suburban habitats (Thompson 1988). Comparison of the CBC trends between habitats suggests that farmland is preferred to woodland: recovery from the fall in the early 1960s took longer in woodland, and was perhaps aided by overflow from farmland, while in the last few years the woodland index values have fallen further than those of farmland.

The cause or causes of the modern downturn are not fully known. The species was affected by cold winters in the early 1960s, and the largest recent fall followed the hard winter of 1981/82 when mortality of ground-feeding birds was especially high (Marchant 1983*a*). Yet the CBC graph does not show the sharp spikes typical of species limited by winter weather, such as Wren. A loss of tree canopy through Dutch elm disease promoted ground vegetation previously inhibited by shading, and reduced the amount of bare ground on which hedgerow Dunnocks forage (O'Connor & Shrubb 1986*a*), though this may also have increased potential nest sites. In the results of nest record card analyses, there were tendencies for Dunnock nestling mortality to rise, and for nest habitat diversity to fall, after the middle to late 1970s; it was suggested that changes in farming practices may have led to competition from other passerine species, with Dunnocks being forced into more marginal sites (O'Connor & Pearman 1987). Both of these suggestions fit the timing of the Dunnock decline, but neither could be more than a contributory factor since neither applies to the urban and suburban situations where Dunnocks have also decreased.

It is also uncertain how well CBC clusters relate to population densities in view of recent discoveries concerning the Dunnock's extremely variable territorial and mating systems (reviewed by Davies 1987). Both males and females defend personal territories in spring, and seek to extend these to include territories of the opposite sex. Monogamous pairs exist, but instances of polygyny (male with two or more females), polyandry (female with two or more males), and polygynandry (two or three males sharing several females) are also frequent. A male can produce more offspring by pairing with more than one female, while a female can achieve higher breeding success by having two or more males helping to feed her brood. Polygynandry is an extension

146

of this, in which neither the dominant male nor the dominant female succeeds in driving its rivals away from what becomes a communal territory. In a study in the Cambridge Botanic Gardens, 1981-1984, 229 mating combinations comprised 27% monogamy, 9% polygyny, 35% polyandry, and 28% polygynandry (Davies 1987). However, these proportions may well be very different on CBC plots, where Dunnocks are present typically at much lower densities.

Regional variation

On farmland there is a north-to-south gradient of increasing density, doubtless reflecting the comparable gradient in frequency of hedges as field boundaries (O'Connor & Shrubb 1986a). In 1988 regional density rankings, this held on farmland though the opposite applied in woodland; this implies regional variation in habitat dependence, with woodland assuming more importance where hedgerows are fewer. There are no obvious regional differences in population trends either on farmland or in woodland.

Trends elsewhere in Europe

The Dunnock has increased generally in Europe, after becoming adapted to human proximity, and benefiting from changes in land management which artificially maintain otherwise transitory stages of vegetation growth (Cramp & Simmons 1988). In Denmark, however, index values from 1976 show a steady decline comparable to that in Britain, and by 1985 the index was at less than half the initial value (DOFF 1989).

Robin *Erithacus rubecula*

Present population trend: some recent cold-weather fluctuations; otherwise stable.
Percentages of plots occupied 1968/78/88: farmland 94/97/99; woodland 92/99/99.
Latest estimate of breeding population: 3½ million pairs in Britain (Hudson & Marchant 1984).
Regional density rankings 1988: farmland W>NI>SE> WE>EE>NE>S; woodland NI>W>NE>S>EE> SE>WE.

So far as one can judge, Robin populations in Britain have been remarkably stable over the last 100 years or so, without widespread changes other than short-term fluctuations associated with harsh winters. It is as well to remember, however, that there were no quantified data before the CBC started in the early 1960s.

The CBC began at a low point in the Robin's fortunes, due to the cumulative effects of the severe winters of 1961/62 and 1962/63. After recovery, there was some unexplained fluctuation in the period 1967-1970, followed by modest overall increase during the early to middle 1970s. This increase was more pronounced on farmland, where a peak was reached in 1975, and it seems likely that this was due to increased overflow from woodland as population levels rose. The trend was then reversed following a cold spell in the winter of 1975/76. Since then index values have fallen in both habitats, but slightly more on farmland than in woodland. It can be seen on the graph that the cold winter of 1978/79 affected farmland Robins more than those of woodland; but large declines occurred in both habitats after the severe winter of 1981/82.

147

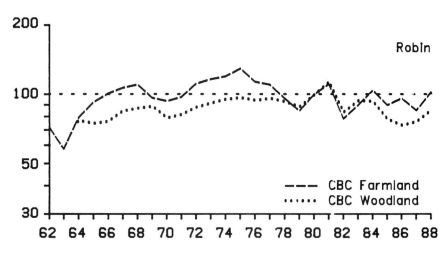

Woodland is the ancestral habitat of Robins from which, as the landscape changed under human impacts, they then colonised timbered hedgerows on farmland, town parks, churchyards and suburban gardens. Farmland probably remains suboptimal Robin habitat: hard-winter survivors tend to fill the woodland niches first, and it seems to be the losers in territorial competition which are forced out into farmland hedgerows (Benson & Williamson 1972, Sharrock 1976). This explains the relative differences between the two CBC indices – it is not that woodland birds necessarily survive better, but that any gaps in their ranks are more likely to be filled than are similar gaps on farmland. Declines on farmland probably occur through both mortality and emigration. Only after a series of mild winters, as in the late 1960s and early 1970s, is farmland likely to be occupied fully. Of course, in urban and suburban areas, garden feeding aids Robin survival even in cold winters. Garden Bird Feeding Survey index values have varied little over the last 17 years, suggesting a stable population level (Thompson 1988).

There is no doubt that, as already noted, the biggest influence on Robin population changes is winter weather. However, it seems likely that modern changes on farmland will have affected the attractiveness of that habitat to the present species. In effect, Robins use mature hedgerows as a woodland substitute. Hence any deterioration in extent or quality of hedgerow will have an adverse effect, whether through tree felling (for example following Dutch elm disease), hedge removal, or severe trimming of the hedgerows retained. Related to this, Robins have become more characteristic of pasture, sheep and dairy farms, where hedges are useful as stockproof barriers and shelter, than they are of arable and cereal farms where hedgerows are less functional and have often been removed or damaged (O'Connor & Shrubb 1986a).

Regional variation

Overall, there are north-to-south and east-to-west gradients of increasing farmland densities, so that mean values are highest in Wales and southwest England (O'Connor & Shrubb 1986a). This reflects the increasing scarcity of hedgerows towards the north, where stone walls are frequent as field boundaries, and towards the east, where field enlargement has been most marked. Woodlands are relatively more important for northern Robins, and this emerges from 1988 regional density rankings. The biggest recent falls on farmland have been in eastern and western England and in Wales, and the biggest woodland fall in eastern England. It is possible that this is the result of recent cold winters having affected the southern half of Britain more severely than the north.

Trends elsewhere in Europe
No major trends are known. As in Britain, there are fluctuations, sometimes large, which correspond to winter weather patterns. However, northern populations are migratory and thus independent of winter conditions in the breeding range.

Nightingale *Luscinia megarhynchos*

Present population trend: long-term range contraction; numbers fluctuate.
Percentages of plots occupied 1968/78/88: all CBC habitats 8/8/10.
Latest estimate of breeding population: fluctuates, now probably 4000-5000 territorial males in Britain (see below).

The Nightingale is not indexed by the CBC because it occurs on too few plots, though ubiquity figures are available (see graph). This species has, however, been the subject of two special BTO surveys, in 1976 (Hudson 1979) and 1980 (Davis 1982).

Between 1910 and 1940 a contraction of the Nightingale's breeding range was documented in Yorkshire and the north Midlands, though at the same time there were temporary increases in Devon, Somerset and southeast Wales in line with a period of climatic amelioration. At least since 1950, population levels have clearly been falling in western and central counties of England, indicating that gradual range contraction is continuing (Parslow 1973, Hudson 1979). It is not clear whether densities have also fallen in southeastern counties, where the largest numbers are now found, though local decreases have been reported. Prior to 1976, counts had been few and restricted in scope. These are difficult to interpret because of fluctuations between years, weather-related variations in song output, and a tendency for localities to be used only for so long as the vegetation remains at a suitable successional stage. In the important and well-studied area of east Kent, numbers were relatively stable during 1966-1976 (Hudson 1979). The CBC ubiquity values show considerable year-to-year fluctuations, but no long-term change. Probably this is because the CBC has its best representation in those parts of England which coincide with what is now the Nightingale's main breeding range.

The scale of change between years was shown well by the two BTO surveys, which produced national totals of 3230 singing males in 1976 and 4770 in 1980. Some counties are thought to have been incompletely covered, especially in 1976 when the true number may have been nearer to 4000. It is suspected that these surveys coincided with respectively poor and good years for this species in England, and that annual totals of territorial males therefore fluctuate between 4000 and 5000.

Typically, the Nightingale in Britain is a thicket-haunting species which is adapted to taking temporary advantage of a variety of scrub, plantation and woodland sites during suitable stages of vegetational succession. Climax woodland is unsuitable for it except along edge habitat. Some actively coppiced woodlands carry large populations of Nightingales. The birds utilise the middle stages of growth (5-8 years) of various

149

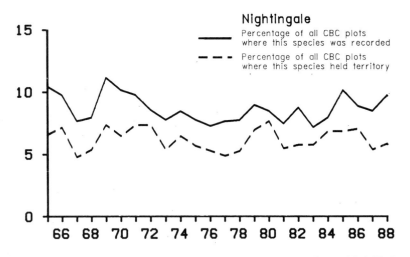

Nightingale

15

Percentage of all CBC plots
where this species was recorded

- - - Percentage of all CBC plots
where this species held territory

10

5

0

66 68 70 72 74 76 78 80 82 84 86 88

types of mixed coppice, although pure sweet chestnut is generally avoided (Fuller & Warren, in press). The massive overall decline this century in commercial coppicing has not helped the Nightingale, nor has scrub clearance and felling of spinneys for building development and agricultural intensification. Yet the species' adaptability, and the fact that plenty of seemingly suitable sites still exist in counties where Nightingales are clearly declining, suggests that habitat availability is not the underlying reason for the modern trend. Climatic conditions may be relatively more important to a species on the edge of its range, and it is significant that the British trend is paralleled elsewhere in northwestern Europe (see below). The period of climatic amelioration over northern Europe during the 1920s and 1930s was clearly in reverse by the 1950s, most apparent in Britain through consistently cooler and later springs. It is noteworthy that 1970 and 1980, both years of above-average numbers of Nightingales, were also marked by warm, dry anticyclonic weather in April and May.

Regional variation

Much the highest densities of Nightingales in Britain are those in Kent and Sussex, which together held 1400 singing males (43% of the national total) in 1976 and 1800 (38%) in 1980. From this region there are gradients of declining density to the west and north. Thus Devon had only 5 singing males in 1976 and 14 in 1980, while South Yorkshire had 2 and 22 respectively. The larger numbers which entered Britain in 1980 were noticed especially in East Anglia (where the total increased from 360 in 1976 to 950 in 1980), the east Midlands (285 to 465), and in the counties of Dorset and Somerset together (120 to 300). Hence the biggest increases in 1980 occurred towards the edges of the normal British range (Davis 1982).

Trends elsewhere in Europe

Declines during the present century have been reported also from West Germany, the Netherlands and Belgium (Cramp & Simmons 1988). Hence the British trend is part of a wider pattern across northwestern Europe. This decline is not linked to the Sahel drought, being of longer standing (Wammes *et al* 1983). More recently, Dutch census index values rose over the period 1984-1987 (Hustings 1988).

Black Redstart *Phoenicurus ochruros*

Present population trend: increase since the 1970s.
Percentages of plots occupied 1968/78/88: all CBC habitats 0/0/1.
Latest estimate of breeding population: fluctuates from year to year, but usually below 100 pairs in England; none elsewhere in Britain.

The Black Redstart is one of the scarcest birds dealt with in this book. It is, however, by no means easy to obtain good annual coverage for it, because it breeds mainly in urban areas and industrial sites where birdwatching opportunities are often restricted. The CBC registrations are mostly of spring migrants, and territories are far too few to provide an annual index or even ubiquity values. The species has been monitored in other ways, including a special BTO survey in 1977.

This attractive chat became a regular British breeding bird in the 1920s, when a few pairs began nesting in natural cliff sites in Cornwall and Sussex and on industrial sites in London. In the 1930s other breeding records came from Kent, Cambridgeshire and Suffolk. From 1940 there was an upsurge in numbers of localities and birds, encouraged by the many new nest sites created by Second World War bomb damage (especially in London and Dover). Subsequently, nesting has occurred north to Lancashire and Northumberland but has often been sporadic; currently, this occurs most consistently in eastern and southeastern coastal counties, and inland in Greater London, the West Midlands and South Yorkshire (Morgan & Glue 1981). Now, as previously, the most common nesting sites are on power stations, factories, and derelict buildings. Natural sites seem to be used rather seldom in Britain, despite their initial importance.

Each year the total of singing males located exceeds the number which are subsequently proved to be paired. Annual totals to 1973, given by Fitter (1971, 1976), show considerable year-to-year fluctuations, as would be expected of a scarce migrant at the periphery of its range. Temporal trends can be discerned, however. Levels were generally higher in the 1940s and early 1950s than they were in the late 1950s and 1960s, and rebuilding after wartime bomb damage possibly contributed to this fall. After 1969 average numbers rose again (see table). An index based on BTO ringing totals is thought to be influenced too heavily by trapping at coastal migration sites, but this does show a broad pattern of fluctuation around low levels in the 1960s, followed by a trend towards increase in the 1970s which is still continuing.

Direct comparison of breeding census numbers across years may be misleading, because the data have been collected in different ways. The longest series (1940-1972) was based on records submitted to county bird reports, which seem likely to have been incomplete. From 1973 to 1976 the species was monitored by the Rare Breeding Birds Panel, which probably stimulated a higher reporting rate, and in 1977 it was the subject of a special BTO survey (Morgan & Glue 1981). After a nine-year hiatus, the RBBP reinstated the species in 1986; and their 1987 total (Spencer *et al* 1989) is the highest yet reported. In contrast, the lowest annual total was in 1962 when there were reports of only 12 pairs plus a further five singing males.

Years	Pairs proved breeding	Pairs not proved to have bred	Territorial males possibly unpaired	Total, pairs plus males
1943-52 mean	23	4	16	43
1953-62 mean	18	2	10	30
1963-72 mean	22	6	11	39
1973	63	5	22	90
1974	49	13	16	78
1975	47	19	25	91
1976	34	18	30	82
1977	61	18	25	104
1986	25	24	25	74
1987	46	35	28	109

Regional variation

In 1977, coastal counties of southeastern England (Norfolk to Sussex, plus the London Area) held 62% of proved breeding pairs and 77% of other territorial birds. The largest county total was that for Suffolk, which had 12 pairs (10 proved breeding) and a further 8 singing males (Morgan & Glue 1981). In 1987, the biggest totals were those for Kent and the London Area (Spencer *et al* 1989).

Trends elsewhere in Europe

There has been a long-term expansion of range to the north and northwest in northern Europe. In West Germany it spread northwards in the second half of the 19th century, and Denmark was first occupied at that time. Sweden was colonised from 1910, the Soviet Baltic States in the 1920s, and there has been more recent spread into Norway and Finland. Hence the colonisation of Britain is part of a broader European trend. In Czechoslovakia, the point-count index rose during 1981-1986 (Hustings 1988).

Redstart *Phoenicurus phoenicurus*

Present population trend: recovering well from 1970s decline.
Percentages of plots occupied 1968/78/88: farmland 29/13/18; woodland 34/12/20.
Latest estimate of breeding population: 140,000 pairs in Britain (Hudson & Marchant 1984).
Regional density rankings 1988: all CBC habitats W> WE>SE>S>NE.

There has been earlier disagreement over long-term trends in Redstart populations. Buxton (1950) suspected that changes had been local in nature, and that claims of widespread decline were due to unjustified generalisation from local observations. However, Alexander & Lack (1944) reported a very marked decline throughout southern, eastern and central England, and various county sources dated this from about 1915-1920. The latter interpretation was accepted by Parslow (1973), who considered that the decline had halted before 1960 and even been reversed in some regions. Using an index constructed from nestling ringing totals, and covering

1950-1980, Mason & Hussey (1984) found Redstart numbers rising in the early 1950s, falling a little up to 1960, then rising again to another peak in 1965 before a serious decline commencing in 1969.

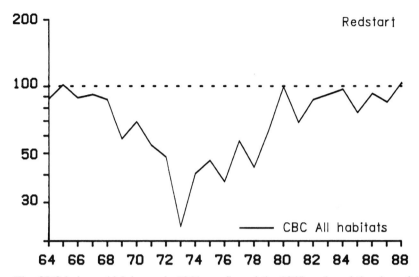

The CBC index, which began in 1964, confirmed the 1965 peak and the sharp fall from 1969. The latter was subsequently attributed to severe drought conditions in the Sahel wintering area (Winstanley *et al* 1974). Redstarts continued to decline as Sahel conditions deteriorated further, and the CBC index reached its lowest point in 1973, as did the Mason & Hussey index. Since then an overall increase has been maintained, so that CBC index levels have returned to those found before the crash. Recovery is probably not yet complete, however, since Redstarts are still scarce or even absent in many former localities in lowland Britain, including former farmland haunts where the birds frequented poplars and old willows. In Devon, for example, the population level has recovered fully in the preferred open woodlands around Dartmoor and Exmoor, whereas levels in the less-favoured lowland sites are still 50% below pre-decline status (Sitters 1988).

It seems likely that over the last four or so decades the biggest influence on Redstart population levels has operated in Africa rather than in Britain. We do not have Sahel rainfall figures for the early years when Redstart declines were reported, but the increase in the early 1950s coincided with a return to normal levels of Sahel rainfall following five years of drought in the late 1940s. Also, the 1965 Redstart peak shown by British monitoring followed the best Sahel rains since 1959, and the 1969-1973 correlation has already been mentioned. Yet there are recent puzzling anomalies. The Redstart's recovery since the mid-1970s has been more pronounced than those of most other drought-affected species, and the others experienced further serious falls in 1984, following a failure of the 1983 rains, which had no counterpart in the Redstart. But, so far, there is no evidence to suggest that the Redstart has modified its winter range in response to the persistent drought.

Conditions in Africa may not therefore be the sole reason for recent population changes in Britain. Yet there is no obvious European factor which might have been adverse in the 1970s but which ceased to be so during the 1980s. There is no evidence that Redstarts are limited in any way by habitat availability in Britain (Sharrock 1976). The availability of tree holes suitable for nest sites can limit population densities in modern managed woodland. Redstarts are not averse to using nestboxes, though these have to be given positions and entrance-hole sizes that are appropriate to this species. The chief beneficiaries of modern nestbox schemes are the Redstart's tree-hole competitors – Pied Flycatcher, Nuthatch, and the *Parus* tits: it is conceivable that their ready use of nestboxes has made more natural sites available for the Redstart. Woodland nestbox schemes are increasing in number, though this trend began well before the recovery of the Redstart population started in the 1980s.

Regional variation

The Redstart has always been most abundant in western and northern counties, where it often shares oak-wood habitats with the Wood Warbler and Pied Flycatcher. On farmland CBC plots Redstarts are commonest in a pasture-dominated region covering the four west Midland counties and Wales, in which there has been a higher rate of retention of hedgerow trees. Regional CBC trends follow the national pattern, with one major exception in that no recovery was apparent in eastern England during the 1980s. Redstarts have long been thinly distributed east of a line from the Humber to the Solent.

Trends elsewhere in Europe

Declines in the late 1960s, continuing into the following decade, were reported widely from western and northern Europe. These have been linked to Sahel drought, with the effects of drought exacerbated in some cases by habitat loss on the breeding grounds (Hildén & Sharrock 1982, Berthold *et al* 1986, Cramp & Simmons 1988). In contrast to the British upturn, Continental populations show little sign of recent recovery. There has, however, been increase during the 1980s in southern Finland (Väisänen *et al* 1989), and some increase in Swedish and Danish index values since 1984-1985 (Hustings 1988, DOFF 1989).

Whinchat *Saxicola rubetra*

Present population trend: decline since 1950s, in England at least.
Percentages of plots occupied 1968/78/88: all CBC habitats 17/13/10.
Latest estimate of breeding population: 20,000-40,000 pairs in Britain and Ireland (Sharrock 1976); 90% of occupied squares were then in Britain.

The two chats in the genus *Saxicola* are so similar in some ways that comparison is invited. Broadly, the Stonechat is a resident (though not sedentary) species which requires cover all year round and so depends more upon woody shrubs, whereas the summer-visiting Whinchat takes advantage of the seasonal flush of plant growth and so is more characteristic of grasses, weeds (especially umbellifers) and bracken. Typically, the Stonechat inhabits lowland and coastal gorse-clad heath, though it extends also into areas of rough grazing and young forestry where it may overlap with the Whinchat. The latter is more of an upland bird, favouring hill pastures, tussocky unimproved grassland, bracken-covered hillsides and moorland grass, where it nests in open situations among grass or bracken, and uses fences or tall weeds as song posts where no bushes are available (Fuller & Glue 1977, Sitters 1988).

The Whinchat has probably always been more common in the more hilly northern and western counties, but it has become increasingly scarce and local in the agricultural lowlands of eastern, central and southern England. During the agricultural recession, which reached its nadir in the 1920s and 1930s, there was an abundance of attractive habitat as neglected pastures were slowly colonised by small hawthorns. But in the post-1940 revival of farming much of this once-neglected land was converted to arable, and thereby rendered less suitable for Whinchats. Then, after 1954, much of the remaining uncultivated downland became overgrown with dense scrub as myxomatosis devastated rabbit populations. More recently, the increased use of herbicides for chemical weed control, and the use of fertilisers on pastures to produce a denser sward, have both reduced the suitability of farmland for Whinchats still further (O'Connor & Shrubb 1986*a*). Roadside verges, once a significant habitat for this species, are now subject to much greater disturbance and are more often mown in the interests of traffic safety; railway embankments and cuttings are becoming overgrown; sewage-farms have been modernised; and much former wasteland has either been reclaimed for farmland or built over.

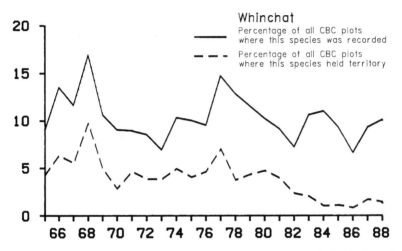

Whinchat
———— Percentage of all CBC plots where this species was recorded
– – – Percentage of all CBC plots where this species held territory

All these trends have contributed towards a continuing decline in Whinchats since the 1950s or earlier, at least in the area south and east of a line from the Humber to the Severn – with the result that too few CBC plots are occupied for regular indexing. Nevertheless, CBC ubiquity values, especially the lower graph line for territory-holders, document all too clearly the decline in occupancy of English lowland sites. Trends in other parts of the country are less certain. National ringing totals, for example, suggest only a small overall fall over the last 30 years, hardly more than might be expected from the English lowland decline alone.

As a trans-Saharan migrant, the Whinchat has been at risk from the persistent drought conditions in the northern tropics of Africa. However, there is no evidence for there having been a marked effect. A ringing index showed that Whinchat numbers fell somewhat in 1970 and 1971 and remained on the low side during that decade; they improved their status in the early 1980s, but fell again in 1984 and 1985. Yet these changes were small compared to those shown by, for example, Sand Martin and Whitethroat. While the timing of these events coincides with Sahel rainfall trends, it is difficult to separate the effects of African climate from those of the deterioration of

British habitat. No effect clearly attributable to the Sahel drought is apparent from Continental trends (see below). In West Africa, the Whinchat occurs over a wider latitudinal belt than most migrants: from the Saharan fringe southwards into cleared cultivations within other vegetational zones, as far south as the Gulf of Guinea. Hence this species has probably been able to avoid the worst consequences of Sahel drought.

Regional variation
The trend in the west and north of Britain is unknown (see above).

Trends elsewhere in Europe
Marked declines have been reported from most countries within the middle latitudes of western and central Europe (Wammes *et al* 1983, Glutz von Blotzheim 1988). On the other hand, no such changes have been reported from Fenno-Scandia or from Mediterranean countries (Sharrock & Hildén 1983). This pattern strongly suggests that losses have been due to habitat changes associated with farming in the regions where decrease has occurred. Local studies in Germany have confirmed this (*e.g.* Bastian 1987, 1989).

Stonechat *Saxicola torquata*

Present population trend: long-term decline, exacerbated by cold winters.
Percentages of plots occupied 1968/78/88: all CBC habitats 9/6/2.
Latest estimate of breeding population: 30,000-60,000 pairs in Britain and Ireland (Sharrock 1976), with 61% of occupied squares then being in Britain. Has declined since.

It has long been appreciated that winter weather has an important influence on Stonechat population levels. Decline in a severe season is followed by recovery and even by overall increase after a succession of mild winters, but only to fall again after the next hard season. Stonechats can recover fairly quickly from declines in cold winters because of their ability to produce three broods in a season (Johnson 1971, Morgan & Davis 1977). However, during the last four or five decades the loss and fragmentation of habitat, especially inland, has been a significant factor inhibiting a full return to earlier numbers. A long-term downward trend has been especially apparent since the early 1940s, when three consecutive cold winters coincided with an end to agricultural recession. Much neglected pasture and marginal land was ploughed during the Second World War emergency.

Typical Stonechat breeding habitat comprises coastal or lowland heaths and commons, particularly where gorse is present, though they occur also in other low scrub, especially bramble. Young forestry plantation with heather for ground cover is accepted, though where the ground cover is of grass it is the Whinchat which is more likely to be found (Phillips 1973). Since the Second World War there has been a progressive reduction of natural Stonechat habitat. Wastelands and heaths have been built over or encroached upon by ploughing, while large tracts have gone for tree-planting or been taken over for human recreation – though some golf courses can offer suitable habitat. Moreover, areas of heathland have been invaded by birch scrub after cessation of the traditional grazing/burning rotation, a trend accelerated in the 1950s by myxomatosis (Magee 1965). Such fragmentation of inland habitats resulted in small, isolated pockets, where Stonechats were vulnerable to being wiped out in severe winters and which were then dependent on chance recolonisation. By the 1970s such inland breeding sites were scattered much more thinly, especially in central and eastern England, and the Stonechat's distribution had acquired substantial coastal, westerly and southerly biases towards areas of least habitat change and of normally milder winters (Sharrock 1976). As a consequence of this inland decline, the species occurs on too few CBC plots for regular indexing.

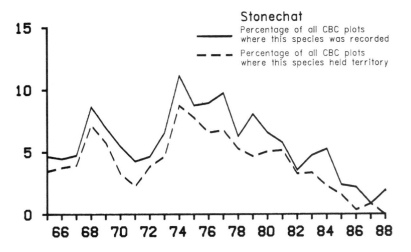

Stonechats were recorded specifically as having suffered very severely in the harsh winters of 1916/17, 1939-42 (three consecutive seasons), 1946/47, and in 1961-63. Each time they recovered within a few years to the extent that habitat availability would permit. In the absence of a CBC index, some indication of how Stonechats have fluctuated during the last 25 years can be gleaned from a ringing index based on numbers ringed per permit-holder. From the very low level of 1963 (Dobinson & Richards 1964) the species recovered in four years. After a temporary setback in the late 1960s, Stonechats continued to increase, as did various other resident passerines, up to a peak in the mid-1970s. According to this index, Stonechats were again hit badly by the severe weather of 1978/79. They have made only moderate recovery over subsequent years, presumably due to intervening rather cold winters, and in 1987 the level of Stonechat ringing was only one-quarter of that achieved at the time of the mid-1970s peak. The CBC ubiquities graph follows the ringing trend closely, except that it fails to show the large fall caused by the 1978/79 winter. The species was present on more plots in the mid-1970s, when populations were high after a series of mild winters, but has almost disappeared from the CBC returns during the 1980s as winters have averaged colder:

Regional variation

Since the Second World War there have been progressive reductions in Stonechat numbers in east-coast and inland counties, which are more prone to extremes of winter weather and to habitat losses. The British distribution is now biased substantially towards the west and south.

Trends elsewhere in Europe
Stonechats have declined in northwest Europe since the 1960s, notably in the Netherlands and West Germany. Since these are mainly migratory populations, and harsh conditions were not known to have occurred in their wintering areas during the main period of decline, habitat changes in the breeding range are considered to have been responsible (Hustings 1986).

Wheatear *Oenanthe oenanthe*

Present population trend: long-term decline in the southern half of England; elsewhere, decline up to mid-1970s now reversed.
Percentages of plots occupied 1968/78/88: all CBC habitats 17/17/18.
Latest estimate of breeding population: 80,000 pairs in Britain and Ireland (Sharrock 1976); 78% of occupied squares were then in Britain.

In Britain, most Wheatears nest in open upland or along western coasts, where there is short turf either as a result of grazing pressure by sheep and rabbits, or through climatic influences at higher altitudes (Conder 1989). In these situations, the most frequently used nest sites are rabbit burrows, dry-stone walls, rock crevices and screes. Yet such uplands are not necessarily of great altitude, and the species was formerly well distributed on the chalk escarpments of the southern English downs, the Chilterns and the Cotswolds, as well as on heathland such as the East Anglian Brecks. There has, however, been a long-term decrease over the southern half of England, from Lancashire and Yorkshire southwards (Parslow 1973). This was detectable before the turn of the century, and became general from the 1930s onwards. Trends elsewhere in Britain are harder to detect, and it is uncertain whether there has been any real long-term change in Wales or Scotland (Parslow 1973, Thom 1986).

In England, at least, the downturn in the fortunes of the Wheatear can be traced back to the 19th century and especially to the onset of the great agricultural depression, which affected most severely the eastern and southern counties. This long period of recession was at its worst during the 1920s and 1930s, but marginal land was being taken out of production even before the First World War. Grassland quality began to deteriorate, and (significantly) the numbers of sheep fell. Less intensive grazing of downland reduced the areas of short turf required by Wheatears and allowed the growth of scrub, a trend which became pronounced by the 1930s. During the Second World War, ploughing of pasture and marginal land on hillsides also reduced Wheatear habitat. In the 1950s the remaining commonland and downland grass deteriorated further after rabbit grazing was reduced or ended by myxomatosis. As a direct result of such changes the Wheatear became decidedly scarce in southern England and extinct in some counties. On the heathland of west Suffolk, where afforestation contributed to habitat loss, numbers fell from about 800 pairs in 1947 to fewer than 50 by the early 1960s (Easy 1964). Inland in southern England, breeding Wheatears persist now only on the steeper chalk slopes, on unplanted parts of the East Anglian Brecks, and on Dartmoor where overgrazing has created good conditions for this species (Sharrock 1976, Tye 1980, Sitters 1988).

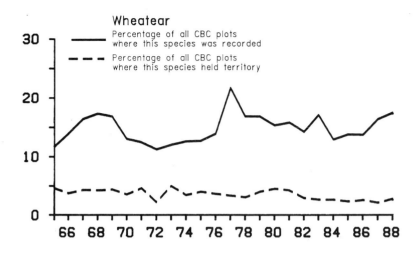

Wheatear

— Percentage of all CBC plots where this species was recorded

- - - Percentage of all CBC plots where this species held territory

30

20

10

0

66 68 70 72 74 76 78 80 82 84 86 88

Much of this habitat-related decline in southern parts of the country took place before the CBC began in the early 1960s, and the Wheatear is now so scarce there that it occurs on too few CBC plots for an index to be calculated. Ubiquity figures can be derived from the CBC, however, and are shown on the graph. Many of the birds seen on CBC plots are passage migrants. The percentage of plots on which Wheatear territories were held has declined very gradually.

Another source of national data is the Ringing Scheme, from which totals are available from the 1950s. Those of the 1950s were distorted by special ringing efforts then at some bird observatories, especially Fair Isle. A ringing index for 1959-1987, based on numbers ringed per permit-holder, shows values falling during the early to middle 1960s, remaining low up to the mid-1970s, but then rising again as a substantial recovery took place and index values returned to the 1961-1963 level. The only long series of breeding censuses is that from the Welsh island of Skokholm (Conder 1989), and it is of interest that this largely parallels the ringing index pattern. There were 26-38 (average 32) pairs on Skokholm during the 1950s, though fewer (12-30, average 24) during the 1960s; only 8 or 9 pairs were present in each of the years 1973-1976, but there was gradual recovery thereafter, to 19 pairs in 1986 and 1987. A short series of breeding counts from Fair Isle during the 1980s indicated overall increase, despite fluctuations, from 50 or more pairs in 1981 and 60-70 pairs in 1982 to 135 pairs in 1988 (Fair Isle BO annual reports). The pattern shown by the ringing index, supported by the island censuses, bears some resemblance to that of the Redstart, which declined in the late 1960s to a low point in 1973 and has since recovered substantially.

It remains uncertain whether the Sahel drought has contributed to these recent population trends, because Wheatears were declining before its onset. Their recovery since the mid-1970ş argues against the 1960s decline having been due to loss of breeding habitat, which occurred only locally, but this recent recovery occurred despite a continuance of rainfall deficits in the Sahel zone (a feature also shared by Redstart). However, the Wheatear's upward trend was interrupted temporarily in 1984, as happened with other Sahel species which were affected by an almost complete failure of the Sahel rains in 1983. The causes of Wheatear population fluctuations remain unclear.

159

Regional variation
Regional differences in trends are discussed above.

Trends elsewhere in Europe
Decreases have been reported from France, Belgium, the Netherlands, West and East Germany, Finland and western USSR, with habitat changes quoted as the likely cause in those instances where a reason was given. Swedish index values, available since 1970, have shown fluctuations between fairly narrow limits but a sizeable peak in 1978 (Hustings 1988).

Ring Ouzel *Turdus torquatus*

Present population trend: pronounced decline to 1950s; no recent evidence of change.
Percentages of plots occupied 1968/78/88: all CBC habitats 3/1/2.
Latest estimate of breeding population: 8000-16,000 pairs in Britain and Ireland (Sharrock 1976); 96% of occupied squares were then in Britain.

With its essentially upland distribution in Britain, the Ring Ouzel does not have much direct contact with man, though a minority nests on hill farms, along plantation edges, in old quarries and on the walls of derelict upland buildings (Flegg & Glue 1975). The species occurs on too few CBC plots for annual indexing or for the production of meaningful ubiquity figures.

The true summer home of the Ring Ouzel comprises the high ground of moorland and mountainside, on broken terrain rather than uniform heather. Often pairs will be concentrated in favoured cloughs or valleys – for example 12 pairs, with nests 160-200 m apart, in a linear 2-km stretch in the Pentland Hills, Lothian (Durman 1978). Such valley-side territories typically include heather slope, scree, rock outcrops, running water and isolated rowan trees (Poxton 1986). All breeding pairs require access to short grass for feeding, whether enclosed pasture or open tracts grazed by sheep or deer. Alsop (1975) considered access to such feeding areas to be a major factor influencing distribution, and he attributed the Ring Ouzel's absence from acid moorland to the low earthworm densities in such soils.

Quantified data are few, but subjective opinions agree that the Ring Ouzel has declined considerably during this century. Thus Baxter & Rintoul (1953) reported serious decreases from many districts in both Highlands and Southern Uplands and feared for its future as a Scottish breeding bird. Subsequently, Thom (1986) received reports in the early 1980s which indicated that the decline in Scotland had continued (though not to the extent forecast by her predecessors) outside the mountainous regions of the Grampians and west Highlands where, by implication, there had been little change. Numbers are thought to have decreased since the 1920s in the southern half of Wales, though apparently not in North Wales (Parslow 1973). There is also documentation of long-term decline and range contraction in the English Peak District where, by the 1970s, it had become virtually restricted to millstone grit (Alsop 1975, Holland *et al* 1984, Hornbuckle & Herringshaw 1985). In the Southwest Peninsula, numbers seem to have held up in Devon but regular breeding in Cornwall has ceased

(Sitters 1988). In Sussex, a long-term decline has been reported in the numbers of migrant Ring Ouzels occurring at traditional passage sites (R.Leverton, *in litt.*), although passage was strong in autumn 1988.

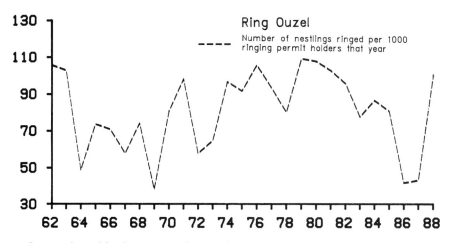

Ring Ouzel
---- Number of nestlings ringed per 1000 ringing permit holders that year

In assessing subjective reports of population change, it has to be taken into account that Ring Ouzel populations fluctuate naturally from year to year by up to 20% (Alsop 1975). In the absence of CBC data, the accompanying graph is for an annual index of Ring Ouzels ringed as nestlings in Britain. The most obvious features of this are the large fluctuations. There are also indications of an increase in the 1970s, then a fall up to 1986, with 1988 a much better year. However, no long-term pattern of change is evident.

With much of the national decline having occurred in the warmer interlude before 1950, Williamson (1975) suggested that this basically montane species had lost ground due to climatic amelioration. Moreover, it was suggested, this same climatic trend assisted the Blackbird, which increased its altitudinal range and competed with the Ring Ouzel where they met; but evidence for such competition is circumstantial (*e.g.* Meiklejohn & Stanford 1954). Competition with Mistle Thrush was reported by Durman (1978), but was not found in a subsequent study in the same area (Poxton 1986). The impact of upland afforestation is also uncertain. The areas of rock outcrop and steep-sided valleys favoured by Ring Ouzels are not those best suited to conifer planting, whereas the more uniform tracts of moorland favoured by foresters are often marginal Ring Ouzel habitat. Some loss of territories has certainly occurred at lower altitudes (Thom 1986), though Poxton (1987) found birds nesting along plantation edges. Alsop (1975) considered that the species' disappearance from limestone dales in the Peak District was due to more intensive farming and, especially, a big increase in disturbance from hill-walkers. These are factors which might have wider application – on Dartmoor for example (Sitters 1988). More recently, disturbance from hang-gliding has been implicated in Ring Ouzel decline on the East Derbyshire Moors (D. Alsop, *in litt.*).

British Ring Ouzels winter around the west Mediterranean, and there has been no suggestion that they have experienced problems at that season.

Regional variation
There is some evidence for regional variation in trends (see above).

   In western and northern Europe, pairs have nested irregularly in recent decades in northwest France, Belgium and Finland, but there has been range contraction in Sweden and Ireland. The alpine population (race *alpestris*) has increased in southern Germany and in Czechoslovakia (Cramp & Simmons 1988).

Blackbird *Turdus merula*

Present population trend: some decline since the mid-1970s, following earlier major increase.
Percentages of plots occupied 1968/78/88: farmland 99/100/100; woodland 88/99/96.
Latest estimate of breeding population: 4½-5 million pairs in Britain (Hudson & Marchant 1984).
Regional density rankings 1988: farmland W>NI>EE> SE>WE>NE>S; woodland NI>W>S>NE>EE> WE>SE.

The Blackbird is one of a handful of species which have adapted well to man-made environments, even towns and cities, and increased accordingly. Its gradual spread into suburban and urban areas began in the last century, becoming part of a wider increase which quickened during the warmer climatic interlude of about 1890-1950 and led to expansion in numbers and range.
   When this phase began, Blackbirds were outnumbered by Song Thrushes, but their ratio changed on annual nest record card and ringing totals until the Blackbird became the commoner species sometime around the mid-1940s. Ringing and nest record card indices for Blackbird suggested that they had stopped increasing by the early 1950s. No marked change was apparent over the period 1950-1965 (Snow 1966, Ginn 1969), by which time CBC monitoring had begun.

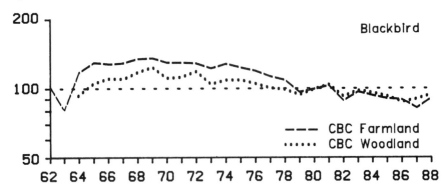

   A review of the effects of the 1962/63 cold winter (Dobinson & Richards 1964) suggested that Blackbird numbers did not fall even to the extent indicated by the infant CBC. Recovery was soon complete, and from the mid-1960s the Blackbird population both in woodland and on farmland fluctuated between narrow limits for the next ten years, resuming the stable trend since 1950 which has already been mentioned. Both indices began falling in 1976, following a short but severe cold spell the previous winter. There has been a shallow downward trend ever since, which has been slightly steeper on farmland than in woodland. Garden Bird Feeding Survey winter counts, dating from 1970, indicate a slight decrease overall, though this does not reach statistical significance (Thompson 1988).

As in other resident species, these downward trends are presumably related to the return of lower average winter temperatures over the last ten years. The highest Blackbird densities occur in suburban areas, where values can exceed 250 pairs per sq.km (Batten 1973), but this habitat is not monitored by the CBC. Woodland edge is probably the ancestral habitat of Blackbirds, and the CBC trends suggest that woodland is still preferred to farmland. However, it is also necessary to take into account the modern changes in farming practices which may have altered the attractiveness of farmland as Blackbird breeding habitat. The only firm correlation found by O'Connor & Shrubb (1986a, b) was for Blackbird densities to be lower in counties dominated by winter cereals. These authors considered that the decline of spring tillage was more important in limiting Blackbird numbers than reductions in ley grass in such areas. Grazed pastures are important feeding sites for Blackbirds, however, and there was a more marked association between Blackbirds and cattle in eastern regions where winters tended to be colder than elsewhere. Hedge quality also has an impact on Blackbird density. In a Dorset study, Williamson (1971) found that linear territories averaged 187 m in tall hedgerows but 346 m along trimmed ones. On the positive side, the switch from hay cropping to silage will have been beneficial locally, since more cuts mean a longer period with very short grass suitable for feeding thrushes.

Regional variation

There is a clear north-to-south increase in abundance on farmland (O'Connor & Shrubb 1986a), though the 1988 regional density rankings reveal an opposite trend in woodland. Variation between CBC trends in different regions appears to reflect geographical differences in the severity of cold winter weather. Thus 1975/76 and 1981/82 made their biggest impacts in Scotland, and 1978/79 caused bigger decreases in western England than elsewhere, whereas the effects of 1985/86 were clearest in eastern England.

Trends elsewhere in Europe

Since the First World War, there has been considerable northward and eastward expansion of the breeding range, and this is still continuing in Fenno-Scandia and the east Baltic. As in Britain, there was also, until recent decades, a general increase in numbers which in most countries included a marked spread into towns and cities (Cramp & Simmons 1988). Index values in Sweden and Denmark since the 1970s have been relatively stable (Hustings 1988, DOFF 1989).

Song Thrush *Turdus philomelos*

Present population trend: overall long-term decline; steep decline from short-lived plateau since mid-1970s.
Percentages of plots occupied 1968/78/88: farmland 96/98/93; woodland 86/98/98.
Latest estimate of breeding population: about 1½ million pairs in Britain (Hudson & Marchant 1984).
Regional density rankings 1988: farmland W>NI>EE>SE>NE>WE>S; woodland NI>W>S>NE>EE>SE>WE.

It is hard now to visualise the situation in the opening decades of this century, when Song Thrushes considerably outnumbered Blackbirds in all lowland habitats. The ratio changed during the 1920s and 1930s, as shown in annual ringing and nest record card totals (Ginn 1969). Initially this was due to increases of Blackbirds during that period of climatic amelioration, but the trend became more marked after about 1940 as Song Thrushes went into a decline which, despite short-term fluctuations and plateaus, has continued through to the present day. Song Thrushes are highly susceptible to cold weather and, despite their ability to migrate, their numbers always drop considerably after a severe winter. Most resident species have a capacity to recover from such setbacks, usually fairly quickly; but it seems that Song Thrushes were unable to recover fully after three consecutive cold winters between 1939 and 1942, or after another in 1946/47, resulting in a stepped pattern of population changes. They have been at lower levels ever since (Ginn 1969, Mason & Hussey 1984).

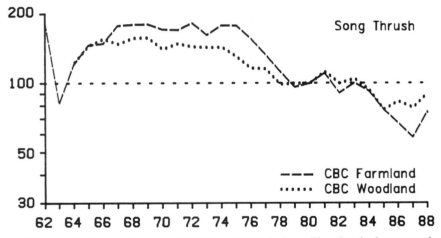

Following further setbacks in 1961/62 and 1962/63, Song Thrushes had recovered quite well by 1968 in both woodland and farmland. CBC index values were then stable for a short period, but by the mid-1970s they had begun to fall in both habitats. Since then the species has been declining progressively. Particularly sharp falls followed the severe winters of 1978/79 (farmland only) and 1981/82 (both habitats), with only small subsequent recoveries, and the increased frequency of cold winters during the 1980s must have contributed to the recent acceleration of the downward trend. This same pattern is observed, to varying degrees, in other British resident passerines. Despite increases in 1988, index values in both habitat types are now only half those of the late 1960s. The recent fall has been especially evident on farmland. Nor has this decline been restricted to the habitats monitored by the CBC, for there have been statistically significant reductions in Garden Bird Feeding Survey winter counts of Song Thrushes in both rural and suburban gardens, dating back to the beginning of the scheme in 1970 (Thompson 1988).

As already mentioned, Song Thrush declines have been attributed to cold winters and failure to recover fully after some of them. Baillie (in press, a) found that simple multiple-regression models, incorporating CBC index data and numbers of freezing days in January-February, explained much of the variation within the farmland index: 89.8% and 57.7% over 1962-1976 and 1962-1987 respectively. This relationship with numbers of freezing days is not unexpected, since it is under such conditions that Song Thrushes will have most difficulty in finding food. However, since 1982 the observed decline of Song Thrushes has been steeper than predicted by Baillie's model. The reasons for this are uncertain.

O'Connor and Shrubb (1986a) drew attention to the possible effects of modern changes in farmland management, and reported Song Thrush declines in regions dominated by barley cultivation that may have been attributable to a shift since 1975 towards autumn-sown varieties. This change reduced the extent of spring tillage, on which the majority of farmland birds previously fed at that season. However, the decline on farmland is not restricted to barley-growing areas; moreover, the species' decrease has been general and reflected even in urban areas. Concern has been expressed over the possible impact of the continuing increase of the Magpie, which is a predator of Song Thrush eggs and young; but recent studies have found that there is no correlation between the Magpie increase and breeding success of Song Thrush or indeed other passerines (Gooch et al, in prep.).

One feature which is shared by farmland, woodland edge and private garden is the presence of land molluscs – slugs and snails. It is a common misconception that these are the preferred foods of Song Thrushes. In reality, they are eaten with a marked seasonality which corresponds to the periods when the birds experience particular hardship: in midsummer when dry conditions often render soil invertebrates less accessible, and in late winter when berry crops are depleted and the weather is often severe (Goodhart 1958, Cameron 1969). Yet this very fact might make Song Thrushes particularly vulnerable to decreases in mollusc abundance. Molluscicides have a long history of usage, in slug pellets for example, though their use did not become widespread on farmland until the 1970s. Moreover, some pesticides intended for other purposes kill molluscs also. These could affect birds through direct poisoning or by causing overall reductions in snail populations. The possibility of a relationship with Song Thrush population trends merits investigation.

Regional variation

Between 1975 and 1986, the rate of Song Thrush decline on British farmland plots averaged 7.0% per annum. However, this rate of decline differed significantly between regions, being almost double in the southwest (12.0%) as compared to the southeast (6.5%) and north (5.6%) (Baillie, in press, a).

Trends elsewhere in Europe

The Song Thrush has increased in parts of north and northwest Europe, for example the Netherlands, Denmark and Finland. Declines have occurred in urban areas of Poland (Cramp & Simmons 1988). In Denmark, the population decreased markedly during 1975-1979, but has subsequently increased (Nøhr & Braae 1984, DOFF 1989).

Mistle Thrush *Turdus viscivorus*

Present population trend: recent decline, after previous increase.
Percentages of plots occupied 1968/78/88: farmland 72/82/83; woodland 66/84/82.
Latest estimate of breeding population: about 300,000 pairs in Britain (Hudson & Marchant 1984).
Regional density rankings 1988: farmland NI>WE>SE>NE>W>EE>S; woodland W>NE>EE>SE>S>WE.

Two hundred years ago the Mistle Thrush was very much a bird of southern Britain, but by 1850 it had acquired something approaching its modern distribution following half a century of spectacular increase and spread. Ireland was also colonised during that period. Increase continued, albeit at a slower pace, well into the present century, latterly manifesting itself through a spread into towns and cities wherever open grass areas, for example parks and sports fields, were available for feeding (Alexander & Lack 1944, Cramp & Tomlins 1966, Parslow 1973). Though it has been suggested that planting of new woodlands helped the species in Britain, especially in the north, this cannot have caused the expansion into new areas and habitats, for the same trend occurred over large areas of Europe (see below).

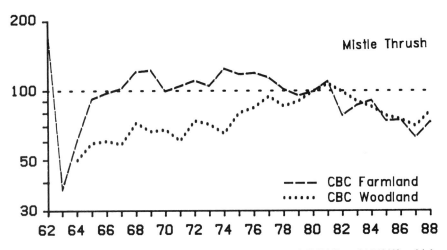

The start of the CBC was marked by the hard winters of 1961/62 and 1962/63, which brought the population to a low level. Following a recovery period, 1964-1966, index values continued to rise slowly until about 1977 (farmland) or 1981 (woodland). The cold winter of 1981/82 caused a small fall, from which there was a partial recovery. Since then levels have fallen further, especially on farmland, so that the gains of the 1970s have been cancelled out. The colder winters of the mid-1980s may have contributed to this setback, despite the Mistle Thrush being a partial migrant, but modern changes in farming are likely to have been more important.

The Mistle Thrush eats terrestrial invertebrates, supplemented by berries in autumn and winter. Farmland and also many woodland breeding pairs are dependent on farmland feeding sites, and may have been affected by two major changes in farming practices (O'Connor & Shrubb 1986a, b). The switch from hay to silage has probably been beneficial. Mowing produces a sudden flush of invertebrates previously unavailable because of the long grass, and silage production calls for at least two cuts in each meadow instead of one. The early silage cut often coincides with the period when Mistle Thrushes are feeding young. But, on the debit side, the change to autumn sowing of cereals has much reduced the extent of spring tillage which was also important for feeding.

National CBC index values mask local differences. In counties dominated by pasture and sheep farming, Mistle Thrush populations seem to have been more or less constant. Some decline has occurred since the 1970s in cereal-dominated counties, though less and later where barley is the main crop, presumably because spring sowings of barley remain at significant levels (O'Connor & Shrubb 1986a). Decline might have been even more pronounced were it not for the Mistle Thrush's ability to forage widely, up to one kilometre or more away from the nest site.

The population trends attributable to different farming regimes seem also to be reflected in the breeding statistics. Thus the average clutch size is 2.9 in cereal-growing eastern England, and 4.5 in southwestern England where pastures predominate. Both clutch size and fledgling productivity rise steeply with the extent of mown grass available for feeding sites. Moreover, fledging success has fallen in cereal-dominated counties, from 39% in 1962-65 to 28% in 1976-80 (O'Connor & Shrubb 1986a).

In winter the successful defence of fruit-bearing trees and shrubs, against conspecifics and other thrushes, is an important element in the survival over that season of adult pairs (Snow & Snow 1984). Young birds mostly emigrate for the winter period.

Regional variation

Division into a few broad geographical regions is too coarse an arrangement to show adequately the variations with farming type described above. Regional CBC indices indicate that populations have remained relatively stable overall on farmland in western England, in northern woodland, and in both habitats in Wales. Other combinations show varying degrees of decline.

Trends elsewhere in Europe

Over the last century or so there has been expansion in northwestern Europe, related to the adoption of a wider range of habitats, and in some regions, such as in the Netherlands, the increase was spectacular. Originally a bird of upland forest, the Mistle Thrush suddenly took advantage of park-like habitats and spread into lowland cultivations, aided by amenity plantings, and then into towns (Peus 1951, Voous 1960, Snow 1969). More recently, a marked decrease has been reported from Finland.

167

Grasshopper Warbler *Locustella naevia*

Present population trend: steep decline since 1970, but with temporary partial recovery around 1980.
Percentages of plots occupied 1968/78/88: all CBC habitats 21/10/14; all WBS plots -/4/10.
Latest estimate of breeding population: 25,000 pairs in Britain and Ireland (Sharrock 1976); 73% of occupied squares were then in Britain. Considerable decline since that time.

Grasshopper Warblers have long been widely though thinly distributed in Britain, but they are secretive and much more often heard than seen. They appear to be more prone than most passerine summer visitors to local fluctuations from one year to the next, and are erratic in their occupation of some breeding sites (Parslow 1973).

CBC data are barely sufficient for the construction of an index. Though up to 36 plots provided data in the early years, the sample sizes have been more than halved as the species declined. By 1987 they were too small to allow the index to be continued.

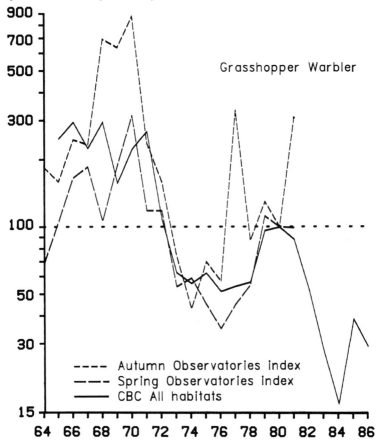

The pattern is of strong fluctuations up to 1971, followed by a major crash during 1972-1974. There was a modest improvement between 1979 and 1981, but then further decrease until by 1985 the index value was only one-sixth the average level of the late 1960s.

Riddiford (1983) calculated indices of spring and autumn migration, using daily census data from nine British observatories over the period 1964-1981, and his figures (converted to a datum year of 1980) are also shown in the graph. Both these indices show a substantial increase up to 1970, followed by a massive decline during 1971-1974. The lower population level was maintained throughout much of the 1970s, but with a suggestion of an increase towards the end of that decade, and large autumn peaks in 1977 and 1981. These indices are affected by annual variations in weather conditions in both spring and autumn; these will influence migration patterns, including the sizes of coastal falls. The autumn index may further be affected by variations in breeding success. Nevertheless, there is good overall agreement between the CBC and observatories indices.

Further confirmation of the trend has been obtained from the national annual ringing totals. An index for 1963-1987 has been prepared by dividing the annual ringing total by the number of permit-holders in that year. This index increased fivefold between 1963 and the peak in 1970, but was suddenly halved in 1971 and continued to fall over the following two years. Since that time it has fluctuated around a lower level comparable to that of the early 1960s. Though there was some improvement in the late 1970s, which is also apparent in the other indices, this proved to be temporary. There has, however, been no further population crash in the 1980s, as is indicated by the CBC.

For whatever reason, Grasshopper Warblers failed to maintain the increased numbers they achieved in the 1960s. It has been suggested that, along with other trans-Saharan migrants, they may have suffered during the prolonged Sahelian drought, but, against this, their numbers stayed high in 1969-1970 when typical Sahel species declined. A loss of breeding habitat may be implicated, although this alone could not account for a sudden fall in numbers. Destruction of wetland, grassland and scrub habitats has undoubtedly occurred, particularly during the gradual reclamation of marginal land for agriculture, but this has been at least partly compensated for by a widespread increase in young conifer plantations which present ideally structured breeding habitat (Parslow 1973, Sharrock 1976). Riddiford (1983) proposed that the observed trend simply represented a return to a more typical population level, following a temporary rise to plateau numbers in the 1960s. The reasons for the 1960s increase remain unknown.

Regional variation

The trends indicated agree with those reported regionally from widely separated parts of the country such as the four west Midlands counties (Harrison *et al* 1982), Sussex (Parmenter 1982), Essex (Cox 1984), Devon (Sitters 1988) and Gwent (Ferns *et al* 1977).

Trends elsewhere in Europe

Simms (1985) describes a probable northward extension of the breeding range in Europe during the present century. The Swedish point count index, which began in 1975, has shown large fluctuations, with peaks in 1979-1980, 1982 and 1986, and troughs in 1975, 1981 and 1985, and perhaps an increase overall (Hustings 1988).

Sedge Warbler *Acrocephalus schoenobaenus*

Present population trend: serious decline over the last 20 years, but substantial gains since 1985.
Percentages of plots occupied 1968/78/88: farmland 45/27/37; woodland 19/8/6; all WBS plots -/37/52.
Latest estimate of breeding population: 300,000 pairs in Britain and Ireland (Sharrock 1976); 71% of occupied squares were then in Britain. Numbers now much reduced.
Regional density rankings 1988: all CBC habitats NI> SE>NE>EE>S>WE>W.

Being less restricted than the Reed Warbler by habitat and climatic needs, the Sedge Warbler has a much wider breeding distribution in the British Isles. It is not known to have changed in status in the decades prior to 1960, beyond some peripheral consolidation in the Western Isles and Orkney, and a suggestion of more frequent breeding records in dry situations such as arable crops and young forestry (Parslow 1973, Sharrock 1976).

While Reed Warblers often nest among pure stands of reed, Sedge Warblers more typically choose rank vegetation around wetland margins, in or close to the interface between aquatic and terrestrial growths. They prefer the vegetation to be low and dense, structure being more important than plant species (Thomas 1984). Small numbers breed away from open water. In one study, pairs took to nesting in farm hedgerows after river vegetation was destroyed by dredging and bank clearance (Williamson 1971). Breeding in atypical situations is more likely to occur at times of high population, as in the 1960s, when competition for territory space is increased (Taylor *et al* 1981, Sitters 1988).

Sedge Warblers are less colonial than Reed Warblers and this, together with the habitat differences, makes them much easier to census. The CBC method works well,

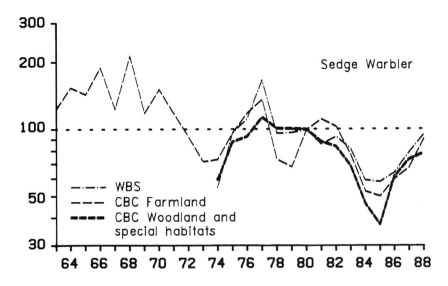

provided that visits are properly timed and spaced to allow for the main song period of the species being so short (Bell *et al* 1968, 1973).

The early years of the farmland CBC documented fluctuating population levels. 1968 was certainly a peak year, this being reflected in annual ringing totals as well as by the CBC. The population level fell sharply in 1969 and, despite a small hiccup in 1970, continued to do so until 1973-1974. After a partial recovery in the middle to late 1970s, the downward trend resumed again. An all-time low was reached in 1985, when farmland index values were only one-third of the 1964-1968 mean. There has, however, been a sustained improvement over the last three years in both CBC indices. The WBS index, which started in 1974, has shown a very close agreement with the CBC trend.

There is no doubt that the cause of the Sedge Warbler's post-1968 decline has been the persistent rainfall deficit in the species' wintering range in the Sahel and adjacent savanna zones of Africa. The regional improvements in West African rainfall in the middle to late 1970s, the failure of the rains in 1983, and the recent easing of drought conditions in the Sahel, are all evident in the Sedge Warbler indices.

Regional variation

The national trend described above is repeated exactly in the regional indices for southern and eastern England. Other regional values were based on smaller sample sizes. Decline occurred, but apparently less steeply, in northern England and Scotland, while in western England the index bottomed in 1979 and 1980 and has since risen.

Trends elsewhere in Europe

Decrease has probably been general in western and central Europe, though quantified data are available only from the mid-1970s. Population indices from Estonia, Finland, Sweden, the Netherlands and Czechoslovakia all show overall declines with minimum values in the mid-1980s (Hustings 1988, Väisänen *et al* 1989). Moreover, constant-effort ringing stations in West Germany (south and north) and in Austria, operated from 1974, have all revealed large decreases (Berthold *et al* 1986).

Reed Warbler *Acrocephalus scirpaceus*

Present population trend: no major change is known; perhaps increasing.
Percentages of plots occupied 1968/78/88: all CBC habitats 11/12/11; all WBS plots -/17/22.
Latest estimate of breeding population: 40,000-80,000 pairs in England and Wales (Sharrock 1976); none elsewhere in Britain.

Although some Reed Warbler pairs nest over damp ground in such vegetation as meadowsweet, willowherb, and even in bushes, the majority do so in *Phragmites* reeds, whether the large reed beds associated with lakes and meres or the narrow reedy fringes of linear waterways. In a sample of twelve reed beds, Milsom (1982) found that breeding numbers were correlated with perimeter length rather than with area of reeds, this doubtless being related to the frequency with which the warblers feed beyond the confines of the reeds. The combination of semicolonial habit and *Phragmites* habitat makes Reed Warbler a difficult bird to census by conventional methods (Bell *et al* 1968, 1973).

Over the long term there has been little evidence of overall change in Reed Warbler status, beyond some gradual expansion in Wales, the northwest (Lancashire, Cumbria) and the Southwest Peninsula. However, there are some examples of large-scale local changes. For example, at Oxwich NNR (West Glamorgan), Reed Warblers colonised as reeds began to invade the site in the 1950s and had built up to 400 pairs by the late 1980s (D.K. Thomas, *in litt.*). It remains very much a breeding bird of the southern half of Britain, with big distributional gaps in the west and southwest. *Phragmites* has a wider distribution than does the Reed Warbler, and it is suspected that climatic factors such as summer temperature and rainfall also limit the warbler's range (Sharrock 1976).

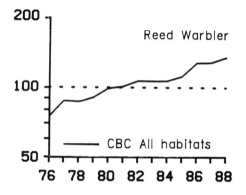

Reed Warblers are present on a small proportion of CBC plots, mainly in coastal counties. A CBC index for the years since 1976 shows a continuous increase, with values almost doubling by 1988. However, this apparent trend must be treated with some reservation. Most of the data came from sites where numbers and densities are manageably small for censusing, as for example along reed-fringed canals and dykes, and may be biased towards suboptimal habitats. A general increase of that magnitude should have been detected in other ways, but has not been (*e.g.* Prater 1988). Moreover, the CBC samples are rather small, with as few as 16 plots contributing to some annual comparisons.

A simple ringing index cannot be used for this species, since ringing effort over the years has been distorted by special projects, both national and local. However, some indication can be gained from the proportions of Reed Warblers in the Ringing Scheme's annual ringing totals for full-grown *Acrocephalus* warblers. This is but a crude measure, inevitably, since ringing totals reflect annual productivity as well as the strength of spring arrivals, and more critically because Sedge Warbler population level has itself changed markedly. When CBC index values for Sedge Warbler were highest, in the period 1964-1968, the Reed Warbler accounted for 36% of *Acrocephalus* trapped. As the Sedge Warbler declined during the 1970s, the proportion rose to an average 47%. By 1983-1987, when Sedge Warbler CBC index values were at their lowest, Reed Warblers accounted for an average 53% of *Acrocephalus* warblers trapped. One might have expected the Reed Warbler's proportion of ringing totals to have risen even higher after a halving of the Sedge Warbler population. However, the ringing ratio for the two species will be affected by any change in ringing effort at northern or western sites where Reed Warblers are rare or absent, and a major Scottish study was initiated in 1982. Using data from single southern ringing sites, the proportion of Reed Warblers in *Acrocephalus* totals at Dungeness Bird Observatory in

Kent rose from an average of 15% up to 1968 to an average of 68% in the 1980s; while at Beachy Head (East Sussex), the proportion of Reed Warblers has risen from 50% prior to 1975 to about 78% during the 1980s (Prater 1988). In summary, it is clear that the Reed Warbler has fared much better than has the Sedge during the last 20 years. Its national population level may not have changed much, but if there has been change then this is more likely to have been upwards. It has sometimes been assumed that this species will have been affected by Sahel drought, but there is no good evidence of this. Its winter quarters lie further south.

The *Phragmites* habitat is a vulnerable one. Without conservation management, large reed beds are encroached upon by willow or alder scrub as part of a natural succession. Linear reed growths along watercourses are at risk from cleaning and dredging operations (but will often regenerate), and marsh dykes are vulnerable to drainage and agricultural reclamation. On the other hand, habitat is created where reeds invade new pools such as those formed by mining subsidence and newly disused gravel pits. There is no certainty that habitat changes have affected Reed Warblers other than locally. Indeed, it is reported from Kent that there has been an increased frequency of breeding records in scrub, hedgerows and even cereal crops as, perhaps coincidentally, the Sedge Warbler has declined (Taylor *et al* 1981). However, one problem facing Reed Warblers is increased nesting failure through Cuckoo predation and parasitism now that it has risen in the league table of Cuckoo hosts in Britain (Wyllie 1981, Bibby & Thomas 1985, Brooke & Davies 1987).

Regional variation
None is known, other than the peripheral expansions referred to above.

Trends elsewhere in Europe
Northward expansion in Europe this century may still be continuing in Norway (Parslow 1973) and Sweden, where census data show considerable increase since 1975 (Hustings 1988). In Denmark and Finland, however, index values have fallen during the 1980s (DOFF 1989, Väisänen *et al* 1989). Reed Warblers have been breeding regularly in Ireland since 1981 (Hutchinson 1989).

Lesser Whitethroat *Sylvia curruca*

Present population trend: marked fluctuations, but no clear trend.
Percentages of plots occupied 1968/78/88: farmland 34/43/56; woodland 15/29/26.
Latest estimate of breeding population: at least 50,000 pairs in Britain (see below).
Regional density rankings 1988: all CBC habitats SE> EE>WE>S>W>NE.

With the exception of Dartford Warbler, the Lesser Whitethroat has the most restricted breeding distribution of any of our *Sylvia* warblers – its principal centres of abundance being encompassed by a line from the Humber to the Wirral and southwards to the Severn estuary and Dorset. Parslow (1973) doubted whether there had been any long-term change in its numbers or range in the decades leading up to the CBC. Subsequently, there has been some peripheral expansion. Lesser Whitethroats have been breeding and spreading in Northumberland since 1962 (Blackett & Ord 1962), they have increased in Cumbria since 1970 (Hutcheson 1986),

173

and since the mid-1970s they have been breeding in southeast Scotland, especially Lothian Region, where there were estimated to be 50-100 pairs by 1980 (da Prato 1980). Subsequently, a spread has continued in Scotland; in 1987 there was proved and probable breeding in Strathclyde (up to 10 pairs), near Aberdeen and on Speyside (Hogg 1988). There has also been expansion in southwestern England, with perhaps 100-200 pairs now in Devon, and a few pairs have nested regularly in Cornwall since 1977 (Sitters 1988).

As a bird of developing scrub, of which overgrown hedgerows are an extension, the Lesser Whitethroat has been sufficiently common on farmland since 1963 to be monitored by the farmland CBC. Since 1974 it has also been possible to build an index from the smaller samples on woodland and "special" plots. Farmland territories are often very large, including a kilometre or more of hedgerow.

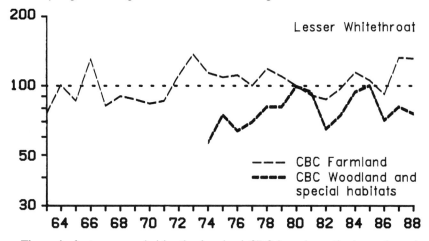

The main features revealed by the farmland CBC have been the large, irregular fluctuations. These have sometimes been between adjacent years (*e.g.* increases of 52% between 1965 and 1966 and of 44% between 1986 and 1987), though more usually across a short series of years. Mason (1976) has already presented an index to 1970, based on numbers of nest record cards submitted, which showed the Lesser Whitethroat to have increased in the early 1960s, to a peak in 1963, before falling away again slowly. Also, ringing totals were high relative to other *Sylvia* warblers at that time. In conformity with this, farmland CBC index values were moderately high in the early years, followed by a short period of lower densities. Index values were high again around the mid-1970s, before falling away. The 1981-1984 mean was almost equal to that of the CBC's opening years; while numbers have since risen again to match those of the mid-1970s. Both indices have shown large fluctuations, with peaks and troughs coinciding well (at least during the 1980s).

Such oscillations seem to be normal in the Lesser Whitethroat, and may be due to natural variations in the scale of spring arrivals at the edge of the species' breeding range. In western and northern Britain, records often relate to apparently unmated males (Parslow 1973, Sharrock 1976). Moreover, recent range expansions there, already referred to, occurred especially in the early to middle 1960s and in the mid-1970s, when the farmland CBC index was relatively high.

Lesser Whitethroats migrate southeastwards in autumn to winter quarters in Sudan and Ethiopia, and so are not influenced by drought in the western Sahel. However, there have been substantial rainfall deficits in northeastern Africa in several years since the mid-1970s. There seems not to have been a consequent change in the pattern or scale of population fluctuation in Britain, though overall reductions have been reported from some other west European countries (see below). Nevertheless, Lesser Whitethroats are more likely to be influenced by climatic conditions in their winter quarters or along their migration routes than by events on their breeding grounds.

In recent years, mean farmland densities have been around 0.8 pairs per sq.km. Applying this to the extent of pasture and arable land in England alone leads to an estimate of 65,000-70,000 pairs. That figure may be on the high side in view of the species' scarcity in northern and western counties, but the British population must be at or above the top of the range (25,000-50,000 pairs) offered by Sharrock (1976).

Regional variation

There are south-to-north and east-to-west gradients of declining density. It is probably coincidental that densities are higher in cereal-dominated regions than in pasture-dominated ones, for these have the same geographical trends as do Lesser Whitethroats (Lack, in press).

Trends elsewhere in Europe

Constant-effort ringing stations in West Germany and Austria during 1974-1984 found marked fluctuations which had temporal correspondence between sites – only partly matching those of Britain – although the trend was towards overall decline (Berthold et al 1986). Census data from Sweden and Denmark agree with this general pattern, both reaching low points in 1985 (Hustings 1988, DOFF 1989).

Whitethroat *Sylvia communis*

Present population trend: fluctuating around new lower level, following 1969 crash.
Percentages of plots occupied 1968/78/88: farmland 92/75/77; woodland 87/49/37; all WBS plots -/44/47.
Latest estimate of breeding population: 400,000-500,000 pairs in Britain (Hudson & Marchant 1984).
Regional density rankings 1988: farmland EE>SE>W>WE>NI>NE>S; woodland S>NE>SE>EE>WE.

The recent history of the Whitethroat has often been told. Its population level plummeted between the 1968 and 1969 breeding seasons, drawing attention to the effects of the Sahelian drought on this and other trans-Saharan migrants (Winstanley et al 1974). Prior to this event the Whitethroat may have been the most abundant British warbler, vying for this title with the Willow Warbler. Both CBC indices reached their highest levels in 1968, and this served to emphasise the scale of reduction in 1969, following a sudden failure of the Sahel rains the previous summer and autumn. In farmland and woodland plots, the 1969 population was around one-third that of the previous year and fluctuations have been close to that lower level ever since. An index from the WBS has been available since 1974, and this shows a remarkable similarity in trends to those from the CBC. All three indices show a peak year in 1977, and considerable recent improvement from a trough in 1985. Even before 1969, there are very striking parallels between the various Whitethroat indices and those for Sedge Warbler.

175

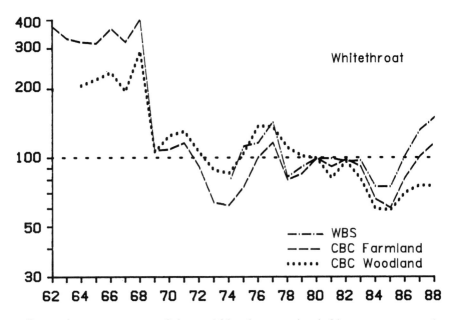

In a region so vast as trans-Saharan Africa there are, inevitably, year-to-year and area-to-area variations in rainfall deficit. Better rainfall in some areas in autumn 1969 helped Whitethroat survival that winter, but generally deteriorating conditions thereafter brought the species by 1974 to only one-sixth of 1968 densities on farmland. Over the following nine years Whitethroat indices fluctuated according to conditions in the winter quarters, and after a serious overall rainfall deficit in summer/autumn 1983, the 1984 spring population in Britain was back to the minimal level of 1974. Since 1985 the Sahel rains have been somewhat better, though still below the long-term average, and Whitethroats have been able to increase again, but they remain far below their former level. So striking have been the changes that they would be detected by almost any kind of quantified assessment. Thus Mason (1976) produced an index based on nest record card submissions, which closely paralleled that of the CBC; while a ringing index (Whitethroats as a percentage of all *Sylvia* warblers), previously relatively stable, slumped from 1969 and bottomed in 1973-1974, by which time the Blackcap had become the most common British *Sylvia*.

In an analysis of nest record cards, mostly collected prior to 1969, only 18% of Whitethroat pairs used hedgerows, while 56% of nests were in scrub and a further 19% in woodland (Mason 1976). Blackcaps and Garden Warblers have increased recently, to the point where they may be overflowing into less desirable sites such as the edge habitats now under-used by Whitethroats. However, there is no evidence that competition with Whitethroats occurs. The breeding success of Whitethroats has risen since the 1960s: this may be related to lower levels of intraspecific competition at the reduced densities which now apply (O'Connor & Pearman 1987).

Regional variation

The 1968/69 decrease affected all British regions and habitats. Both before and after this crash, population density was lower in pasture-dominated regions, notably Wales and the western half of England, than in regions of mixed or cereal farming.

Probably this was a geographical effect rather than a habitat one; before the crash, densities within mixed and cereal farming regions had actually been higher on individual farms that were predominantly under pasture (Lack 1989). Densities have been particularly low since 1969 at higher altitudes, where fewer sample plots remain occupied by Whitethroats; the national decline has thus been accompanied by greater concentration within the (presumed) preferred areas (Lack 1989).

Trends elsewhere in Europe

The 1969 crash was general over western and central Europe as far as 15°E (Berthold 1974, Berthold *et al* 1986). Monitoring data during the 1970s and 1980s show fluctuations around the post-1968 levels (Hustings 1988).

Garden Warbler *Sylvia borin*

Present population trend: recent recovery from 1970s decline.
Percentages of plots occupied 1968/78/88: farmland 42/33/49; woodland 59/64/74.
Latest estimate of breeding population: 200,000 pairs in Britain (Hudson & Marchant 1984).
Regional density rankings 1988: farmland W>NE>SE>EE>WE; woodland W>WE>EE>NE>S>SE.

Among the *Sylvia* warblers, the Garden Warbler and Blackcap can be grouped together for the similarity not only of their songs, at least to the human ear, but also of their breeding ecologies, including their preference for woodland and woodland edge. Of the two species, the Garden Warbler is more often found away from mature trees – in tall scrub and young conifers, for example. Farmland Garden Warblers establish their territories in copses with thick undergrowth, and only seldom along hedgerows. Within the primary habitats the defended breeding territories of the two species are reported as being mutually exclusive and this being only partly due to microhabitat preferences (Cody 1978, Solonen 1979, Garcia 1983), but CBC clusters (the sum of activity over a whole season) frequently do overlap. Interspecific competition between them certainly occurs to some extent. Blackcaps arrive earlier in spring and establish their territories, but when territorial Blackcaps were removed experimentally, additional Garden Warblers moved into the study area to occupy part of the space that had been made vacant (Garcia 1983). In view of this, an inverse relationship might have been expected between their respective CBC trends. That no such relationship is apparent shows that interspecific competition is not an important determinant of national population trends; the different conditions applying in their widely separated winter ranges have probably had greater influence.

There is no good evidence in the literature for any status change by the Garden Warbler in the decades preceding the CBC (Parslow 1973). Mason & Hussey (1984) gave an index from 1950 based on annual nestling ringing totals. This showed considerable fluctuation in the early 1950s, a deep trough in 1957 and 1958, but an increase thereafter to high levels between 1962 and 1966. These results agree with the initial high index values shown by the infant CBC. After a peak in 1964, farmland index values fluctuated around a high level up to 1970, while woodland values fell

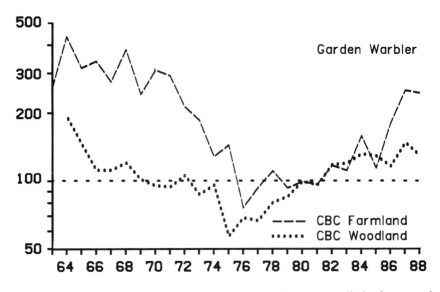

Garden Warbler

CBC Farmland
CBC Woodland

sharply in 1965-1966 and then fluctuated between rather narrow limits for several years up to 1972. Declines then became apparent in both habitats (and in the Mason & Hussey index also), earlier and steeper on farmland, and low points were reached in 1975-1976. Subsequent recovery was slower on farmland than in woodland, though since 1985 it has been the increase on farmland which has been more pronounced. These differences between habitats can be interpreted in terms of temporal changes in the usage of suboptimal habitat. As the Garden Warbler went into decline after 1970, there was progressive concentration into the preferred woodland sites. With numbers falling, a higher proportion of birds was able to establish territories in the preferred habitat. Conversely, as recovery neared completion in the mid-1980s, so more and more were forced out into farmland.

The overall Garden Warbler pattern of decrease in the early to middle 1970s, and subsequent slow recovery, is somewhat similar to those of other trans-Saharan migrants which have been affected by drought conditions in their winter quarters. Yet the present species winters further south than, for example, Sedge Warbler or Whitethroat, while it declined later and recovered sooner in comparison with these others. Possibly Garden Warblers experienced problems with crossing the Sahara during the period when the Sahel rainfall deficit was at its worst. Changes in British population levels may well be influenced more by climatic factors operating outside Britain than by any breeding season problems. Indeed, the 1980s recovery argues against the species having been affected by adverse habitat changes during its period of decline.

Regional variation

The highest farmland densities are in pasture-dominated areas, notably Wales; little or no difference is apparent between areas dominated by mixed and cereal farming (Lack 1989). In woodland also, higher densities occur in the west. While all regions reflect the national population trends, the 1970s decline seems to have been less pronounced in northern England and possibly in Scotland, but the number of Scottish census plots is small.

Trends elsewhere in Europe
Continental monitoring covers a shorter time-span than the British CBC. There are strong indications from European census projects (Hustings 1988, DOFF 1989) and constant-effort ringing in West Germany (Berthold *et al* 1986) that population levels have increased, to varying extents, after the mid-1970s. This matches the period of British recovery from the earlier decline.

Blackcap *Sylvia atricapilla*

Present population trend: consistent increase over the last 30 years at least.
Percentages of plots occupied 1968/78/88: farmland 56/58/79; woodland 71/85/88.
Latest estimate of breeding population: 800,000 pairs in Britain (Hudson & Marchant 1984).
Regional density rankings 1988: farmland W>SE> EE>WE>NE>NI>S; woodland W>EE>NI>SE> WE>NE>S.

There is no doubt that the Blackcap has been the most successful of our warblers over recent decades, with only the newly colonising Cetti's Warbler (whose numbers have now been much reduced by hard winters since 1984) showing comparable population growth. Though Parslow (1973) was unaware of any evidence for general long-term changes in the status of British Blackcaps this century, there is now reason to believe that the species has in fact been increasing since the mid-1950s.

An indication of the trend in the run-up to the CBC can be gleaned from Ringing Scheme records. The proportions of Blackcaps in annual ringing totals for all *Sylvia* warblers combined averaged 5% in the period 1951-1956, rising to 10% for the years 1957-1962, and to an average of 25% during 1963-1968, after which the ratio was disturbed by drought in the Sahel. An index based on nest record cards submitted between 1961 and 1970 (Mason 1976) also showed Blackcaps increasing from the outset. Thus it seems probable that Blackcaps have been increasing since the mid-1950s, though the ringing figures should be treated cautiously since gross ringing totals reflect both productivity and passage of Continental birds as well as the size of the British breeding population. Langslow (1978) has drawn attention to the increase since 1970 of Blackcaps passing through coastal bird observatories.

The CBC indices show that the upward trend has been especially marked on farmland. Mason (1976) noted that the Blackcap was the *Sylvia* warbler most likely to be found in woodland and the least likely to be found in scrub. Hence farmland plots probably contain a higher proportion of suboptimal sites than do woodland ones. The difference between farmland and woodland habitats in the increase detected by the CBC is clearly attributable to an increasing use of farmland by birds unable to establish territories in woodland due to this preferred habitat being fully occupied.

The Blackcaps which winter in Britain, in increasing numbers (Leach 1981), are thought to be from Continental breeding grounds. Our breeding population is migratory, wintering both in the western Mediterranean basin and in West Africa. Ringing recoveries indicate that the former area is the more important. Of all our migrant warblers, the Blackcap is the one which participates least in trans-Saharan migration. Lack (1989) has attributed the recent success of the species to its choice of winter quarters, which for most individuals lie well north of the drought-afflicted

179

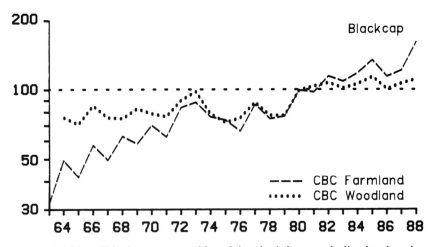

200

Blackcap

100

50

CBC Farmland
CBC Woodland

30

64 66 68 70 72 74 76 78 80 82 84 86 88

regions of Africa. This, however, would explain why it has not declined rather than why it has increased so markedly.

The Blackcap increase began long before the latest Sahelian drought became a problem to other migrants. Though it has been shown that there is breeding season competition between Blackcap and Garden Warbler (see under that species), there is no suggestion in CBC indices of Blackcaps having benefited from the decline of Garden Warblers in the 1970s. Harrison *et al* (1982) suggested that Garden Warblers prefer coppiced woodland, and as coppicing declined so Blackcaps became more numerous since they favour a higher, denser canopy. However, the decline in coppicing is of longer standing than are the warbler trends reported here. The long-term increase of Blackcaps is a European (not just British) trend; so the underlying causes, whatever they may be, are not peculiar to Britain.

Regional variation

On farmland, densities are lower in cereal-dominated eastern England than in pasture-dominated areas (western half of England plus Wales) and mixed farming areas (the remainder) (Lack 1989). At a local level, densities are doubled on farms with some woodland, compared to those without. The 1988 regional density rankings for both groups show the values for northern England and Scotland to be comparatively low.

Trends elsewhere in Europe

There was little indication of change in the Blackcap's Continental status before the mid-1970s (Langslow 1978); for Sweden, however, ringing data indicate a progressive increase at least since 1960 (Österlöf & Stolt 1982). Since the 1970s reports have all referred to increase. The Swedish index, 1970-1986, showed fluctuations initially and overall increase since 1975; while data from Denmark, Netherlands and Czechoslovakia all reveal upward trends during the 1980s (Hustings 1988, DOFF 1989). Constant-effort ringing stations in Austria and West Germany, operating from 1974, have also found significant increases (Berthold *et al* 1986).

Wood Warbler *Phylloscopus sibilatrix*

Present population trend: no recent change is known.
Percentages of plots occupied 1968/78/88: farmland 5/2/5; woodland 27/21/30.
Latest estimate of breeding population: 17,200 ±1370 territorial males in Britain in 1984-1985 (Bibby 1989).

Wood Warblers are essentially breeding birds of the deciduous, mainly oak woodlands of higher ground in western and northern Britain. They have always been scarce in eastern England south of Humberside, with a discontinuous distribution there, and may have become even scarcer in these peripheral areas in recent decades (Parslow 1973).

Because of this distribution pattern, the Wood Warbler occurs on rather few CBC plots. An all-habitats index has been constructed for the years since 1970: the trend indicated is one of sizeable annual fluctuations, with a suggestion of slight increase over the period. There is good agreement between Wood Warbler peaks and troughs and those of Whitethroat and Sedge Warbler. It would be unwise to attach too much significance to results based on small samples, and in any case Wood Warblers winter well to the south of the Sahel zone, but the possibility that their population has been influenced by Sahel drought cannot be discounted.

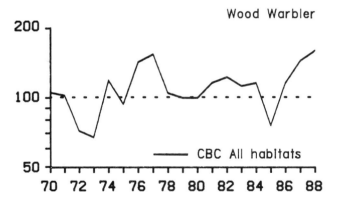

The Wood Warbler was the subject of a special BTO survey in 1984-1985 (Bibby 1989). This survey concentrated on 10-km squares where proved or probable breeding was found during the 1968-1972 Breeding Atlas, and had the objective of counting territorial males. A random sample of squares was checked in western and northern Britain, with full coverage being attempted elsewhere. Extrapolations were made for squares not visited. This resulted in an estimate (with 95% confidence limits) of 17,200 ±1370 territorial males. The only previous population estimate was that of Sharrock (1976), who suggested 30,000-60,000 pairs; but that was based on a guess of an average of 25-50 pairs in an occupied square, which the later survey has shown to be too high (see below).

Counts must be expressed as territorial males, for two reasons. First, there is evidence that a proportion of singing males remains unmated, more in some years than others (Oakes 1953, Simms 1985). Secondly, paired males do not help to incubate their clutch and at that time may continue singing in an attempt to attract a second female, resulting in instances of polygyny (Temrin 1984). Such males sing from different points of their territory (being very inconspicuous between these), presumably in an attempt to deceive females about their breeding status. This can exaggerate density estimates of males from the territory-mapping method, since discrete groups of registrations are liable to be interpreted as referring to different birds (Bibby 1989).

The Wood Warbler, together with the Redstart, Pied Flycatcher and, less markedly, the Tree Pipit, are characteristic members of the woodland bird community in western hills and valleys. There, sessile oak dominates natural woodlands, offering high canopy cover and little in the way of a shrub layer or herbaceous ground flora – due in part to grazing by herbivores. In contrast, many lowland deciduous woods seem to have too dense a shrub layer for Wood Warblers. There are exceptions, however, such as in the New Forest and Forest of Dean, where long histories of heavy grazing have produced woodlands with little understorey (Bibby 1989). Soil quality may also have an influence, for lowland woods used regularly by Wood Warblers tend to be on poorer substrates, such as sand, where woodland does not luxuriate as it does on fertile soils. In Scotland, also, the best Wood Warbler sites are in oak woods, though birch woods are important locally. The species disappears in Britain where deciduous woodland is replaced by conifers (Goodfellow 1986, Thom 1986), though it is known to breed in pine woods elsewhere (e.g. Wesołowski 1985).

Regional variation

Earlier expansion in Scotland, reaching northern Sutherland by the 1940s, may now have ceased (Pennie 1962, Thom 1986). In 1984-1985, median numbers of males in an occupied 10-km square were: Wales 29, southwest England 22, Lake District 13, English/Welsh border 12, Scotland 9, and rest of England 3 (Bibby 1989). Along the periphery of the species' main range, and especially in central and eastern England, presence at individual sites is often sporadic from year to year.

Trends elsewhere in Europe

Limited census data indicate that fluctuations are the main feature of Wood Warbler trends in western Europe (Hustings 1988). In Denmark, a decrease during 1976-1984 was followed by almost-complete recovery by 1988 (DOFF 1989). Northward expansion this century in Fenno-Scandia appears still to be continuing (Tiainen et al 1983, Hogstad & Moksnes 1986).

Chiffchaff *Phylloscopus collybita*

Present population trend: declined in 1970s; has fluctuated since, but is currently increasing.
Percentages of plots occupied 1968/78/88: farmland 57/50/64; woodland 70/80/83.
Latest estimate of breeding population: 400,000-500,000 pairs in Britain (Hudson & Marchant 1984).
Regional density rankings 1988: farmland W>SE>WE>NI>EE>NE; woodland WE>EE>NI>SE>W>NE>S.

In the temperate latitudes of western Europe there is considerable overlap between the breeding habitats of the Chiffchaff and its close relative, the Willow Warbler. Both favour deciduous woodland with a good shrub layer, and extend into parkland, commons, and also farmland where there are copses as well as tall hedgerows. However, the Chiffchaff is to be found less in young woodland growth and along woodland edges. This is because the presence of mature trees is of greater importance to the Chiffchaff, which is generally absent from scrub and treeless hedgerows. There is a major difference between the two species in their feeding ecology, for the Chiffchaff forages mostly within tree foliage whereas the Willow Warbler feeds more frequently low down in the shrub layer (Lack 1971).

The Chiffchaff is much the less abundant of the two species, with CBC densities indicating a national population level of only one-fifth that of the Willow Warbler (Hudson & Marchant 1984). It is particularly local in Scotland, being absent from much seminatural woodland except where grazing is prevented or rhododendrons provide a lower storey (Parslow 1973, Sharrock 1976). Nevertheless, the Chiffchaff has increased and spread somewhat in Scotland since about 1950 (Thom 1986), this being the only marked change known in its British status in the decades preceding the CBC.

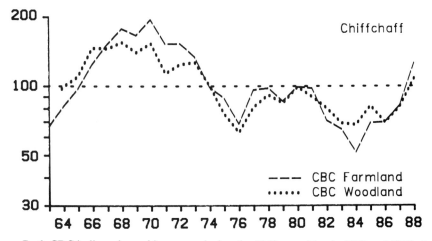

Both CBC indices showed increases during the 1960s, peaking in 1968 and 1970. A sharp decline then set in, with the population reaching its nadir in 1976. There was partial recovery from then into the early 1980s, followed by another pronounced fall.

Since 1984, population levels have been rising again, more steeply on farmland. Over much of the CBC period the woodland and farmland trends have run parallel. However, it is well established from detailed studies that farmland is suboptimal habitat for Chiffchaffs. When densities are low, the territories are centred on woods and copses, though as densities rise an increasing proportion of birds is found further away from preferred sites (P. Osborne, cited by O'Connor & Shrubb 1986a). Hence the farmland index has tended both to rise and to fall more steeply than that for woodland, the woodland population being to some extent buffered against change.

Like the Blackcap, the Chiffchaff winters both north and south of the Sahara, in the Mediterranean basin and in West Africa, but the two species differ in that a higher proportion of Chiffchaffs make the Saharan crossing. Lack (1989) suggests that wintering conditions are the most decisive factors in population change, for the Chiffchaff's southern winter quarters lie within drought-affected regions. The CBC trends are broadly in line with the temporal patterns in Sahel rainfall deficit: a decline through the early to middle 1970s was followed by partial recovery in the late 1970s, then a slump in 1984, but with subsequent improvement. That the drought-related trend in Chiffchaff is not so spectacular as in certain other migratory passerines is due to the fact that a proportion of our birds winters north of the Sahara, and therefore serves as a buffer against the effects of adverse conditions further south.

Regional variation

The regional indices all reflect the national trend described above. Recent population changes show no significant differences with altitude or with region (Lack 1989).

Trends elsewhere in Europe

Constant-effort ringing at two West German sites during 1974-1984 documented low population levels in the mid-1970s, rising to peaks in 1979-1980 before falling away again (Berthold et al 1986). In Denmark, decrease was reported between 1969 and 1976 (Møller 1979) but post-1976 census work has revealed an upward trend (DOFF 1989). Increases were recorded in Czechoslovakia during 1981-1986 and in the Netherlands during 1984-1987 (Hustings 1988). In Finland, the population trend has been clearly downwards during the 1980s (Väisänen et al 1989).

Willow Warbler *Phylloscopus trochilus*

Present population trend: fluctuates, but little long-term change.
Percentages of plots occupied 1968/78/88: farmland 83/84/94; woodland 98/95/96.
Latest estimate of breeding population: 2½ million pairs in Britain (Hudson & Marchant 1984).
Regional density rankings 1988: farmland NI>W>S>WE>NE>EE>SE; woodland WE>W>NE>S>EE>SE>NI.

At the present time the Willow Warbler is certainly our most numerous summer migrant, though it ranks only as ninth in the national league table of abundance. Moreover, it is the only summer visitor in the top fifteen of Britain's most numerous breeding species. As befits its numerical status, the Willow Warbler has a wide distribution, and was found in 92% of all British and Irish 10-km squares during the

Breeding Atlas. Basically it is a bird of young woodland, woodland edge and scrub, with areas of closed canopy being avoided. It has adapted also to young conifer plantations, carr and well-timbered hedgerows. Even in desolate uplands it may be found in the scrub, often birch, of lower slopes and intersecting valleys. Often it is the dominant species of birch woods in the Scottish highlands (Yapp 1962, Bibby *et al* 1989). In Surrey, the densities of Willow Warblers are highest in birch-invaded heathland, where bird species diversity is low and they experience little competition (M.R.Lawn, *in litt.*).

The earlier suggestion that there may have been a decline, in southern England at least, during the 1950s and early 1960s depended on the evidence of two small-scale surveys made in Gloucestershire and Surrey (Parslow 1973). These were too restricted to allow generalisation. A better indication of the trend then can be gained from the national ringing data, by comparing annual ringing totals for nestling Willow Warblers with those for all nestlings of warbler species. Data for 1947-1966, using 5-year means to smooth the effects of chance variation in nest-finding, show the proportion of Willow Warblers to have remained rather constant at 45-48%. Major population change during that period therefore seems unlikely.

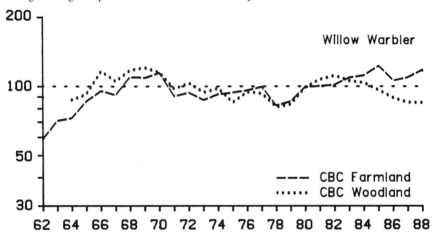

Nevertheless, the opening years of the CBC recorded an apparently large increase from a low initial level in 1962. It is now suspected, however, that this was an artefact of observer inexperience during the early seasons and the change in methods in 1964. Since 1965, Willow Warblers have fluctuated between rather narrow limits: indeed, the population has been remarkably stable. There was a drop in index values in 1971 and these remained on the low side through that decade. They rose again around 1980 and have continued to do so on farmland. In woodland, however, the population level fell away again after the mid-1980s, for reasons which are unclear. Willow Warbler populations have held up well over the last two decades because the species winters well to the south in tropical Africa, thus avoiding the worst of the drought-related problems which have affected several other trans-Saharan migrants (Lack 1989).

An interesting concept has been advanced by Herrera (1978) and by O'Connor (1981) that, in general, resident birds have population levels which are regulated by climate in winter and by territorial behaviour in summer, whereas migrant species are primarily exploiters of breeding season resources that are left unused by the residents. The implication is that migrants are able to increase rapidly to fill the void when residents are at reduced levels. Against the background of this hypothesis, it is interesting to note that Willow Warblers were at somewhat reduced levels in the 1970s, when resident species became more numerous after a succession of mild winters, but they increased after 1979, when the densities of resident birds had fallen following a return to a period of colder winters.

Regional variation

Two studies of farmland densities (O'Connor & Shrubb 1986*a*, Lack 1989) both found the highest values in pasture-dominated areas, followed by mixed farming, with arable farming as the least preferred. Thus there is an east-to-west gradient of increasing density, and to some extent a south-to-north one. This trend is related to the higher densities of trees and spinneys away from cereal-dominated regions. In the woodland CBC also, densities are generally higher to the north and west, as shown by the 1988 regional density rankings. The very recent fall in woodland index values for Willow Warbler is more pronounced in Scotland and eastern England than elsewhere; this is not purely a geographical effect since there has been no comparable decline in the farmland index for these two regions.

Trends elsewhere in Europe

The limited evidence indicates the existence of fluctuations, sometimes pronounced, but no overall trends. Long-term census data from Sweden indicate that, as in Britain, there was decline in the 1970s followed by increase in the 1980s (Hustings 1988).

Goldcrest *Regulus regulus*

Present population trend: recent cold winters have reduced the high levels of the 1970s; strong recovery from a population crash in 1986.
Percentages of plots occupied 1968/78/88: farmland 32/51/46; woodland 68/72/77.
Latest estimate of breeding population: 500,000-600,000 pairs in Britain in 1982 (Hudson & Marchant 1984).
Regional density rankings 1988: farmland NI>EE>SE>NE>W>S; woodland EE>NE>W>SE>S>NI.

Over the last quarter of a century the British Goldcrest population has been influenced by two opposing factors. First, as an arboreal species favouring conifers it has benefited from afforestation, which has expanded the habitat in which it can achieve its highest densities. But second, as a tiny resident insectivore it is susceptible to the effects of cold winters, which have been more frequent over the last decade. This is a species in which, in Britain, winter temperatures limit population levels through influencing the level of overwinter mortality. Hence the lengths of interludes between severe winters determine the extent to which Goldcrests can make use of the expanded habitat area available to them. It should be noted, however, that CBC indices rarely include data from plantations in their initial phases, during which Goldcrests and other species may colonise, and therefore are influenced relatively little by the creation of new habitat.

Consecutive cold winters in 1961/62 and 1962/63 ensured that Goldcrest populations were still at low levels when the woodland CBC began. Thereafter the trend was one of continuous increase up to the mid-1970s, by which time population

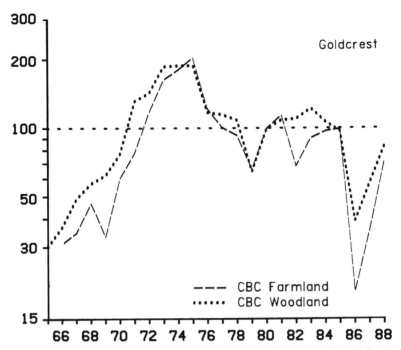

Goldcrest

--- CBC Farmland
...... CBC Woodland

levels were very high and overflow was apparent into deciduous woodlands, farmland, and even into gardens with ornamental conifers. At that time the Goldcrest was the most numerous species in commercial forestry plantations, with local densities of up to 320 pairs per sq. km (Sharrock 1976). CBC index values fell sharply in both woodland and farmland in 1976, following adverse conditions in the previous winter, and this was followed by another decline caused by the severe winter of 1978/79.

Since 1980 most winters have produced one or more periods of cold weather. Yet these recent winters have affected Goldcrests in different ways. After the 1979 fall, index values rose again over successive years, despite more winter cold spells, though not reaching the heights of ten years earlier. In 1985/86, severe winter weather caused a serious crash, one of the most striking population changes recorded by the CBC, during a protracted cold spell in which many areas experienced their coldest February since 1947. Though, in the following winter, January 1987 produced some record low temperatures and snow falls in southeastern England, these were localised in effect and the national Goldcrest indices actually rose that summer.

Recent experience has confirmed that the effects of cold weather vary considerably according to the duration and geographical pattern of low temperatures and precipitation. Cold periods interrupted by brief thaws are less likely to prove damaging than those of continuous freeze, and temperatures probably matter less than snow and ice conditions. Also of importance is whether or not an ice coating (rime) or hoarfrost persists on trees, this being particularly serious for arboreal feeders such as Goldcrests. In the absence of such glazed-ice conditions in the severe winter of 1981/82, Goldcrests seemed hardly affected in woodland (judging from the CBC index), though there was a decline on farmland. Possibly some farmland birds moved preferentially into woodland that spring to fill territorial vacancies there.

187

While the national trends described above can be detected in all regions, index values have shown least temporal change in northern England and Scotland. The steepest recent falls seem to have been those in western England and Wales, where the species is known to have suffered worst in the 1985/86 winter.

Trends elsewhere in Europe
No long-term trends are known, though numbers fluctuate with winter conditions. Northern European Goldcrests are partially migratory. At 60°N about half of the birds depart, while north of 65° nearly all do so (Blaedel 1963, Haftorn 1971). Nevertheless, the wintering areas for these migrants are in latitudes affected by periodic cold winters. Birds which attempt to winter in Scandinavia experience high mortality, a mean overwinter reduction of 86% in one study, and mortality is significantly correlated with snowfall and ambient temperature (Hogstad 1984). Almost all the Goldcrests wintering in Finland in 1986/87 fell victim to an exceptionally cold January (Hildén 1989). Swedish and Danish census data, since 1970 and 1976 respectively, agree with the British results in that new low points were reached in 1986 (Hustings 1988, DOFF 1989).

Spotted Flycatcher *Muscicapa striata*

Present population trend: fluctuates, but the long-term trend is downwards.
Percentages of plots occupied 1968/78/88: farmland 56/66/63; woodland 52/53/52.
Latest estimate of breeding population: possibly 200,000 pairs in Britain (see below).
Regional density rankings 1988: farmland S>NI>W> SE>EE>WE>NE; woodland W>S>EE>NE>SE.

Up to the 1960s there was no evidence for any marked change in the British status of the Spotted Flycatcher, beyond some additional colonisation of Scottish islands. Elsewhere, a few local decreases were reported but it was impossible to assess how real or extensive they were against the background of local fluctuations (Parslow 1973).

From 1964 onwards, some marked short-term variations in both farmland and woodland CBC indices have not obscured a general downward drift through to the present. A third type of habitat for Spotted Flycatcher is rural and suburban garden, but this the CBC does not monitor. Mature gardens with trees are attractive to this species, and may be as important as woodland.

It seems possible that the gradual decline of this species has a climatic basis (see below), but this is difficult to test in a species in which annual changes have been small and which is abroad for two-thirds of the year. Climatic factors might operate in Britain, influencing breeding success, or abroad, affecting overwinter survival, or in combination. This might not be the whole answer, however, for regional CBC data indicate that the decline has been more a feature of the southern half of Britain. Possibly habitat degradation or more plausibly a widespread use of insecticides have also had their impacts, at least in the south.

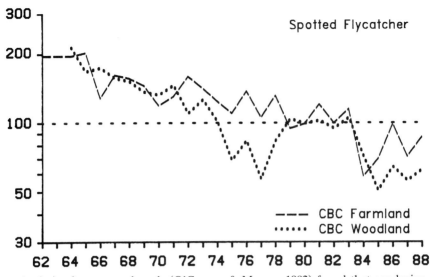

Analysis of nest record cards (O'Connor & Morgan 1982) found that egg-laying began earlier when May was a warm month, and that clutches were larger when that month was sunny. Thereafter the size of new clutches decreased over the season. Overall nesting success was significantly higher in years when June was warm and sunny. Since Spotted Flycatchers feed almost entirely on flying insects, the activity of which increases in warm weather, it follows that when May weather is fine the female birds are more likely to have an energy surplus for egg formation and when June weather is fine there is a more reliable food supply for flycatcher nestlings. An early start to the breeding season also provides more opportunity for second broods.

Spotted Flycatchers winter entirely in Africa, well to the south of the drought-affected Sahel region and with some reaching South Africa, which has experienced its own drought problems in the 1980s. Nevertheless, they have to cross the Sahara twice a year, and the degraded condition of the Sahel may make this more difficult now. The big drought-linked crash of the Whitethroat and other Sahel species was noted in 1969, but there was only a small fall of Spotted Flycatchers in that year. The largest annual drop has been that between 1983 and 1984, which coincided with a failure of the Sahel rains that season. Deforestation in tropical Africa is unlikely to have affected a species which prefers secondary woodland, savannas and clearings.

In summary, it seems likely that Spotted Flycatchers are experiencing problems in Africa, and finding it difficult to make up the losses in the face of the typically cooler and wetter early summers which Britain has experienced of late. However, a possibility that environmental conditions for this species have deteriorated in southern Britain, especially on farmland, has not been investigated yet.

Sharrock (1976) estimated the British and Irish population at 100,000-200,000 pairs, while Hudson & Marchant (1984), using 1982 CBC mean densities, arrived at a figure of 300,000 pairs in Britain alone. The real British total probably lies somewhere between these figures.

Regional variation

CBC samples are small when subdivided regionally. There is scant indication of temporal change in Wales, where samples are particularly small, while in northern

189

England and Scotland population levels are generally either static or higher now than they were in the early 1970s. The biggest falls are those on farmland in western, eastern and southern England. Densities in 1988 were lower in England than elsewhere in the United Kingdom.

Trends elsewhere in Europe

Long-term census indices are available for Sweden and Denmark. In Sweden, Spotted Flycatchers have fluctuated but in 1984-1986 were above the 1970 level (Hustings 1988). In Denmark the position is similar to that in Britain: fluctuations overlie a generally downward trend (DOFF 1989).

Pied Flycatcher *Ficedula hypoleuca*

Present population trend: probably stable, except where nestbox schemes promote local increase.
Percentages of plots occupied 1968/78/88: all CBC habitats 5/5/7.
Latest estimate of breeding population: 20,000 pairs in Britain (Sharrock 1976); probably too low a figure, and the reality may be double that (Hudson & Marchant 1984).

The Pied Flycatcher is not indexed by the CBC since its main breeding centres lie beyond the regions covered well by CBC fieldwork. CBC ubiquity values (see graph) show an increase since 1982 in the proportion of plots on which the species is recorded; but the underlying causes for this are unclear.

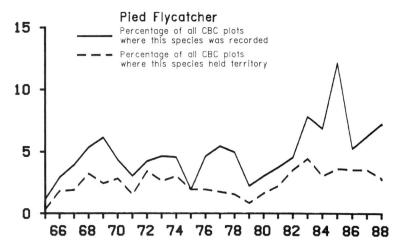

Changes in the species' British status were assessed by two BTO-aided surveys in 1952 and 1962, which also included historical summaries (Campbell 1954-55, 1965). There is little doubt that range expansion occurred during the 1880s and 1890s, when

Pied Flycatchers began breeding regularly in southern Scotland, and in Wales expanded both southwards and eastwards and reached Shropshire. Notable spring influxes in 1885, 1898 and 1899 may have aided the establishment of new breeding areas. Increase and spread accelerated in the period 1940-1952, when first breeding records were obtained from seven counties, together with reappearances (after long intervals) in ten others. In particular, this involved a narrowing of the separation between the Welsh and Pennine populations. In the West Midlands, a peak was reached in 1951-1952 and they then declined a little (before nestboxes were provided), while the Forest of Dean (Gloucestershire) nestbox population, studied annually since 1942, peaked in 1950-1953. The 1962 BTO survey concluded that the phase of increase and expansion had slowed considerably and even been reversed locally.

Since the 1960s it has become impossible to separate any natural increase from that generated by large-scale provision of nestboxes. Under natural conditions, Pied Flycatchers have to compete with tits, Redstarts and Nuthatches for the available tree holes. However, the flycatcher seems to prefer nestboxes when these are available. Hence their provision can stimulate considerable local increase, as in Devon where numbers rose from one pair in 1955 to 150-200 pairs by 1985 (Sitters 1988). Yet success with nestbox schemes is only achieved in woods with an open structure and sparse shrub layer, such as Pied Flycatchers require. Such conditions are mainly the result of grazing. The natural habitat in Britain is open deciduous woodland, especially of sessile oaks, in uplands and steep valleys. Pied Flycatchers remain absent from lowland woods in the southeastern quadrant of England; occasional instances of breeding there, at irregular intervals, have never led to colonisation.

Two independent studies – Edington & Edington (1972) in this country and van Balen *et al* (1982) in the Netherlands – found no evidence that Pied Flycatcher increases after nestbox provision were related to previous shortages of natural tree holes. This finding accords with later researches (T.J. Stowe, pers. comm.). The key to the Pied Flycatcher's success seems to be its preference for nestboxes. Since the onset of breeding in resident species, such as the tits, is usually delayed in British uplands by poor spring weather conditions, Pied Flycatchers return in time to compete successfully for the boxes and to outnumber tits within them. In this way, high densities are achieved.

Pied Flycatchers, especially females, exhibit a marked degree of infidelity to their natal area, a trait which aids the exploitation of new opportunities which arise. The proportion of first-time breeders not returning to their birthplace appears to be highest after a successful breeding season the previous year (Stenning *et al* 1988). Even adult females are quite often found in subsequent years far from the area in which they had settled and bred in a previous season. On the other hand, adult males are highly faithful to a site once they have bred there.

Grimmett (1987) has speculated that deforestation in the African winter quarters might affect this species adversely, though conversion of forest to savanna may actually benefit other European migrants.

Regional variation
The picture has been modified by nestbox schemes, so that natural trends are unclear. In many Welsh oak woods this is the dominant species in the bird community. However, the Pied Flycatcher is still a sporadic breeder over much of Scotland, and may have declined in the southeast; its main areas are now in Dumfries & Galloway, the oak woods of the Trossach Hills in Central Region, and Loch Lomondside in Central and Strathclyde (Thom 1986).

Trends elsewhere in Europe

Long-term trends are unclear for, as in Britain, densities have often been manipulated through the provision of nestboxes. There seem to have been declines in the 1980s in Denmark and Netherlands, though not in Sweden (Hustings 1988). In Finnish point count data, a large fall in the early 1980s has since been made good (Väisänen *et al* 1989). In Switzerland there was a stable population from the mid-1940s to 1968, but a subsequent decline which was attributed to urbanisation, loss of orchards and increased use of pesticides (Bruderer & Hirschi 1984). In Ireland, the species bred for the first time in 1985, in nestboxes in both Antrim and Wicklow (Hutchinson 1989).

Long-tailed Tit *Aegithalos caudatus*

Present population trend: marked fluctuations associated with winter weather conditions, but no long-term trend is apparent.

Percentages of plots occupied 1968/78/88: farmland 45/58/ 62; woodland 63/90/91.

Latest estimate of breeding population: around 200,000 territories in Britain (Hudson & Marchant 1984).

Regional density rankings 1988: farmland W>EE> SE>WE>NI>NE; woodland NE>EE>W>SE> WE>S.

As might be expected in such a tiny resident bird, the size of the breeding population in the Long-tailed Tit is heavily dependent on weather conditions in the preceding winter. Population levels rise above the long-term average after a series of mild winters, but severe winters cause heavy mortality from which it may take several years for the population to recover. Unlike the *Parus* tits, the present species does not use garden feeding sites much, so has no last resort to fall back to if natural foods are scarce or inaccessible. No other significant influences on British Long-tailed Tits are known, nor have there been more than minor peripheral changes in their recorded distribution this century.

Different cold winters affect this species in conspicuously different ways, however. Long-tailed Tits suffer most when hoarfrost or glazed ice (rime) persists longer than a day or two on trees and bushes, covering their feeding sites. In a prolonged period of glazed-ice conditions in winter 1916/17, perhaps 80-90% of birds died (Jourdain & Witherby 1918). Mortality was also heavy in the similar conditions of 1939/40. Yet the effects of the abnormally cold 1946/47 winter were less severe on this species, in the absence of freezing fog (which produces rime), and sharp population falls were localised (Ticehurst & Hartley 1948). The winters of 1961/62 and 1962/63 caused heavy losses and some local extinctions, these worst in the south and becoming progressively less severe further north (Dobinson & Richards 1964). The CBC has documented the period of slow recovery from the low point reached then.

Long-tailed Tit populations were high by the early 1970s, following a run of mild winters, but there was a moderate fall after cold weather in January 1976. This was followed by a more severe decline (of 49% on farmland, 32% in woodland) in the harsh winter of 1978/79, when hoarfrost persisted and most other species with body weights of less than 10 grams were affected (Cawthorne & Marchant 1980). Since that time, cold winters have become more frequent, and Long-tailed Tit population indices

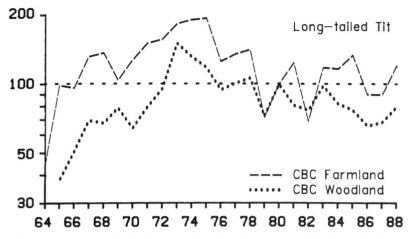

200

100

50

30

64 66 68 70 72 74 76 78 80 82 84 86 88

Long-tailed Tit

--- CBC Farmland
······ CBC Woodland

now fluctuate at around the 1969-1970 level. However, that for farmland shows sharper peaks and troughs. This may be due to woodland and woodland edge being more sheltered than farmland, or to woodland being the preferred habitat in which cold winter survivors then establish their territories while densities are low. Related to habitat preference, the CBC graph also shows that peak years on farmland are often one or two years later than in woodland, though troughs usually coincide.

Territorial groups each comprise an adult pair plus other adult helpers which are likely to be siblings of the male parent. For this reason, population estimates have to be of territories rather than pairs. These groups, with the young they rear, remain together as discrete flocks over the following winter, and each such family unit maintains a winter territory that is subdivided into "pair territories" the following spring (Glen & Perrins 1988). Ringing data show that, even when long-distance dispersal occurs in autumn or winter, the whole family party tends to stay together. The resulting close genetic relationship between members of individual flocks was discussed by Gosler (1988). The only birds to change flocks are unmated females in early spring, and these carry the gene flow between families (Glen & Perrins 1988). Since the Long-tailed Tit does not have a song audible over a distance, does not exhibit conflict at boundaries of breeding territories, and is generally inconspicuous while breeding, it is suspected that densities in woodland are poorly estimated by CBC territory mapping (Dougall & North 1983). But year-on-year comparability and hence a CBC index is not known to be affected by this. Prior knowledge of local winter "group territories" is helpful to summer censusing.

Regional variation

When cold winters exhibit geographical variation in the intensity of frost and glazing, these result in regional variations in the degree of population change. This applied in 1947 and 1963 (see above), and in 1978/79 there was a south-to-north gradient of increasing mortality across Britain which showed also some relation to altitude (Cawthorne & Marchant 1980).

Trends elsewhere in Europe

No underlying trends are known. Some Continental populations are partially migratory. Lowered census index values since 1982 in Denmark and the Netherlands (Hustings 1988) are probably related to recent cold winters there.

Marsh Tit *Parus palustris*

Present population trend: shallow long-term decline.
Percentages of plots occupied 1968/78/88: farmland 26/24/19; woodland 57/59/57.
Latest estimate of breeding population: 140,000-150,000 pairs in Britain (Hudson & Marchant 1984).
Regional density rankings 1988: woodland SE>WE>EE>W.

Reliable historical information on the distribution and status of the Marsh Tit in Britain dates only from the beginning of this century, for only then was it discovered that the Willow Tit was also a British resident. Earlier information is a composite for these two species. There is no evidence for the Marsh Tit having changed its range or abundance significantly during the first six decades of the present century, beyond a marginal extension into southeastern Scotland. It was identified in Berwickshire in the 1920s, though not proved breeding there until 1945. Also in the Borders, there was a spread into Roxburghshire in the 1960s, and birds are now present in Selkirkshire also although no nest has yet been found there (Thom 1986).

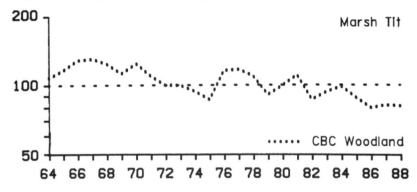

Annual index values have been available from the woodland CBC since 1964, and these have shown that an otherwise unsuspected long-term decline in population is occurring. In this respect the species differs from all other British tits which are monitored by the CBC. The fall seems to have begun in the late 1960s, and to have been steepest in the early to middle 1970s, when most other resident birds were increasing in line with the run of mild winters which characterised that period. A slower rate of decline has been maintained since. Fluctuations occur, but these have become smaller of late.

The underlying reasons remain unknown. The sharpest annual troughs usually followed cold winters, for example in 1979, 1982 and 1986, though this was not the case in 1975. Such cold-weather falls were not so pronounced as in some other resident passerines, however, and on each occasion there was evidence of some partial recovery in the following year. Nor is there yet any convincing evidence that British Marsh Tits have been affected adversely by habitat deterioration, declining food supply or competition from related species. But in the latter context, it should be noted that Coal Tit, Blue Tit and Great Tit have all increased, and Continental studies have shown that interspecific competition influences the foraging niches of the different tit species there (*e.g.* Alatalo *et al* 1985, Dhondt 1989). Finding a suitable nest-hole may be more difficult in managed woodlands, for the Marsh Tit does not excavate its own (though it will enlarge one). Compared to other tits it takes less readily to nestboxes (Perrins 1979), although these are used, and in one Gloucestershire larch plantation 45 nestbox clutches (1978-1982) averaged eight eggs (Sells 1984), which is also the average for natural nest sites. The CBC trend suggests that Marsh Tit biology merits further study in Britain. However, in the site where the species has been studied most closely in the past, Wytham Woods in Oxfordshire (Southern & Morley 1950), it has if anything increased recently (A.G. Gosler, pers. comm.).

Regional variation
    The steepest decline in the early 1970s seems to have been that in eastern England, where densities have remained reduced ever since.

Trends elsewhere in Europe
    Danish point counts between 1977 and 1988 have shown an irregular decline (DOFF 1989). Information from Sweden is conflicting: the point-count index halved between 1975 and 1986, while the index from mapping censuses since 1970 shows that numbers were highest during 1981-1984 (Hustings 1988). A strong increase was recorded in Czechoslovakia during 1981-1986 (Hustings 1988).

Willow Tit *Parus montanus*

Present population trend: some regional changes; otherwise no clear trend.
Percentages of plots occupied 1968/78/88: farmland 22/21/25; woodland 34/42/32.
Latest estimate of breeding population: 50,000-100,000 pairs in Britain (Sharrock 1976).
Regional density rankings 1988: all CBC habitats WE> EE>W>SE.

Although the species was already well known on the Continent, it was not until 1897 that the Willow Tit was found to be a British bird also. In that year two skins from Middlesex (now Greater London) were discovered in the British Museum collection, mislabelled as Marsh Tits, and two from another Middlesex locality were received by Tring Museum (Hartert 1898). The broad outline of its British range was only gradually disentangled from that of the Marsh Tit (Witherby & Nicholson 1937). Since then local surveys in more detail by better-skilled observers have filled out our knowledge of the Willow Tit's status.
    Whereas Marsh Tits prefer dry deciduous woodland, especially of oak and beech, Willow Tits frequent damp woodland habitats (including carr) as well as lowland conifer plantations, and will accept smaller wooded areas such as farmland spinneys and scrub. Willow Tit is generally the more widespread of the two species on farmland. While this difference in habitat selection often results in their spatial separation on a local basis, at the level of the 10-km square there is much overlap: both were found in 64% of the squares which contained one or both species during the Breeding and Wintering Atlases (A.G. Gosler, in Lack 1986).
    Although these species have distributions which overlap substantially, and are both well represented in central and southern England where the CBC has its strongest fieldwork support, Willow Tits usually occur at lower densities than Marsh Tits. An

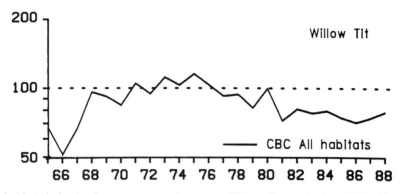

all-habitats index has been constructed to assess Willow Tit trends since 1965. Almost certainly, some of the year-to-year fluctuations are artefacts of small to moderate sample sizes. One can, however, discern the broad trends. Willow Tits increased between the mid-1960s and mid-1970s, as did many other resident passerines during that lengthy period in which mild winters were the norm. The Willow Tit peaked in 1975, in which year its index value was almost double its 1965-1967 mean; but a subsequent shallow decline has taken the index value back to the mid-1960s level. This is a different picture from that presented by the Marsh Tit. The latter has been declining steadily since the 1960s and is now at an all-time low in the CBC, whereas the Willow Tit has lost earlier gains and returned to its original level.

Regional variation

Sustained Willow Tit increase is reported from Hertfordshire since the mid-1970s (Gladwin & Sage 1986); and in the adjacent county of Essex the Willow Tit has waxed since the 1970s as the Marsh Tit has waned (Cox 1984), though there is no evidence that this was more than coincidental. Apart from these local increases in southeast England, the only marked change has been in Scotland. Though Willow Tits were thinly distributed in the Highlands, north to Ross-shire, until the 1940s (Baxter & Rintoul 1953), there have been no reports from that region since. None are now known north of the Rivers Clyde and Forth. Even in southern Scotland, Willow Tit numbers are probably smaller than in the past: only in Dumfries & Galloway can the species be said to be flourishing (Thom 1986).

Trends elsewhere in Europe

No major trends are known, other than weather-related fluctuations of Continental races in northern Europe.

Coal Tit *Parus ater*

Present population trend: now relatively stable at new, higher densities, after earlier increase.
Percentages of plots occupied 1968/78/88: farmland 27/43/42; woodland 70/87/93.
Latest estimate of breeding population: 500,000-700,000 pairs in Britain (see below).
Regional density rankings 1988: farmland NI>W>WE>S>EE>SE>NE; woodland NE>EE>W>NI>S>SE>WE.

Britain has two abundant passerines which are prime exploiters of coniferous woodland: the Goldcrest and the Coal Tit. Both reach their highest densities in that habitat, and have been able to increase and spread in the wake of expanded afforestation programmes. The Coal Tit in particular is known to have been extending its range in Scotland since the mid-19th century, and more rapidly since the Second World War, as new habitat was created in upland country that had previously been unsuitable. Both species occur also in deciduous woodland, albeit usually at much lower densities, though the Coal Tit can outnumber its congeners in Scottish birch woods and in western sessile oak woods (Yapp 1962). Amenity plantings of conifers in parks, churchyards and ornamental gardens are also utilised, especially when population levels are high.

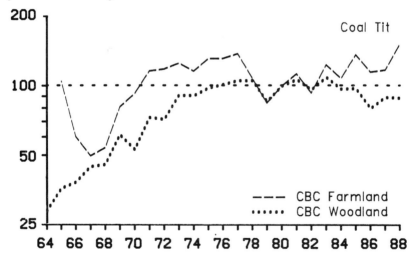

The CBC indices show a conspicuous rise in Coal Tit numbers from the late 1960s up to the mid-1970s, as in many other resident passerines during this period of mild winters. A fall recorded for farmland in 1965-1967 is based on small samples and is perhaps unreliable. It remains unclear whether the initially low level in woodland was due to the 1962/63 severe winter, although this species suffers less in cold weather than many others, or an indication that the subsequent phase of increase actually began earlier than hitherto supposed. The increase ceased in the late 1970s; densities now fluctuate around a new, higher level, though there is a suggestion of a slight fall over

197

the final three years of the woodland index (see below). It must be stressed that this overall increase refers to densities within CBC sample plots, and the species' spread into new areas of coniferous afforestation is very largely additional.

Coal Tits survive cold spells quite well, especially in conifer forest where their agility allows them to feed on the undersides of snow-laden branches. A review of the effects of the 1962/63 winter found that there were locally severe losses of Coal Tits in the western Midlands and in Wales, but little change over most of England and Scotland (Dobinson & Richards 1964). In line with this, recent hard winters (1978/79, 1981/82, 1983/84 and 1985/86) caused only fairly small decreases to the CBC indices, though some cumulative effects have been apparent in recent years in the woodland index at least. Percentage changes have been larger in the farmland index, but that is not a key habitat for the species.

When numbers are high in autumn, at peak population levels or after a productive breeding season, the birds make such inroads into food stocks that overwinter survival is reduced in a density-dependent manner (Perrins 1979). Hence the higher densities maintained since the early 1970s, revealed by CBC results, could hardly have been sustained without access to additional seed and invertebrate food supplies. One way in which this could be achieved is shown in areas where Coal Tits winter in conifer plantations that are too young to provide nest sites, and breed in deciduous woodland nearby (Perrins 1979). This supports the view that, in conifers, the Coal Tit has competitive advantage over the other common tits. The Coal Tit is a sedentary species, with 83% of ringing recoveries showing movements of less than 5 km. There is annual variation in the amount of longer movement, generally occurring in October-November, which shows less relation to population size (as measured by the CBC) than to food shortage (Sellers 1984). The availability of beech mast in autumn and winter seems to be important, for in poor mast years there is more Coal Tit movement, and numbers visiting gardens, especially suburban ones, increase to a larger extent than they do in relation to winter temperatures alone (Glue 1982, Thompson 1988).

Sharrock (1976) offered an estimate of 1 million pairs in Britain and Ireland. Based on numbers of occupied 10-km squares, the British share of this total would have been 700,000-750,000 pairs. Hudson & Marchant (1984) suggested 450,000-500,000 pairs in Britain, based on 1982 CBC densities, but suspected that these probably did not allow for the more extensive areas of coniferous woodland in northern regions. The reality may lie somewhere between these figures.

Regional variation

CBC regional indices show that cold winters in the 1980s had least impact on Coal Tits in western England and Wales. That of 1983/84 affected Scotland more than anywhere else, while that of 1985/86 affected southern England the most. These examples underline the variations which occur when there are geographical trends in the severity of individual winters.

Trends elsewhere in Europe

No major trends are known. Marked fluctuations occur in northern countries, doubtless related to conditions for overwinter survival. Unlike those in Britain, Continental Coal Tits are eruptive in autumns when food supply is poor, such eruptions being most pronounced in central Europe.

Blue Tit *Parus caeruleus*

Present population trend: fluctuating around higher levels reached in the 1970s; perhaps now increasing again.
Percentages of plots occupied 1968/78/88: farmland 93/96/98; woodland 84/99/99.
Latest estimate of breeding population: 3½ million pairs in Britain (Hudson & Marchant 1984).
Regional density rankings 1988: farmland W>WE>SE>EE>NI>NE>S; woodland W>EE>NE>SE>WE>S>NI.

In contrast to the previous species, the Blue Tit is principally a bird of broad-leaved woodland, especially oak, and is correspondingly scarce in conifer plantations. Overall, it is the commonest British tit and the one most frequently found in such peripheral habitats as farmland, parks, orchards and gardens. Under natural conditions, densities can be limited by nest-hole availability. Blue Tits take readily to nestboxes, though they differ from the Great Tit in that some continue to use natural holes even when there is a surplus of boxes available (Perrins 1979).

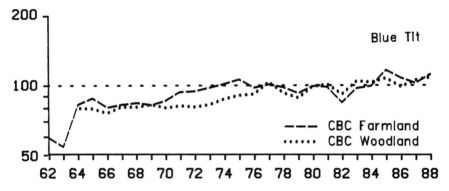

An annual index based on levels of nestling ringing during 1950-1980 (Mason & Hussey 1984) showed both Blue and Great Tits increasing almost throughout that period, initially as recovery from substantial mortality in the harsh winter of 1946/47. Hence the low initial level suggested for Blue Tit by the infant CBC was probably exaggerated by early problems with the census methodology, especially since other sources of evidence (Dobinson & Richards 1964, Perrins 1979) indicated only slight declines in the 1962/63 winter. CBC levels were more or less stable during 1964-1970, after which they rose until the mid-1970s when the increase was checked, at least on farmland, by the rather cold 1975/76 winter. Since then the populations have fluctuated around the new higher level, with only small and very temporary setbacks in the further cold winters of 1978/79, 1981/82 and 1985/86. It is noticeable that the increases during the 1970s and again during the 1980s were most marked on farmland, this being presumably the result of overflow from the preferred woodland habitat.

The nestling ringing index referred to above may have exaggerated the scale of increase, due to the growing use of nestboxes over the index period making nests more accessible to ringers. However, Mason & Hussey (1984) argued that greater provision of nestboxes was itself part of an enormous rise in interest in birds among members of the public who, by also providing food in winter, had aided the Blue Tit to increase. An intensive study near Oxford had shown that the enhanced winter survival of the increased local Blue Tit population could be attributed to the provision of food at a nearby housing estate (Lack 1966). Blue Tits are more mobile than Great Tits, and in winter regularly leave woodland by day to feed in gardens (Perrins 1979). On farmland, Blue Tits tend to concentrate in winter around farmsteads and stockyards, the importance of the latter being reflected in the higher breeding densities of Blue Tits in cattle-rearing areas compared to those dominated by other types of farming (O'Connor & Shrubb 1986a).

It would be wrong to imply that Blue Tits depend on artificial foods in winter. Rather, these act as a safety net, especially in late winter when natural food sources are depleted and conditions become difficult for the birds. In years when beech mast and other natural foods are plentiful, Blue Tits are less dependent on garden feeding. As Perrins (1979) showed from Great Tit survival data, beech mast is probably a reliable indicator rather than a determinant of good natural winter feeding conditions. In Garden Bird Feeding Survey data, Blue Tit fluctuations are not related to winter weather, which suggests that the birds are already making full use of the food potential of gardens (Thompson 1988). This is in line with the wider view that, in Britain at least, winter survival is related to food availability rather than to temperature alone. Thus in the two severest winters this century, Blue Tits were badly affected in that of 1946/47 when there was no beech mast crop, but only to a small extent in 1962/63 when beech mast was plentiful and the agile tree-feeding Blue Tits were not disadvantaged, as were Great Tits, by snow cover on the ground.

Regional variation

None is apparent in population trends. In 1988, mean densities were highest in Wales in both habitat divisions, and comparatively low in Scotland.

Trends elsewhere in Europe

There was northward expansion in Fenno-Scandia during the first half of this century, which also had a counterpart in northern Scotland. Otherwise populations fluctuate but without any clear overall trend. Fluctuations in Denmark are related to winter food supply (such as beech mast) rather than to winter temperatures (Bejer & Rudemo 1985), much as in Britain. However, cold weather effects may be of more importance further north, where winter conditions are regularly more rigorous. Although the species is largely sedentary in Britain, Continental populations are eruptive in autumns when numbers are high but seed crops poor.

Great Tit *Parus major*

Present population trend: gradual increase, especially since late 1970s; perhaps beginning to stabilise.
Percentages of plots occupied 1968/78/88: farmland 87/96/99; woodland 86/96/99.
Latest estimate of breeding population: 2 million pairs in Britain (Hudson & Marchant 1984).
Regional density rankings 1988: farmland W>SE>EE>WE>NI>NE>S; woodland W>EE>NE>S>SE>NI>WE.

Apart from a marked spread in northern Scotland this century, attributed to a warmer climatic period and to afforestation (Pennie 1962, Parslow 1973), the Great Tit is not known to have changed in status in modern times. Its principal habitats are deciduous woodlands. Densities are lower in conifer woods, on farmland, where trees and well-timbered hedgerows are essential, and in orchards, parks and large gardens. Great Tits take readily to nestboxes, which can be used to increase densities – though each site has a limit to its capacity which the birds do not exceed even when additional boxes are available (Perrins 1979).

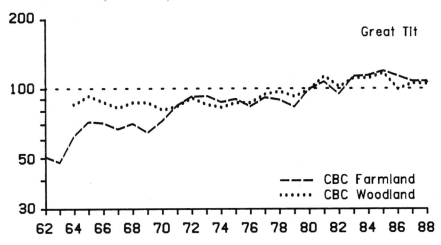

CBC monitoring since 1962 has revealed a straightforward recent history. Though index values were low initially, due to the cold winters of the early 1960s, recovery was achieved quickly. After a plateau period up to 1970, the Great Tit began a modest increase on farmland. Woodland values also rose from the late 1970s, since when the farmland trend has become more marked. Nevertheless, there were small, temporary decreases following the cold winters of 1975/76 (farmland only), 1978/79 and 1981/82 (both habitats), though other resident birds were affected to much greater extents. Studies have shown that winter temperatures play a greater role in Great Tit survival in years when beech mast is scarce (van Balen 1980), as it was in those three seasons. Beech mast was scarce also during the 1946/47 severe weather, from which recovery took several years (Mason & Hussey 1984).

The Great Tit is one of the most intensively studied of European passerines (*e.g.* Krebs 1971, Perrins 1979, O'Connor 1980*b*, Klomp 1981, Bejer & Rudemo 1985). As a result it is now clear that its populations are regulated by a combination of territorial behaviour and food availability. The latter factor is influenced both by the irregularity of tree fruiting, and by winter weather: cold increases energy demands, and lying snow conceals fallen seed. The availability of food operates as a control largely in autumn and winter, and chiefly on first-winter birds, and determines how many individuals will survive to the following spring. When spring population density is low, most pairs defend a large territory. But when densities rise, territories become smaller, though they are defended with greater vigour. In this way an upper limit to population size is established within preferred habitats. Unsuccessful birds either do not breed, or are forced away into suboptimal habitats such as conifer woods and farmland, where their productivity is often lower. The CBC farmland increase in the 1970s may have been such an overflow; woodland indices do not plateau during years of high population levels, but annual changes are proportionately higher on farmland. Moreover, BTO nest record card data show that clutch size and chick-rearing success are linked to population density, with breeding success being lower in years when population levels are high (O'Connor 1980*b*).

Although overwinter survival is improved following a good beech mast autumn, or is lowered after a poor one, the relationship is not so straightforward, for two reasons. First, the Great Tit survival trends in beech woods are often paralleled in regions where beech trees are absent; and, second, most juvenile mortality occurs in the late summer, before beech mast falls, so that improved survival must begin before that food source becomes available for eating. It is likely that the volume of beech mast is but an indicator, and one of several factors fluctuating in parallel (Perrins 1966, 1979). Thus a year which is favourable for the setting of beech seed may be favourable for other food sources as well. In years when natural foods are abundant, Great Tits depend much less on supplementary feeding. This leads to big annual fluctuations in the numbers visiting gardens in winter (Glue 1982, Thompson 1988). The CBC data do not show even any subtle variations of density around beech mast years, probably because in poor years the provision of artificial food in gardens goes some way towards making up the difference.

Regional variation

No regional variations are apparent in changes across time. In terms of densities there tends to be a north-to-south gradient of increasing values on farmland (O'Connor & Shrubb 1986*a*). However, this seems not to apply to woodland (see regional density rankings).

Trends elsewhere in Europe

There was northward expansion in Scandinavia during the first half of this century, in line with comparable spread in Scotland. Population changes now are in the form of periodic fluctuations linked to variations in food supplies. In contrast to those in Britain, north European birds are partially migratory, and undertake distinct eruptive movements in some years when food resources are poor.

Nuthatch *Sitta europaea*

Present population trend: long-term gradual increase.
Percentages of plots occupied 1968/78/88: farmland 9/21/26; woodland 42/53/64.
Latest estimate of breeding population: about 50,000 pairs in England and Wales (see below).
Regional density rankings 1988: woodland W>SE> WE>EE>NE.

British Nuthatches seem to have been increasing and spreading slowly since the 1930s, and especially since about 1940. Although there were no quantified data from southern or central England prior to the CBC, ornithologists in the 1940s and 1950s were able to record an obvious expansion throughout Wales, as well as a gradual northward spread that reached the Lake District and Northumberland in the 1950s (Parslow 1973) and which is still continuing (Hutcheson 1986). Since the 1960s there have been more frequent records from Scotland, and the first proven instance of breeding there came from the Borders in 1989 (*Brit. Birds* 82:462). There is a north-to-south gradient of increasing abundance within Britain, and also an east-to-west one (see regional density rankings, above). Nuthatches are scarce in eastern England, where only fragments of the original deciduous woodland remain.

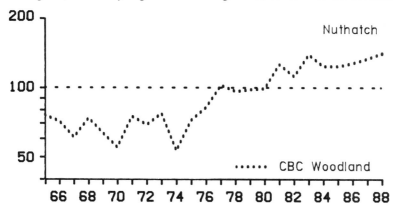

The first ten years of the CBC documented a series of fluctuations, without any obvious overall trend. Then a recovery from a trough in 1974 became the starting point for a period of considerable increase. This was most pronounced between 1976 and 1983, and still continues at a reduced pace. This same pattern is also apparent in the annual totals of Nuthatches ringed (Mason & Hussey 1984).

It is not clear whether the recent increase shown by CBC results is a continuation of that which began in the 1930s, or a second phase following a plateau period in the 1960s. The two periods seem to be bridged by the slow expansion in northern England already referred to. The ecological basis for the original spread remains obscure, but was possibly linked to climate since it began, in Wales at least, during a warmer interlude. Parslow (1973) suggested that a contributory factor may have been an enhanced tendency to visit garden bird tables, especially in winter. Nuthatches visit rural gardens more frequently in winters when the beech mast crop is poor (Thompson 1988).

The main features of the CBC period are the short-term fluctuations throughout, and latterly these superimposed on the general increase since the mid-1970s. The temporary fluctuations correlate well with the size of the beech mast crop the previous autumn. Thus autumns of good to moderate seeding in 1967, 1976 and 1982 were followed in the next breeding seasons by rises in Nuthatch numbers. Conversely, poor beech mast production in the autumns of 1968, 1973 and 1981 was followed by reduced densities in the immediately ensuing summers. However, it is possible that, as explained under Great Tit, beech mast is an indicator, rather than a determinant, of winter food resource levels. Swedish studies of the relationship between the Nuthatch and the amount of beech mast available were published by Nilsson (1976) and Enoksson & Nilsson (1983). They found that autumn densities are related to the size of the mast crop; autumn territories are three times larger in poor mast years, but diminish in size with experimental provision of food. Yet, these Swedish studies could find no evidence that overwinter survival there is dependent upon the level of the previous autumn's beech mast crop.

In relation to the recent overall increase, Osborne (1982) predicted that the Nuthatch, like both the spotted woodpeckers, would benefit in the short term from the outbreak of Dutch elm disease which began in 1969 and was rampant by 1980. Indeed, Nuthatches were breeding significantly more often in elms after 1972, perhaps benefiting from nesting near an abundant summer food source – the larvae of scolytid beetles, which were a major vector of the DED fungus (Osborne 1982). Nevertheless, association is not so straightforward, since these birds are surface gleaners of tree trunks whereas the beetles were beneath the bark; possibly Nuthatches were attracted by woodpecker excavations for use as their own nest sites. The considerable increase of Nuthatches from the mid-1970s coincided well with the spread of DED, and remains the most plausible explanation of the trend. Yet it is by no means clear how the birds were able to sustain the higher population level beyond the mid-1980s, by which time many dead or infected elms had been felled.

Multiplying an estimate of density from woodland CBC plots in 1987 by the Forestry Commission's estimate of the extent of broad-leaved woodland in England and Wales, a total of 40,000-45,000 pairs is indicated. To this must be added the scattered pairs which breed in such marginal habitats as gardens, orchards and well-timbered farmland. An estimate of 50,000 pairs in Britain seems reasonable, and even this may be too low since Sitters (1988) thought, perhaps optimistically, that there could be 12,000 pairs in Devon alone. The revised population estimate given here is more than twice that offered by Sharrock (1976), but CBC woodland index values have doubled since the Breeding Atlas period.

Regional variation
Trends in population levels are similar in all occupied regions.

Trends elsewhere in Europe
Danish point-count data show an increase during 1976-1988 (DOFF 1989), but otherwise no clear trends are apparent. Declines have occurred in regions which have suffered from excessive tree-felling, *e.g.* parts of France (Yeatman 1971). Otherwise the main feature of European populations is fluctuation in response to temporal changes in food availability.

Treecreeper *Certhia familiaris*

Present population trend: fluctuates around cold winters, but overall trend is towards increase.
Percentages of plots occupied 1968/78/88: farmland 41/52/50; woodland 66/76/88.
Latest estimate of breeding population: 200,000-250,000 pairs in Britain (Hudson & Marchant 1984).
Regional density rankings 1988: farmland W>WE>NI>SE>EE>NE; woodland W>S>EE>NE>SE>WE.

This inconspicuous denizen of well-timbered habitats is not known to have changed in status in the decades preceding the CBC. It has, however, always been prone to periodic numerical fluctuations in line with the mildness or severity of winter weather conditions. Broad-leaved and mixed woodland are the preferred habitats in Britain, in the absence of any competing congener, in contrast to the Continent where this is a bird of upland conifer forest, being replaced in deciduous woodland by the Short-toed Treecreeper. In Britain the Treecreeper occurs at relatively low densities in conifers. A contributory reason for this may be that much of our coniferous woodland is commercial plantation in which trees are felled before they reach full maturity, so that potential nest sites are few (Sharrock 1976). In addition, and especially when population levels are high, Treecreepers hold territories also in other habitats that include mature trees, such as farmland spinneys and tree-lines, parks, churchyards and large gardens.

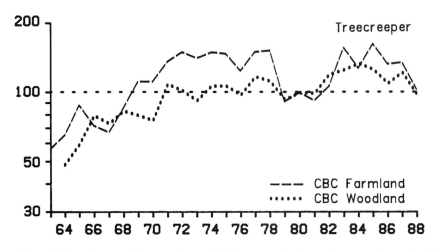

The CBC results over 25 years show well this temporal change in usage of marginal habitats, with contraction into woodland when population levels are low. Shortly before the CBC indices began, Treecreepers were greatly reduced by cold winters in the early 1960s. Recovery in woodland seems to have been well advanced by 1966, since the level there varied little over the ensuing four years. In contrast, farmland densities were still relatively low in 1966, as shown by the scale of increase in that habitat over the following breeding seasons. Treecreepers again suffered badly in the winter of 1978/79, but it was on farmland that index values plummeted. The subsequent recovery produced a woodland surplus which once more overflowed onto farmland.

A second feature of the CBC results is a trend towards shallow overall increase. This is seen best in the woodland index, which is less subject to weather-related disturbances. The reason for the overall upward trend since the mid-1970s remains obscure. A similar trend in the Nuthatch has been attributed to the effects of Dutch elm disease. For Treecreeper it has been suggested that there would be temporary benefit from the availability of extra nest sites behind the peeling bark of dead and dying elms (Osborne 1982). However, nest record cards show that only 15% of Treecreepers nest on elms, with oak trees being preferred (Flegg 1973). One might expect the massive loss of elms to affect farmland densities in particular, since this used to be the most frequent of mature hedgerow trees, but no general Treecreeper decline has occurred in that habitat.

As indicated earlier, the most profound disturbances to Treecreeper population levels are those caused by severe winter weather conditions. Yet not all hard winters have caused serious diminutions in numbers. It is clear that temperature alone is not decisive. As an arboreal species, Treecreepers suffer when freezing rain or persistent freezing fog leads to prolonged ice coating of tree trunks and branches. Such glazed-ice conditions existed in the severe winters of 1916/17, 1939/40, 1962/63 and 1978/79, all of which caused major Treecreeper declines (Jourdain & Witherby 1918, Ticehurst & Witherby 1940, Dobinson & Richards 1964, Cawthorne & Marchant 1980). Extremely low temperatures were also recorded (sometimes for short periods or regionally) in the winters of 1928/29, 1946/47, 1975/76, 1981/82, 1983/84 and 1985/86, but with less severe glazing on trees in those instances this species was affected less – as can be seen from the CBC graphs in the case of the last four.

Regional variation

It is known that cold winters can have variable regional impacts on Treecreepers. In the best-studied case, the winter 1978/79, there were east-to-west and south-to-north gradients of increasing decline, so that the smallest effects were felt close to the south coast and the largest in western England and Wales (Cawthorne & Marchant 1980). There is no clear pattern to the 1988 regional density rankings, other than scarcity on northern and eastern farmland.

Trends elsewhere in Europe

No major trends are known. The results of long-term census schemes in Sweden and Denmark have revealed fluctuations, sometimes large, analogous to those seen in British data (Hustings 1988, DOFF 1989).

Jay *Garrulus glandarius*

Present population trend: stable or increasing slightly.
Percentages of plots occupied 1968/78/88: farmland 39/46/54; woodland 66/81/87.
Latest estimate of breeding population: 100,000 pairs in Britain and Ireland (Sharrock 1976); 81% of occupied squares were then in Britain.
Regional density rankings 1988: farmland W>SE>EE>WE>NE; woodland EE>W>NE>SE>NI>WE>S.

This most arboreal of British crows has fared well during the last fifty years or more. In the 19th century, during the heyday of the large sporting estates, its numbers were suppressed by gamekeeping, a state of affairs which continued until the First World War. In the changed social and economic conditions which followed, there was a large decline in the number of gamekeepers employed in Britain, from over 20,000 in 1911 to around 5000 in the 1970s. With shooting and trapping pressure against them eased somewhat, Jays were able to increase again. The upward trend became more noticeable after the Second World War, since when Jays have been able to benefit further from afforestation programmes which have created new habitat for them. Jays prefer deciduous woodlands, especially those containing oaks, but will also breed in conifer plantations, albeit at lower densities. In recent times they have moved into larger town and city parks and into suburban areas where gardens are large and contain trees, as has the Magpie. Jays on farmland CBC plots occur mostly in spinneys or shelterbelts or are feeding visitors from fringing woodland.

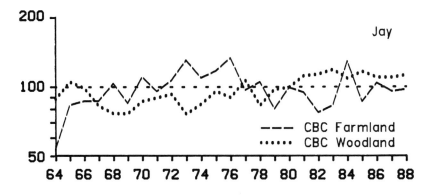

The woodland CBC has included this species from 1964. During the first 15 years, Jay index values showed overall stability but considerable short-term fluctuations, but since about 1979 there seems to have been a modest increase. The farmland index does not show a consistent pattern, and its fluctuations bear little relationship to those of the woodland index: the apparently large size of the year-to-year changes probably owes much to the small sample sizes on farmland and the biology of this species. Though there is no reason to question the validity of the overall CBC trends, nevertheless the Jay is a difficult species to census using the territory-mapping method. It ranges widely and seems not to defend discrete territories, while its song is weak, rarely uttered, and undoubtedly not recognised by many observers. But problems in analysing Jay census maps will be serious only where densities are high.

Jays seemed not to have been affected much by pesticide problems in the 1950s and early 1960s (Prestt 1965), nor by 1962/63 cold weather (Dobinson & Richards 1964). In line with this, there are no decreases in the CBC woodland index that are attributable to recent severe winters. There were small falls in the farmland index in 1979 and 1982, following cold winters, but the significance of these is uncertain.

Undoubtedly, the highest densities of Jays are those in deciduous woodland, and acorns are a staple winter food item. The symbiosis between Jays and acorns is discussed by Bossema (1979). In 1983 there was failure of the acorn crop over a large part of northwestern Europe, and this brought about an abnormal eruptive movement in Britain in early October that involved thousands of birds of both British and Continental origin (John & Roskell 1985). Possibly as a consequence of this, the 1984 woodland index value fell by 8% from the previous year, although it has recovered since. It is noticeable that fewer Jays visit rural gardens in winters when natural foods such as acorns and beech mast are plentiful, though no such relationship exists for Jays in suburban gardens (Thompson 1988).

Regional variation

The recent trend towards increase in woodland seems, in regional indices, to have been most marked in eastern and northern England.

Trends elsewhere in Europe

There are few data. Danish point counts indicate a decline in 1979-1980 and peak years in 1983-1984 (DOFF 1989). In Ireland, Jays have been increasing and expanding their range throughout the present century (Hutchinson 1989).

Magpie *Pica pica*

Present population trend: increasing in rural, suburban and urban habitats.
Percentages of plots occupied 1968/78/88: farmland 64/78/90; woodland 46/73/83.
Latest estimate of breeding population: over 250,000 pairs in Britain and Ireland (Sharrock 1976); 67% of occupied squares were then in Britain. Now much increased.
Regional density rankings 1988: farmland W>SE>NI>WE>NE>EE; woodland NI>NE>W>EE>SE>WE>S.

Like most other British corvids, the Magpie emerged from the 19th century with a lowered population as a result of systematic persecution by game-preserving interests. It was able to increase again after the First World War, and this increase became even more marked after the Second World War. By the 1940s Magpies were spreading into suburban areas, and in more recent times they have penetrated the urban districts also, even in a few places into industrial sites. There was a hiatus in the late 1950s when there was a noticeable decline in eastern England, accompanied by complete disappearance from some agricultural districts. This was attributed to the then unrestricted use of organochlorine chemicals in farming, with hedgerow removals and the ploughing of old grasslands as contributory factors (Prestt 1965, Parslow 1973, Cooke 1979).

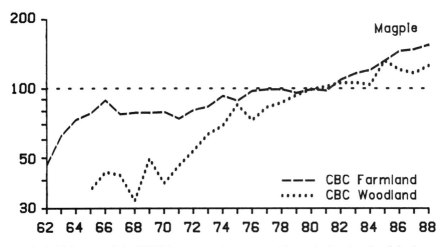

200 ┐   Magpie

100 ┤

50 ┤
                                      ――― CBC Farmland
                                      •••••• CBC Woodland
30 ┤
    62 64 66 68 70 72 74 76 78 80 82 84 86 88

The initial years of the CBC documented a recovery from the low levels of the late 1950s, followed by a plateau for a few years from 1966. Nest record card data reveal that during 1966-1970 there was an unexplained fall in Magpie breeding success, which then recovered to its former level (O'Connor & Shrubb 1986a). Since the early 1970s, both farmland and woodland CBC indices have shown steady increases which have been maintained up to the present time. These parallel the increases also occurring in urban and suburban habitats.

Magpie is a highly sedentary and territorial species, so that offspring are forced away to seek their own territories. It is probable that the expansion into residential districts was due initially to an overflow from rural areas, although some birds may instead have been seeking refuge from persecution on farmland. Modern concern with landscaping and tree-planting in the urban environment seems to have aided this colonisation of cities and suburbs; certainly the best correlations between urban Magpies and habitat features were those with numbers and variety of trees present (Tatner 1982). Yet such close association with man probably could not have arisen but for the Magpie's unspecialised diet, and the relative freedom from persecution and nest predation within conurbations. The densities now achieved in some cities, such as 8 pairs per sq.km in Sheffield (Clarkson & Birkhead 1987) and 6-7 pairs per sq. km in Manchester (Tatner 1982), exceed the national means for rural farmland and woodland. A comparison of Magpie breeding biology in urban and rural areas was made by Eden (1985), who found that breeding began significantly earlier in towns, though breeding success did not differ between the two habitats.

All this has led to concern in some quarters at the impact of Magpies on town and garden populations of small passerines. Undoubtedly this corvid is omnivorous and opportunistic, and it can readily be observed apparently searching for birds' nests. However, the only quantified urban food study published so far (Tatner 1983) found that these Magpies remain essentially ground feeders. Their diet comprises over 70% invertebrates in summer and over 70% plant material in winter, with only a minority of gizzards or faecal samples containing traces of birds or eggs. Clarkson & Birkhead (1987) suggested that systematic and successful Magpie predation on nests of garden songbirds would occur only where the latter breed at high densities, as in large suburban gardens. More recently, Gooch et al (in prep.) have found no correlations between the Magpie increase and the breeding success of any small garden passerine.

Regional variation
All regions have experienced the modern increase. The Welsh index has changed least since the CBC began, but this index should be treated cautiously because of the small samples of plots. The increase has been most pronounced in southern and eastern England.

Trends elsewhere in Europe
Many parts of Europe are experiencing the same increase as in Britain, with expansion into towns and suburbs. The steepest index trend recorded is that for Czechoslovakia, where point-count data suggest a fourfold increase between 1981 and 1986 (Hustings 1988).

Jackdaw *Corvus monedula*

Present population trend: increasing since the mid-1970s; perhaps now stabilised.
Percentages of plots occupied 1968/78/88: farmland 36/56/69; woodland 25/48/55.
Latest estimate of breeding population: 500,000 pairs in Britain and Ireland (Sharrock 1976); 72% of occupied squares were then in Britain.
Regional density rankings 1988: farmland W>SE>NI>NE>EE>S>WE; woodland NI>S>SE>EE>W.

There seems to have been a general increase of Jackdaws in Britain over the first half of this century (Parslow 1973). For England and Wales there were a good many statements to that effect in the county and regional bird literature, though quantification only for a very few single localities or islands. In Scotland the trend was clearer, for there the increase was accompanied by range expansion which included new island colonisations. This upward trend apparently petered out during the 1950s.

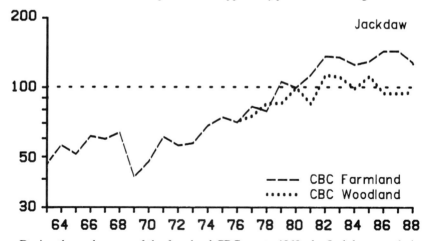

During the early years of the farmland CBC, up to 1968, the Jackdaw population seemed to be relatively stable, with only small fluctuations. This period was followed by lower levels in 1969 and 1970, since when an upward trend was maintained until the early 1980s. Index values in the 1980s have been higher than at any time since the CBC began, and are now twice those of the 1960s. The woodland index, which began in 1976, is in general agreement, except that it shows a stronger indication of recent stability around the new, higher level.

The causes of these long-term changes remain obscure. As in Rooks, the main foods of farmland Jackdaws are grain (and weed seeds) and grassland invertebrates, and presumably there is an optimum tillage:pasture ratio for Jackdaws just as Brenchley (1984) has shown for Rooks. Tapper (1981) linked a Jackdaw decline in East Anglia in the 1960s to reduction in the acreages remaining as grass leys, after cereals had become unduly prominent in that region. Yet O'Connor & Shrubb (1986a) found that Jackdaw breeding success was higher in cereal-dominated, especially barley-growing, counties than in pasture-dominated ones, which may contradict the concept of pasture being the more important habitat. While Rook numbers crashed nationally in the 1960s and early 1970s and have made only limited recovery since, Jackdaws declined less and later. Not only did they recover quickly, but they continued to increase beyond previous levels.

As a hole-nesting species, Jackdaw might have been expected to benefit from the increased availability of dead trees following Dutch elm disease. Jackdaws do commonly nest in elm, and dead elms make very good nest sites. Although there is a temporal correspondence between the onset of the disease and the Jackdaw increase, there is no evidence of any causal link (Osborne 1982). Any advantage the Jackdaw may have received will have been lost when the dead elms were felled.

Perhaps the success of the Jackdaw, relative to the Rook, lies in its being a less specialised feeder. It has a shorter bill and takes food on the surface more than by probing into the soil. Probably this has meant that it is less influenced by recent changes in the farmland ploughing calendar. The Jackdaw feeds more upon weed seeds than does the Rook, and will exploit accessible livestock fodder. It certainly relies less upon earthworms, and is less likely to be affected by any decreases that may have occurred in earthworm abundance on farmland. Moreover, Jackdaws also feed opportunistically in other habitats, such as rubbish tips and rural gardens, and in woodland where they take defoliating caterpillars among other foods.

Regional variation

Regional farmland indices indicate that the 1969-1973 fall was most marked in Wales, northern England and Scotland. The CBC decline was rather small in eastern England overall, despite the report by Tapper (1981) of a 50% drop in numbers shot on East Anglian estates. The subsequent recovery and continued increase are apparent for all regions. Southern England has shown the least temporal change, and figures strongly in the 1988 regional density rankings.

Trends elsewhere in Europe

The Jackdaw has increased in western Europe in line with agricultural expansion, with northward range extensions in Fenno-Scandia following earlier climatic amelioration (Yeatman 1971). Danish point counts reveal a substantial increase during 1976-1987, but a downturn in 1988 (DOFF 1989).

Rook *Corvus frugilegus*

Present population trend: serious decline (from the mid-1950s to early 1970s) has now halted; partial recovery is occurring in some regions.
Percentages of plots occupied 1968/78/88: farmland ?/19/51; woodland ?/5/16.
Latest estimate of breeding population: 850,000-860,000 pairs in Britain (Sage & Whittington 1985).

The Rook is not indexed by the CBC. As a species nesting in widely scattered colonies, it is surveyed more effectively by single-species fieldwork than by counting nests on CBC plots. The BTO conducted national surveys of Rook numbers in 1944-1946 (Fisher 1947) and 1975 (Sage & Vernon 1978), and a sample survey in 1980 restricted to randomly selected squares (Sage & Whittington 1985). Brenchley (1986) has since published an overview on population trends since 1920, incorporating the results of various local surveys also, though this paper confuses bird and nest counts in some 1944-1946 and 1975 comparisons.

The 1944-1946 census covered two-thirds of Britain and, with extrapolations for the remainder, produced estimates of 923,750 nests in England (including Isle of Man), 98,250 nests in Wales and 391,000 nests in Scotland. Comparison with various local and regional surveys in the 1920s and 1930s suggested that there had been an increase to 1946, probably in excess of 20%. Subsequent local surveys showed that the increase continued into the 1950s in some, though not all, counties.

Following reports in the 1970s of Rook decline, a new BTO survey was held in 1975. This confirmed a serious fall in Rook numbers, from 1,413,000 nests in 1944-1946 to around 800,000. This was a decrease of 43%, though the fall from the 1950s peak must have been even larger. By 1975, populations were reduced to the level of the 1920s in those counties for which comparison was possible (Brenchley 1986). The sample survey in 1980 found regionally uneven trends during 1975-1980. Numbers had risen in many western areas, but had fallen still further in some parts of the east and southeast. Nevertheless the gains outweighed the losses, with an overall increase of 6.8% in the areas sampled. Assuming this to be representative of unsampled areas also, the British population would then have been about 850,000 pairs (plus immature birds, for Rooks do not breed until two years old).

Sage & Whittington (1985) reported a finding that, despite partial recovery in total numbers of nests, the numbers of active rookeries has fallen (compared to 1975) so that more nests were concentrated into fewer colonies. Presumably this trend was of longer standing. The CBC percentages of all plots containing rookeries (see graph) declined to minimal values in the mid-1970s, before rising again. It seems likely that this was a consequence of small rookeries being deserted during the period when the national population level was at its lowest.

Since the Rook is essentially a bird of agricultural land, it seems likely that the underlying reasons for population trends are to be found in farming changes. The optimum habitat is one containing a mixture of tillage (cereals, root crops) and pasture in a ratio of 45:55 (Brenchley 1984), for the major components of the diet are grain and grassland invertebrates. Farming was depressed between the two world wars, but was of necessity revitalised in the 1940s. This probably improved conditions for Rooks and led to their increase then. Since the 1960s, however, a major change from pasture

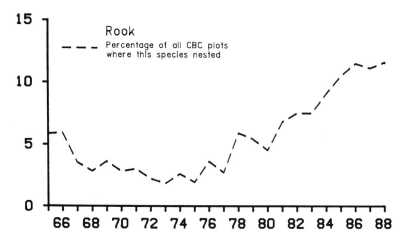

15

Rook
— — — Percentage of all CBC plots
where this species nested

10

5

0

66 68 70 72 74 76 78 80 82 84 86 88

to cereals has altered the land-use ratio away from that most favourable to Rooks. In addition, intensification of cereal growing, the use of pesticides and improved mechanisation have reduced the availability of both cereal and invertebrate foods. The loss of spring cultivations and their associated temporary superabundances of invertebrates, through the switch to autumn sowings, has depressed food availability during the breeding season (O'Connor & Shrubb 1986a). Food supply is more likely to be the factor limiting Rook populations than altered nest site availability through Dutch elm disease (Tapper 1981).

Regional variation

The 1960s decline was probably general, but seems to have been most severe in eastern and southeastern England where cereal acreages had become greater than those of pastures. In these regions the species was still declining in the 1980s, against the overall trend.

Trends elsewhere in Europe

Decline in the mid-20th century has been widespread in northern Europe, from the Netherlands, Denmark and Sweden eastwards to Poland and the USSR (Brenchley 1986). More recently, Danish point counts suggest an upturn in numbers (DOFF 1989).

Carrion Crow *Corvus corone*

Present population trend: continuing increase.
Percentages of plots occupied 1968/78/88: farmland 73/88/95; woodland 47/76/92.
Latest estimate of breeding population: about 1 million pairs in Britain and Ireland (Sharrock 1976); 74% of occupied squares were then in Britain. Has increased since.
Regional density rankings 1988: farmland WE>SE>W>EE>S>NE>NI; woodland NI>W>NE>S>EE>WE>SE.

The distributions in Britain of the Hooded Crow (race *cornix*) and the nominate race of the Carrion Crow (*corone*) are linked by a broad zone of intergradation which runs from SW to NE across Scotland (Cook 1975, Lack 1986). Hooded Crows dominate in Northern Ireland, the Isle of Man, western Scotland (including the Western Isles), Orkney and Shetland. The distribution of CBC plots is such that only a very few Hooded Crows appear in the index samples.

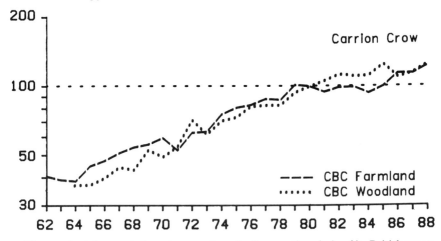

The species is known to have increased markedly over the whole of its British range since the First World War, and especially since the early 1940s, in line with progressive reduction in gamekeeping pressures and also, perhaps more significantly, with much reduced persecution from farmers. Pressure of the latter fell away during the agricultural recession between the two world wars, and more recently crows have been seen less as a pest due to modern stock-rearing practices and a big increase in arable farming. Many avian predators (raptors, owls, some crows) decreased to some extent, even if only locally, during the main organochlorine pesticide era of the 1950s and early 1960s (Prestt 1965). The Carrion Crow however was an exception for it did not decline anywhere: its population level remained unchanged in East Anglia, where regular keeping continues, and showed small or moderate increases in all other regions. This long spell of population increase was accompanied by, and was perhaps to some extent due to, changes in the species' habits and habitats. These involved spreads into open and treeless countryside, where nests may be placed on bushes, posts, or pylons, into the outskirts of towns and cities, and even into major conurbations such as inner London (Prestt 1965, Parslow 1973). Moreover, upland afforestation has provided many new and secure nest sites and, possibly, increased food supplies there during the breeding season. CBC monitoring shows that the Carrion Crow has increased continuously since 1962, with farmland and woodland indices almost trebling by 1988.

There is some evidence, for example from Derbyshire (Frost 1978), that the largest concentrations tend to occur on higher ground, where persecution is least. One would expect this difference to have been more pronounced at the peak of the game preservation era, when such species as Buzzard and Raven were driven out of the lowlands. This is discussed further by O'Connor & Shrubb (1986a). They found evidence that Carrion Crow densities are stable in sheep-rearing districts though increasing in those dominated by cereals and tillage, and that since the mid-1960s breeding success has been highest in sheep country. They speculated that, with many more young crows being reared in the uplands than previously, young territory-seekers are being forced into lowland habitats; there, the population levels are known to be rising despite breeding success having been constant over time. This interpretation must be treated with caution, however, since population size is influenced by post-fledging survival as well as by breeding success.

Regional variation

The long-term increase is reflected in data for all regions. There is a suggestion in the regional indices that in eastern and southern England the major upsurge began rather later (about 1970-1972) than it did elsewhere. This is consistent with the report by Prestt (1965) that, in the early 1960s, East Anglia was the only region in which the species seemed not to be increasing.

Trends elsewhere in Europe

Dutch data for 1984-1987 show increase comparable to that in Britain (Hustings 1988). Otherwise the only index data are for Hooded Crows (and intermediates) in Denmark and Sweden, which have shown fluctuations between years but shallow increases overall (Hustings 1988, DOFF 1989). Hooded Crows have increased markedly in Ireland since 1924 (Hutchinson 1989).

Raven *Corvus corax*

Present population trend: overall, a small decline; but trends are geographically uneven.
Percentages of plots occupied 1968/78/88: all CBC habitats 3/3/6.
Latest estimate of breeding population: 5000 pairs in Britain and Ireland (Sharrock 1976); 74% of occupied squares were then in Britain.

The limited distribution of the Raven, mostly in upland and seacliff habitats, and the poor representation of the CBC in western and northern parts of the country, combine to preclude CBC indexing. The CBC plots on which Ravens are present are mainly in Devon and the southern half of Wales. There are considerable chance variations in the CBC ubiquity values (see graph), but the overall trend is one of stability.

Like the Buzzard, the Raven was formerly a widespread breeding bird in lowland and eastern counties, before persecution by livestock farmers and gamekeepers in the

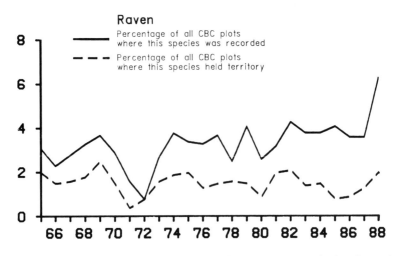

Raven

Percentage of all CBC plots
where this species was recorded

Percentage of all CBC plots
where this species held territory

19th century caused its range to shrink westwards. Nevertheless, the last few pairs in Essex, Kent and Sussex did not disappear until as late as 1890-1895. Persecution still occurs in some regions though, overall, the scale of this has lessened since the First World War. Since about 1920, Ravens have been able to spread a little from their main upland and coastal refuges into adjoining areas, as in southwest England, the Welsh Borders and south Scotland. This overflow has been marked by an increased incidence of nesting in trees, as population levels have risen in the uplands where rock-nesting predominates (Ratcliffe 1962). In Devon, where numbers have increased to about 300 pairs, about 50 pairs are on seacliffs and the others are mainly tree-nesters in districts where livestock rearing, and especially sheep farming, predominates (Sitters 1988). Some former inland sites there on granite tors and in quarries have been deserted through recreational disturbance such as by rock-climbing. Elsewhere, three main factors seem to be involved in regional variations in recent population trends. These are persecution, farming practices, and patterns of afforestation.

Regional variation

In Snowdonia, where nest sites are plentiful and sheep numbers have increased on the hills, there has been an 80% increase in Raven breeding pairs since the 1950s. But in an adjacent lower-altitude area of moorland and enclosed sheep farms, the Raven population has remained stable at a lower density (Dare 1986). This difference is attributed to scarcity of secure nest sites, some continuing persecution, and lower availability of sheep carrion at the lower altitudes, where most dead sheep are removed by farmers and lambing flocks are moved closer to farmsteads (Dare 1986). Mid-Wales has the highest recorded Raven densities in Europe, reaching 21 pairs per 10-km square on hill sheepwalk. There, many sheep are overwintered on the hills, making carrion available, and while there has been afforestation this has, as in North Wales, tended to be in relatively small blocks. Occupancy of Raven territories showed a small fall between 1975 and 1979, from 42 to 36 pairs in the study area (Newton *et al* 1982). In contrast, Ravens in an area covering Northumberland and that part of Scotland south of the Forth and Clyde have experienced declines of over 50% since the 1950s, from at least 110 regular territories to 48 in 1981, with coastal and inland areas affected equally (Mearns 1983). In these regions, Ravens have been affected adversely by improved sheep husbandry, large-scale afforestation and, near the coast, the conversion of moorland and pasture to arable. On Speyside, only five of 22 traditional territories were occupied in 1977, and in this case the use of poisoned baits (also directed towards raptors) was suspected of being a major factor (Thom 1986). No significant changes are known for other important populations, for example those in the Lake District, western Scotland and the northern isles. A recent survey has shown the Shetland population to be larger than previously thought, and larger than that of Orkney where sheep carrion is less plentiful (Ewins *et al* 1986).

Trends elsewhere in Europe
As in Britain, persecution has excluded the species from many areas of lowland cultivation. There have also been some regional increases, in East Germany for example (Sellin 1987), and in Ireland Ravens have increased considerably this century (Hutchinson 1989). Swedish point counts have shown large fluctuations, but no overall trend (Hustings 1988).

Starling *Sturnus vulgaris*

Present population trend: marked decline during the late 1960s, continuing in the 1980s.
Percentages of plots occupied 1968/78/88: farmland 67/90/92; woodland 54/71/54.
Latest estimate of breeding population: 3½ million pairs in Britain (Potts 1967); 4-7 million pairs in Britain and Ireland (Sharrock 1976), with 74% of occupied squares then being in Britain.
Regional density rankings 1988: farmland NI>NE>S> W>SE>EE>WE; woodland EE>S>SE>WE>NE.

Starlings declined over the whole of Britain in the 18th century, and withdrew from many northern and western districts. They increased again from about 1830 onwards, and in the ensuing seven decades recolonised much of their lost ground. The underlying reason for these big temporal changes is unknown, but it may have been a climatic one. Expansion continued into the present century, with infilling between initially scattered recolonists, and was still detectable in west Wales and Scotland in the 1960s (Parslow 1973).
Since 1965 when the woodland index started, similar trends have been shown by both CBC data-sets. Population levels were high during the early years of monitoring, but fell sharply during the late 1960s (see under *Regional variation*). A slow, gradual recovery during the 1970s proved to be only a partial one, for both sets of index values fell again after 1980-1981 and are still falling. In both habitats, the 1988 indices were the lowest yet recorded by the CBC – on farmland at half, and in woodland at only one-third, of the levels found during the mid-1960s. It must be remembered, however, that the CBC does not monitor the large and important populations which breed in urban and suburban areas, and so the relationship of the CBC data to the true national trend is more than usually uncertain. Garden Bird Feeding Survey data since 1970 reveal no long-term trend in Starling numbers visiting urban and suburban gardens in winter (Thompson 1988), but these birds must include many Continental winter visitors whose presence might mask any change.

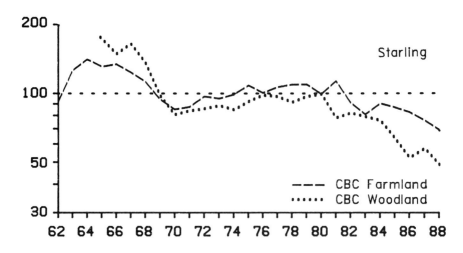

Analysis of nest record cards found that Starling breeding success fell between about 1956 and 1966 but then rose again. This fall coincided well with the use of persistent organochlorine insecticides on farmland before restrictions were imposed in 1966. Breeding success continued to improve up to about 1980, during the period of population recovery, since when it has fallen again as have the CBC index values (O'Connor & Shrubb 1986a, O'Connor & Pearman 1987). These authors concluded that there was a pesticide-related pattern initially, with an improvement after the 1966 ban which was then interrupted by the agricultural changes of the 1970s.

Starlings in the breeding season feed especially on grassland invertebrates, notably leatherjackets, and thus suffer where grassland is converted to cereals. O'Connor & Shrubb (1986a) suggested also that the more widespread rural decline in recent years has been due to a reduction in spring ploughing following the switch towards autumn sowing of cereals. Further it is possible that the densities of some soil invertebrates have been reduced by the modern use of fungicides and the decline of arable/pasture rotations. The decline of Starlings during the 1980s must be seen as part of a more general decline over northern Europe (see below), and this is likely to have a climatic basis, but nevertheless changes on farmland have surely contributed to the trend.

Regional variation

The decline in the late 1960s seems to have been mainly a feature of eastern and southern England and may have been exaggerated in the national indices by a bias of CBC plots towards those two regions. Starling populations subsequently remained low on farmland in the south and east, and the trend seems likely to have been due to the large-scale conversion of pasture to arable, especially cereals, in those two regions.

Trends elsewhere in Europe

There has been a well-documented decline across northern Europe over the last two decades, especially in Fenno-Scandia where Starlings have disappeared from some districts (Orell & Ojanen 1980, Feare 1984). Farming changes, agrochemicals, afforestation, mortality in winter quarters and reversal of earlier climatic amelioration have all been suggested as possible reasons for the recent downturn. The Swedish mapping-census index halved between 1970 and 1986 (Hustings 1988), and the Danish index is decreasing at a similar rate (DOFF 1989).

House Sparrow *Passer domesticus*

Present population trend: thought to be in decline.
Percentages of plots occupied 1968/78/88: farmland ?/41/71; woodland ?/18/16.
Latest estimate of breeding population: 5½-6 million pairs in Britain and Ireland (Lack 1986); 74% of occupied squares were then in Britain.
Regional density rankings 1988: all CBC habitats EE> NE>SE>NI>WE>W>S.

Birdwatchers tend to think of the House Sparrow as an abundant and ubiquitous species, as indeed it is over much of England and the Scottish lowlands. Yet such is its dependence upon man that there are large upland areas of Wales, northern England and Scotland where it is quite locally distributed or even absent, as for example from major tracts of the Scottish Highlands. It seems to be in suburban areas that House Sparrows are most successful, due to a combination there of abundant nest sites and green areas to provide insect food for the nestlings. Indeed, rural populations may depend for their maintenance upon dispersal away from the higher-density suburban ones (Summers-Smith 1988).

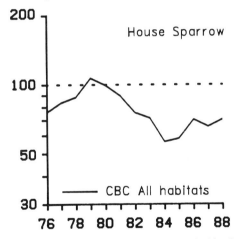

Because its distribution is so closely linked to human habitations, and also because of its semicolonial breeding, it is not always practical to include the House Sparrow in CBC fieldwork. Hence information on population trends is sparse. Even combining data from all habitats, CBC data are adequate for indexing purposes only from 1976. This index shows a temporary increase up to 1979-1980, while the subsequent fall took the index to well below its 1976 level. There is some indication of an improvement in numbers since 1984.

Summers-Smith (1988) suggested that House Sparrow numbers may have reached a plateau in Britain in the early 1970s, and thereafter declined slightly, with a reduced food supply as the most likely explanation. There can be no doubt that, in farmed areas, crop-spraying has reduced invertebrates as well as seed-bearing weeds; while earlier clearing of stubbles after harvest, with the switch to sowing cereals in autumn rather than spring, has further reduced feeding opportunities. Agricultural changes are likely to affect nearly all elements of the population: it is well known that House Sparrows from the outer suburbs as well as villages visit ripening cereals and stubble fields in the late summer and autumn. The use of insecticides by gardeners may also be implicated, since nestling House Sparrows need invertebrate foods. The evidence from the BTO's Garden Bird Feeding Survey is that numbers visiting suburban gardens have fallen noticeably since 1977/78 (Thompson 1988); the index values given suggest that the decline may have been about 15-20% over the last ten years. No significant change has been detected in numbers visiting rural gardens, though this could be because rural birds have become more dependent on feeding in gardens following agricultural changes.

Various local surveys (for example in London, Hertfordshire, Surrey and Berkshire) have also found declines in numbers. However, in a wider context, reduced densities within older conurbations may have been compensated for to some extent through the spread of urbanisation creating fresh House Sparrow habitat. Despite the trend reported here, this species remains one of Britain's five most abundant breeding birds.

Regional variation

There is no conclusive information. Most reports of local declines have come from southern England; but this may be an artefact of observer distribution. Summers-Smith (1988) noted its disappearance from some higher-altitude villages in Yorkshire.

Trends elsewhere in Europe

Consolidation may be continuing along the edges of the species' range, but the only notable expansion in recent years has been the colonisation of the Azores following an introduction. Point-count data from Denmark indicate strong decreases during 1977-1979, followed by approximate stability (DOFF 1989). Swedish point counts, since 1975, suggest an increase in the late 1970s and early 1980s, but some reduction since then.

Tree Sparrow *Passer montanus*

Present population trend: upward in late 1950s and 1960s, but strongly in decline since 1976-1977.
Percentages of plots occupied 1968/78/88: farmland 64/71/42; woodland 28/43/6.
Latest estimate of breeding population: 285,000 pairs in Britain and Ireland in 1985 (Summers-Smith 1989); 93% of occupied squares during the Breeding Atlas period were in Britain (Sharrock 1976).
Regional density rankings 1988: farmland WE>NE>EE>S.

In those parts of the world where the Tree Sparrow is not in competition with its larger and dominant congener, the House Sparrow, it fills the urban role successfully. Yet where the two species overlap, as in Britain and most of continental Europe, the Tree Sparrow is virtually excluded from towns and villages, and occupies instead the rural niches of farmland and lightly wooded countryside. At the northern limit of their range, however, in Scandinavia, northern Germany and northern Russia, the separation is much less clear and both species tend to occur in towns and villages.

It is a peculiarity of Tree Sparrows that apparently thriving colonies are apt to dwindle and disappear. No doubt these are often parallels of wider trends. After high population levels around the turn of the century, much of the British Isles experienced a long phase of decrease and range contraction. This had become very marked by 1930, when the species disappeared from many parts of Scotland, Wales, southwest England and Ireland (Parslow 1973, Thom 1986). Then, in the late 1950s and early 1960s, the population began to increase and expand again, recolonising lost ground to the north and west. As the CBC did not begin until 1962, its indices only measure the later stages of increase and demonstrate the subsequent population plateau which held until 1976 or 1977 when a steep decline began. Tree Sparrows are once more at a low ebb, though perhaps not yet back to the levels found prior to the 1950s (see below).

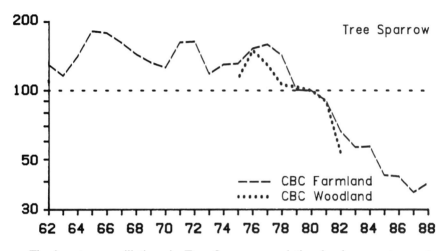

The long-term oscillations in Tree Sparrow population levels are not easy to explain. Probably it was coincidental that the earlier decades of Tree Sparrow decline included the long period of agricultural recession which lasted into the 1930s, for there was a lag of 15-20 years between the resurgences of agriculture in the early 1940s and Tree Sparrows in the late 1950s. Tree Sparrow numbers grew and remained high during the main organochlorine pesticide era, 1956-1963, and began to fall long after the worst chemical excesses had been curtailed. Moreover, climatic amelioration was long past its peak before Tree Sparrows began their last phase of increase. Nor can Dutch elm disease be implicated. Tree Sparrows do not depend on elms for nest holes – only 6% of tree sites in nest record cards were in elms. Indeed, they utilise a wider variety of tree species than other hole-nesting birds (Osborne 1982). However, the now-widespread use of herbicides in weed control on farmland is probably a major contributor to the recent decline. Other farmland seed-eaters, notably Skylark, Linnet, Reed Bunting and Corn Bunting, have shown a similarly timed decline.

Very recently, Summers-Smith (1989) has published a review of regional bird literature assessed against temporal patterns of change shown in three sets of BTO data (CBC, ringing, and nest record card intakes). He estimated that there may have been as few as 130,000 pairs of Tree Sparrows in Britain and Ireland at the low point of 1950, rising to over 850,000 pairs by the mid-1960s before decline set in again. He noted that, while the Tree Sparrow is resident in Britain, big passage movements occur on the east and southeast coasts in some autumns. There is a certain amount of randomness about such movements, but also a tendency for abnormally large numbers to occur in groups of consecutive years which tend to be towards the onset of periods when the British population is recovering (as in the years 1957-1962). From this, Summers-Smith concluded that upsurges in the British population are due to irruptions from the Continent following high population levels there, with each British upsurge gradually subsiding again when immigration has ceased. No answer is presently available to the question of why such Continental fluctuations should occur at all.

Regional variation
The 1960s increase certainly affected all parts of the country, as has the more recent decline. The impact of the latter seems to have been most severe in eastern and southern England; indeed, the species was absent in 1988 from all CBC farmland plots in southern England.

Trends elsewhere in Europe
A decrease has been reported from Niedersachsen, West Germany, since the 1970s, and passage numbers through Heligoland have fallen contemporaneously (Moritz 1981; Summers-Smith 1988, 1989). The Danish point-count index, beginning in 1976, indicates an initial small decrease but substantial gains since 1979 (DOFF 1989). Swedish results suggest some increase up to 1981, and subsequent decrease, though numbers have fluctuated (Hustings 1988).

Chaffinch *Fringilla coelebs*

Present population trend: following recovery in the early 1960s and a short plateau period, a shallow increase is occurring.
Percentages of plots occupied 1968/78/88: farmland 94/97/99; woodland 93/99/100.
Latest estimate of breeding population: about 5 million pairs in Britain (Hudson & Marchant 1984).
Regional density rankings 1988: farmland NI>W>WE>SE>EE>S>NE; woodland NI>S>W>NE>EE>SE>WE.

As well as being one of the most abundant of British breeding birds, certainly in the top five, the Chaffinch is also among the most widely distributed: it was encountered in 92% of 10-km squares during the Breeding Atlas and 91% during the Winter Atlas. Only in the northern and western islands of Scotland is it local or absent.

Though avoiding heavily urbanised areas which lack green spaces, it occurs commonly in city parks and suburban gardens. But it is in rural areas that the Chaffinch is most abundant. Mean densities are higher in woodland than on farmland (58 *versus* 21 pairs per sq. km in CBC data: Hudson & Marchant 1984), but the very much larger area of land in agricultural usage, compared to other habitats, means that well over half of the British breeding population is to be found on farmland. In woodlands, deciduous and mixed habitats are preferred; and Chaffinch is co-dominant with Willow Warbler in Scottish birch woods (Yapp 1962, Bibby *et al* 1989). One study (Glas 1960) found that densities in pine woods fluctuated more between years than in other types of woodland, indicating that this habitat was suboptimal and used more when alternative niches were fully occupied.

Chaffinches were reported widely in the late 1950s as being in decline, especially on farmland in the eastern half of England, reaching a low point around 1960-1962. This decline was believed to be genuine, though there were few figures to indicate its extent (Parslow 1973). CBC studies, which began in 1962, documented an increase until 1965-1966, which may be seen as a recovery from the earlier fall. Thereafter the population was stable for almost ten years, showing only minor fluctuations during that time. Since the early to middle 1970s, a small increase has been maintained in both farmland and woodland indices.

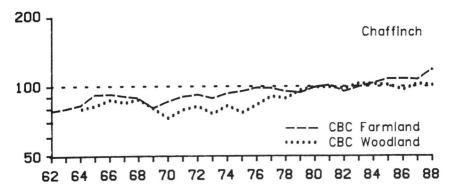

It is likely that Chaffinch population levels have been affected partly by overwinter survival and partly by breeding success. In winter, Chaffinches feed largely on seeds: there were several instances in the late 1950s of population reductions being reported for a range of seed-eating birds, and it was suspected at the time that these were related to the then-widespread use of persistent organochlorine insecticides as seed dressings. Also, hard weather may cause heavy mortality as in the particularly cold winters of 1961/62 and 1962/63. Chaffinches of the British race are usually sedentary, 90% of ringed birds moving less than 5 km (Newton 1972), so winter conditions in Britain can affect their breeding populations directly. In summer, they feed themselves and their young on a diet of insects, particularly defoliating caterpillars and aphids. Although the species appears to be almost ubiquitous in the national Breeding Atlas, some more detailed surveys show local scarcity in rural areas adjacent to industrial sites: this is perhaps attributable to the effects of pollution, and might suggest that the slow increase in breeding Chaffinches in the last ten years has been assisted by gradual improvements in air quality (D. Norman, pers. comm.).

Regional variation
No regional differences in trends have been demonstrated conclusively, but the woodland indices for southern and western England and the farmland index for eastern England all suggest temporary falls in the mid-1970s, then subsequent increases in conformity with overall national trends. The 1988 regional density rankings for farmland placed Scotland and northern England last, but in those regions woodland assumes greater relative importance for Chaffinches. Densities were highest in Northern Ireland in both divisions of habitat.

Trends elsewhere in Europe
No major trends are known. In the Danish point count index for 1976-1988, the species was stable from 1976-1980 but since then has shown a distinct upward trend in line with that in Britain (DOFF 1989). Small increases in the 1980s are also apparent in

Swedish and Dutch census data (Hustings 1988). Chaffinches are reported to be expanding their range in the Dalmatian region of Yugoslavia (Cvitanic 1986), and nesting has recently occurred for the first time in Iceland (Magnusson 1986).

Greenfinch *Carduelis chloris*

Present population trend: stable; perhaps a small downward trend recently.
Percentages of plots occupied 1968/78/88: farmland 84/83/90; woodland 53/70/67.
Latest estimate of breeding population: about 800,000 pairs in Britain (Hudson & Marchant 1984).
Regional density rankings 1988: farmland W>EE>S>SE>NI>WE>NE; woodland NE>EE>WE>SE>S>W.

Various unquantified reports in the 1950s suggested that Greenfinches were increasing then, most obviously in urban and suburban areas but also through further colonisation of islands such as the Scilly Isles and certain of the Hebrides (Parslow 1973). Nevertheless, farmland population levels were clearly depressed in 1962 when the index began, since the early years documented a doubling in numbers up to a plateau from 1966 onwards. Why the population was at a low ebb initially remains uncertain, though the use then of organochlorine pesticides as seed dressings and two consecutive cold winters may both have been implicated. Suggestions of a decrease since 1982 have apparently been removed by an increase in 1988. In woodland, Greenfinches fluctuated in numbers but continued to make overall gains until about 1980, since when there has been a slight drop in population.

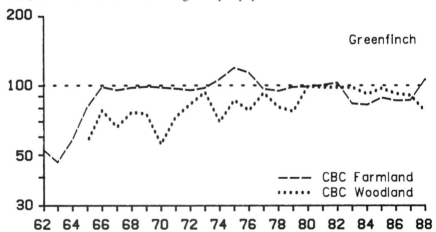

Farmland Greenfinches have been influenced by factors which were, until quite recently, counterbalancing (O'Connor & Shrubb 1986*a*, *b*). They feed more upon cereal grain than do other *Carduelis* finches, and therefore benefit from the increased acreage given over to cereal production. In nest record card data, average clutch size is 14% larger in cereal-growing regions than in regions where root and vegetable crops predominate. Greenfinches have also taken to exploiting for food the increased acreages given over to oil-seed rape since the mid-1970s. This new crop bridges the interval from early summer until the cereal harvest. Yet improved summer survival and breeding success are balanced by other factors which affect overwinter survival. Improvements in mechanised harvesting have reduced the amount of grain left behind in the fields, and winter stackyard threshing was eliminated many years ago. More recently, winter feeding sites have become rarer: the increased trend towards autumn sowing of cereals leaves fewer fields in stubble or fallow over winter, and the more effective use of modern herbicides has much reduced the availability of weed seeds which are also an important food.

The peak mortality period for the Greenfinch in earlier years was shown to be spring, when seeds are hard to find (Mead 1974). However, survival earlier in the winter may now have become more difficult. The Garden Bird Feeding Survey has noted an increased winter usage of rural gardens since 1981/82, but a small decline in suburban gardens (Thompson 1988). There is also a suggestion from ringing recoveries that mobility has increased within the British Isles. In the period 1969-1975, 63% of recoveries were within 10 km of ringing place and only 6% moved more than 100 km. But in the period 1977-1986 the corresponding figures were 49% and 11%. This would be consistent with Greenfinches, which are partial migrants in Britain (Boddy & Sellers 1983), having to become more mobile outside the breeding season in what has become, for them, the hardest period of the year.

Regional variation
No regional variation is known in population trends. There is no clear pattern to the 1988 density rankings.

Trends elsewhere in Europe
Swedish and Danish census data show increases since the late 1970s, whereas those for the Netherlands indicate a progressive decline since 1984 (Hustings 1988, DOFF 1989).

Goldfinch *Carduelis carduelis*

Present population trend: declining, steeply outside farmland, after reaching high population levels in the 1970s.
Percentages of plots occupied 1968/78/88: farmland 67/80/85; woodland 27/39/41.
Latest estimate of breeding population: 300,000 pairs in Britain (Hudson & Marchant 1984).
Regional density rankings 1988: farmland W>WE>EE>SE>S>NE; woodland W>S>EE>WE.

This most attractive of British finches, the Goldfinch, has had a chequered history. Though never reduced to rarity status, it suffered much in the last century from the attentions of commercial bird-trappers, for it was a popular cagebird. Agricultural change may have played a part also, for much marginal land came under the plough during that century, but the intensity of trapping pressure then was such that Goldfinch numbers were probably held below the level where food availability could become a limiting factor. Population levels were able to rise again through the first half of this century, following restrictions on commercial trapping, and probably aided by a long period of agricultural recession which must have resulted in an abundance of thistles, one of the Goldfinch's major food sources.

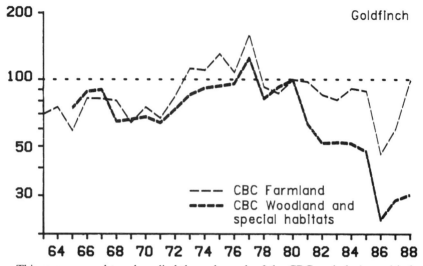

This same upward trend applied through much of the CBC period. Annual index values rose during the 1960s and beyond to give especially high population levels during the 1970s. But index values began to fall away around 1980, with the trend accelerating in 1985-1986 so as to virtually wipe out the gains of the previous two decades. There was, however, a small improvement on farmland in 1987 and a larger one in 1988, so that the population level in that habitat is now around that which applied in the early 1970s. The 1987-1988 increases were much less pronounced in the second index, for woodland and "special" plots, but recently this has been based on small sample sizes.

This overall pattern contrasts strongly with that for Linnet, which has been in decline for 20 years due, it is thought, to chemical control of the arable weeds whose seeds are its most important food resources (O'Connor & Shrubb 1986a, b). In comparison, the Goldfinch feeds more on tree seeds, especially birch and alder (Newton 1972), and the main weeds on which it feeds (thistles, to which its long bill is adapted) are less amenable to herbicide control than are other weeds because its windborne seed disperses so widely. The principal species exploited is the spear-plumed thistle, which occurs on old pasture and waste ground. The 1980s fall in Goldfinch densities was probably due to herbicide use and other agricultural changes affecting food supply (Lack 1986), not only in Britain, but also in this population's wintering areas in southwest Europe. The species is influenced less by winter food availability and cold weather in Britain than are most other finches, because perhaps as many as 80% of the British population (and especially females and young birds) spend the winter period in France and Iberia (Newton 1972).

Glück (1985) discussed seed nutrition in relation to the energy expenditure of foraging in the Goldfinch. He concluded that partial migration is necessary because many birds find the winter daylength in northern latitudes too short to gather sufficient food, despite adequate seed supplies remaining available. As in many other birds, winter is the most difficult season for the Goldfinch, and it is then that food supply exerts its greatest influence on population size.

226

Regional variation
There is a suggestion in regional index values that the decline in the 1980s was more pronounced in eastern and southern England than elsewhere.

Trends elsewhere in Europe
No major changes are known. The species is not monitored by other European schemes except that in Czechoslovakia, where the index has tended to increase since 1981 but fell sharply in 1986 (Hustings 1988).

Siskin *Carduelis spinus*

Present population trend: expanding in the wake of afforestation.
Percentages of plots occupied 1968/78/88: all CBC habitats 2/5/8.
Latest estimate of breeding population: 20,000-40,000 pairs in Britain and Ireland (Sharrock 1976); 72% of occupied squares were then in Britain.

Though the Siskin occurs on some woodland plots, it is not indexed by the Common Birds Census. Its main breeding centres lie outside those for which adequate CBC coverage is available.

Early writers knew the Siskin as a breeding bird of the Scottish Highlands and as a winter visitor elsewhere. It seems likely that it colonised Ireland around the mid-19th century, following large-scale introductions there of conifers, and the breeding distribution in Ireland is now wide. In the present century the same trend has been apparent in western and southern Scotland, and much of England and Wales. Supply difficulties in the First World War led to a large increase in conifer afforestation, which is still continuing: between 1977 and 1982 the area of new plantings averaged 12,000 ha annually. Spruce woodland is a favoured breeding habitat of Siskins in continental Europe, and the extensive use of spruce, especially Sitka spruce, in British forestry plantings has created good conditions for this finch. As early as the 1930s, pioneer Siskins were spreading into Argyll (Thom 1986), but major expansion in Britain took place mainly after 1950, as the conifers planted on a larger scale over the two previous decades grew to cone-bearing age.

In the 1950s and 1960s Siskins began colonising maturing plantations in Galloway, the Cheviots and northern Pennines, the Lake District, the Peak District, North Wales, the East Anglian Brecks, the New Forest and Devon; and scattered breeding records have since been reported from other regions. This trend is apparent in the graph of CBC ubiquity values, which shows a gradual spread of territory-holding as well as of the presence of visiting birds – the latter showing also the influence of irruption years such as 1986. In the Scottish Highlands also there has been a substantial spread beyond the original Caledonian Forest as a result of the afforestation of large tracts of both upland and lowland moorland. Scottish Siskins have increased considerably in numbers as well as range, over the last two decades especially, and the trend seems likely to continue as further plantations mature (Thom 1986).

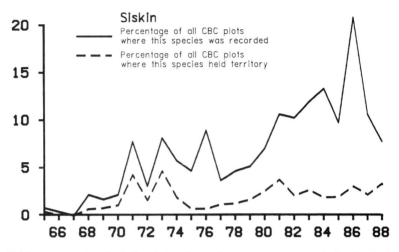

Siskin

Percentage of all CBC plots where this species was recorded

Percentage of all CBC plots where this species held territory

Siskins move extensively in winter, becoming more numerous in England at that season. There are very large annual variations in the numbers present in England in winter, for Siskin movements include an eruptive component such as is typical of tree-seed specialists which utilise a limited range of tree species (Newton 1972). In the case of Siskin the preferred trees are larch and spruce, plus birch and alder in winter. While it has often been assumed that irruptive movements in Britain concern birds of Continental origins, that is not the whole picture. The Siskin's principal food trees seed irregularly in Britain as they do elsewhere; hence our breeding birds – and especially those in the large Scottish plantations – are just as likely to erupt in autumns when tree-seeding is poor. However, the British birds involved are outnumbered by the immigrants, in view of the much greater extent of Continental forests.

In British lowlands, wintering Siskins have been able to take advantage of ornamental conifers planted in parks and gardens. Perhaps as a consequence of being attracted to gardens in that manner, they have more recently taken to feeding on supplementary foods, especially peanuts, in late winter and early spring when natural food resources have been depleted (Spencer & Gush 1973). Gardens may now be a very important habitat for Siskins. For example, in the irruption winter of 1985/86 this species was recorded feeding in 35% of all gardens contributing to the Garden Bird Feeding Survey (P.S. Thompson, pers. comm.). Peanuts are highly nutritious and very suitable for premigratory fat deposition in the Siskin (Cooper 1985, Sellers 1986).

Hence the modern success of British Siskins can be seen as owing much to a combination of afforestation, helping them in summer, and a change in feeding opportunities and behaviour, aiding overwinter survival despite the enhanced numbers of birds now involved.

Regional variation

Within Britain the continuing spread is southward, but regional trends cannot be quantified.

Trends elsewhere in Europe

No long-term trends are known; densities fluctuate markedly in line with eruptive behaviour. The Swedish point-count index for 1975-1986 shows low points in 1976, 1978 and 1986, and peaks in 1980-1983 and 1985 (Hustings 1988).

Linnet *Carduelis cannabina*

Present population trend: steep decline since 1977 or earlier.
Percentages of plots occupied 1968/78/88: farmland 87/86/85; woodland 35/45/27.
Latest estimate of breeding population: 700,000-800,000 pairs in Britain in 1982 (Hudson & Marchant 1984). Has decreased since.
Regional density rankings 1988: farmland W>S>WE>NI>EE>SE>NE.

Like its close relative, the Goldfinch, the Linnet was reported to have declined last century from the combined effects of agricultural improvement (which reduced arable weeds) and large-scale trapping for a thriving cagebird industry (Newton 1896). With hindsight, farming changes were probably less important than supposed, since food availability would be less of a problem where population size was being depressed by trapping. Following restrictions on the latter in the 1880s, and the beginnings then of agricultural recession, which deepened during the economic doldrums which followed the First World War, both species were able to increase again. With arable weeds being important in the diets of both these finches, they benefited greatly from the widespread neglect of farmland during that era. However, in recent years their population trends have been quite different.

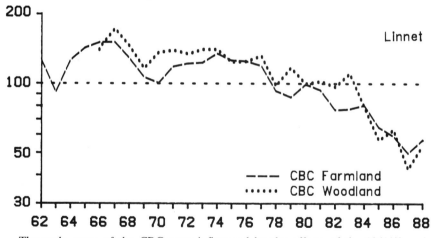

The early years of the CBC were influenced by the effects of the 1961/62 and 1962/63 severe winters, though not seriously for this species because it is a partial migrant. After that, index values rose to a peak in 1966-1967, but the trend has been steeply downward since 1977 and Linnets are now at an all-time low. The underlying reasons for this were investigated by O'Connor & Shrubb (1986*a*, *b*). The proximate reason seems to be reduced breeding success. Nest record card data indicate a post-hatching nestling mortality of about 36% since the mid-1960s, in contrast to the period before 1950 when nest success was higher and Linnets and their food plants were increasing. But the ultimate reason behind the modern decline is the chemical control of weeds associated with agricultural crops. The seeds of arable weeds

229

(especially chickweed and fat hen) are particularly important foods for Linnets (Newton 1972); the modern relative scarcity of these weeds has increased mortality through starvation, not only in the breeding season, but also in winter when foods for Linnets are at their scarcest. By 1980, local CBC results showed the Linnet decline to be general in all farming regions dominated by tillage, though numbers were stable in areas primarily of grassland. The steeper fall since about 1980 may be due to improved weed control in France and Iberia, where many of our Linnets winter (I. Newton, *in litt.*).

It remains to be seen how Linnets will fare under new EEC moves to reduce the "grain mountain" by limiting the acreages under cereal production. However, we may have one pointer. Since the 1970s some 250,000 ha of former cereals have been given over to the relatively new crop of oil-seed rape. Rape seeds are taken avidly by Linnets and other finches, and Linnets establish their territories close to rape fields when this crop is present (P.C. Lack, pers. comm.). This new crop must have gone some small way towards mitigating the effects of weed-seed reductions. Linnets begin to feed on the rape as soon as the seed is formed, in June, and rape stubble after the crop harvest, although short-lived, has provided a partial alternative to cereal stubble. However, what matters more is the food supply during the difficult late winter period, in France and Iberia as well as in Britain.

Regional variation

Population changes follow the pattern of agricultural land use (see above). Linnets have declined most in cereal-dominated areas, especially eastern England, and least in the pasture-dominated western regions.

Trends elsewhere in Europe

Swedish census data, beginning in 1970, show strong fluctuations but an overall decrease, with particularly sharp downturns in 1971 and 1977-1978. Dutch results during 1984-1987 suggest a progressive decline over the short period for which information is available (Hustings 1988). Danish point counts indicate a halving of the population between 1976 and 1979, but little change since then (DOFF 1989). In Finland, the population crashed after the severe winters of 1984/85 and 1986/87, and the species disappeared almost completely from the northern parts of the range (Hildén 1989).

Redpoll *Carduelis flammea*

Present population trend: now declining from high population levels achieved in the 1970s.
Percentages of plots occupied 1968/78/88: farmland 20/29/ 20; woodland 41/52/37.
Latest estimate of breeding population: 140,000-150,000 pairs in Britain (Hudson & Marchant 1984).
Regional density rankings 1988: all CBC habitats S> NE>NI>WE>SE>EE.

This often elusive finch has undergone several medium- or long-term fluctuations in Britain (Parslow 1973). Certainly in central and southern England, whence the best information has come, it increased considerably during the first decade of this century, when it bred especially in damp woodlands. It disappeared again from many lowland counties in the 1920s but, after two further decades at low population levels, numbers began to rise again about 1950, this time with a preference for breeding in young conifer plantations. This upsurge seems to have begun decidedly earlier in Scotland, with breeding populations expanding northwards into birchwoods and young forestry in Sutherland and Caithness around 1930. By 1950, Redpolls were colonising the west coast islands (Thom 1986).

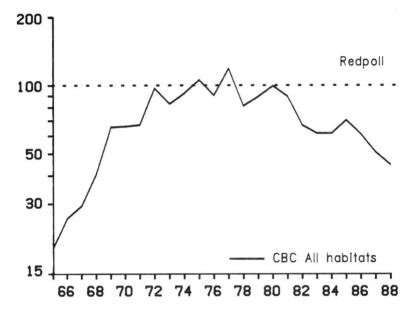

The early years of the CBC recorded progressive increases, and the population continued to rise, with fluctuations, to an index value in 1977 that was four times the level of ten years earlier. Yet these values began a downward trend after 1980 and are now back to a level comparable to that of the late 1960s, although still higher than when the Redpoll index began. There are few CBC plots in Scotland, and Thom (1986) doubted whether the population was declining there, since only in Dumfries and the Black Isle (Easter Ross) had decreases been reported. She felt that habitat preferences compelled Redpoll populations to be mobile over time, due to conifer plantations becoming less suitable as they mature.

In arctic and subarctic latitudes, Redpoll populations fluctuate in size, and to some extent in range, through an eruptive strategy, with density changes related to variations in the seed crops of birch and spruce (Antikainen et al 1980, Enemar & Nystrom 1981). Such eruptive movements are believed to occur, on a smaller scale, in Britain also. Certainly there are variations between years in the numbers of ringed birds recovered abroad in autumn and winter; these seem to be related to levels of seed abundance, especially of birch seed (Evans 1966, 1969; Boddy 1984). A particularly large emigration in 1977/78, after a successful breeding year, produced recoveries as far south and southeast as Portugal, south France, Switzerland and north Italy, and a temporary fall in the CBC index for 1978 was attributed to the scale of emigration the previous autumn (Lack 1986). Nevertheless, the longer-term decline remains unexplained, and the vicissitudes of Redpoll populations in Britain merit a detailed study.

Regional variation

The pattern seems to be an irregular one, which may be a consequence of the small sample sizes available for some regional comparisons. All regions experienced the 1950s-1970s increase. The subsequent fall appears to have been less pronounced in eastern and southern England, and steepest in northern England. Nevertheless, northern England and Scotland came highest for Redpoll in 1988 regional density rankings, and eastern and southern England lowest.

Trends elsewhere in Europe

Coincidental with the return to higher population levels in the 1950s, the British race *cabaret* (the "Lesser Redpoll") also found in the Alps and central Europe, began to colonise the northwest Continent from across the North Sea. Breeding was detected first in the Netherlands (Blok & Spaans 1962) and soon afterwards in Denmark (Hald-Mortensen 1970), and the subsequent spread has been both eastward into Germany and south Sweden (Gotmark 1981, Rettig 1985) and southward through Belgium into northwest France and the Channel Islands (Milbled 1979, Bourgaize 1982). The expansion still continues, and Redpolls are now present throughout much of central Europe, eastward to the Carpathians (Ernst 1988). In Bonn, West Germany, the species first bred in 1981 but by 1989 had increased to almost 1000 pairs (G.Rheinwald, pers.comm.). Ernst (1988) attributed the Lesser Redpoll's success on the Continent mainly to large-scale plantings of conifers: ornamentally in parks and gardens, as windbreaks and coastal protection, as well as in plantations. The central European and Alpine population is no longer isolated and, indeed, probably contributed to the expansion process.

Common Crossbill *Loxia curvirostra*

Present population trend: fluctuates widely, but increasing due to coniferous afforestation.
Percentages of plots occupied 1968/78/88: all CBC habitats 0/0/3.
Latest estimate of breeding population: fluctuates between irruptions; probably under 1000 birds in Britain in low years, but several thousands in good ones (Lack 1986).

Following studies of crossbill taxonomy (Knox 1975, Voous 1978), it is now accepted that three species in the genus *Loxia* breed or have bred in Britain. The Highlands of Scotland have their endemic Scottish Crossbill, a resident but not sedentary population of up to 400 pairs (see *Additional species*). The Parrot Crossbill, a rare irruptive visitor from Fenno-Scandia, bred successfully in Norfolk and almost certainly in Suffolk, Derbyshire and South Yorkshire also during 1983-1985, following a substantial influx of birds in autumn 1982 (Catley & Hursthouse 1985). The third species is the Common Crossbill, which has a wide though irregular breeding distribution in Britain that includes the Scottish Highlands.

It is questionable whether there was a regular British population of Common Crossbills before the 1950s. Rather, irruptions from the Continent at irregular intervals often led to the establishment of small and unstable breeding groups which typically, over a period of years, declined and eventually disappeared unless reinforced by further invasions. In the first half of this century the more persistent nesting groups were those in the Norfolk/Suffolk Brecks and in the New Forest in Hampshire. These also fluctuated in size from year to year, with very few pairs being found in some seasons. Breeding Common Crossbills were much scarcer then than they are nowadays.

Common Crossbill

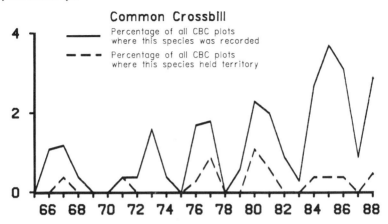

The CBC is unable to monitor Common Crossbill adequately. Few plots are occupied, and the species' propensity for early nesting, often in January or February before census visits begin, makes numbers especially difficult to assess. Ubiquity figures are available, but these reflect irruptions in June and July as well as presence in the breeding season.

Since the First World War there has been a great upsurge in conifer afforestation, involving various species of pine, spruce and larch. As these plantations have matured, much new crossbill habitat has come into being. However, Common Crossbill numbers still fluctuate greatly between years, in line with irruptions from abroad. The difference now is that the existence of large coniferous forests in some regions has allowed a regular stock of birds to become established here. Yet they remain opportunistic colonisers, moving between forests as their numbers or food supplies fluctuate (A.G. Knox, in Lack 1986). The British distribution remains a basically unstable one; smaller, more isolated woods and plantations are more likely to be used during and immediately after the irruption peaks (A.G. Knox, pers. comm.). This can be seen in the graph of CBC ubiquity values, in which there is good correspondence between the occurrence of non-breeding birds following irruption years and the smaller peaks for territory-holders.

The composition of modern silviculture is also relevant. Common Crossbills are adapted to feeding on spruce, the cones of which have long but rather thin scales (Lack 1971). The stouter bills of the Scottish and Parrot Crossbills are better suited to seed extraction from the cones of Scots pines which have thick, wooden scales. Hence commercial afforestations of Norway and Sitka spruce provide more typical feeding habitat for the Common Crossbill. These ecological adaptations are presumed to have evolved in northern Europe, where the crossbill species overlap geographically to a greater extent than they do elsewhere (Lack 1971). However, in British situations the Common Crossbill has shown itself able to live and breed in Scots pine; hence its distribution here is by no means restricted to spruce plantations. It is the irregular nature of seeding by conifers which underlies the periodic eruptions of crossbills. The cone crops of Scots pine fluctuate less than those of spruce, which is presumed to be the reason why Parrot Crossbill eruptions occur much less frequently than those of the common species (Reinikainen 1937).

Regional variation

Common Crossbills are now well established in the large plantations of Dumfries & Galloway, and from the Borders Region southwards into Northumberland. There may be several thousand birds in these areas in good years (Thom 1986). Other substantial groups occur on the North Yorkshire Moors and in the Peak District (Mather 1986), in the traditional areas of East Anglia and Hampshire, the Forest of Dean, and in South Devon where there are now over 100 pairs (Sitters 1988). Smaller numbers are known to be present at other sites in England, Wales and Scotland.

Trends elsewhere in Europe

Numbers and distribution both vary greatly from year to year, depending on food supplies and large-scale or local movements. The Swedish point-count index, 1975-1986, shows large peaks in 1975, 1977 and 1984-1985, with the 1984 index nearly forty times larger than that for 1978 (Hustings 1988).

Bullfinch *Pyrrhula pyrrhula*

Present population trend: has declined since mid-1970s.
Percentages of plots occupied 1968/78/88: farmland 60/78/74; woodland 69/83/80.
Latest estimate of breeding population: 300,000-350,000 pairs in Britain (Hudson & Marchant 1984).
Regional density rankings 1988: farmland NI>W>EE> SE>WE>NE; woodland NI>NE>EE>S>WE> SE>W.

There is a substantial body of evidence that Bullfinches increased and spread in England and Wales, Ireland and southern Scotland in the 1940s and 1950s, especially from about 1955 (Parslow 1973). This seemed to arise to some extent from an expansion in the range of habitats the species was able to occupy. In rural areas, where they had previously been more or less confined to thick cover, they moved increasingly into more open farmland habitats. This may have been facilitated by the huge decline then of an important predator along hedgerows, the Sparrowhawk. Around this time Bullfinches also spread into town parks and larger suburban gardens, and increasingly became a pest in orchards.

When the CBC started in 1962, Bullfinches were still increasing. High population levels were maintained up to the mid-1970s, but about 1975 the index values began to fall on farmland; this drop became steeper from 1978, but may now have stabilised at a new, lower level. In woodland also, index values have fallen since about 1978, but there the decline seemed still to be continuing in 1988. It is interesting to note that the Bullfinch decreases over the last ten years coincide with a recovery in Sparrowhawk numbers. However, the Bullfinch declines also span a period of extensive farmland hedgerow destruction. Intensive farming, especially where there is a regional concentration on arable crops, provides poor conditions for Bullfinches, though agricultural land which retains a good deal of secondary growth can be more attractive to the species than mature woodland (P.W. Greig-Smith, *in litt.*).

An analysis of nest record cards showed that there was a sharp improvement in Bullfinch fledging success in the early 1950s and a slow continuation of this trend

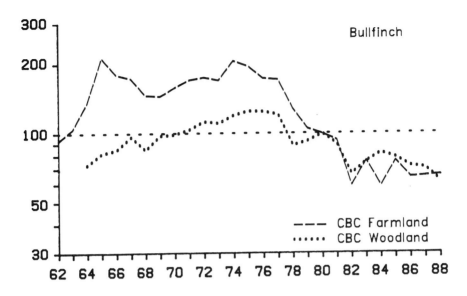

subsequently, while in the period from the early 1950s to 1977, but not later, there was a statistically significant increase in nest habitat diversity (O'Connor & Pearman 1987). These findings are in good agreement with the information previously available on the timing of the increase and that of the recent decline, and on the species' wider habitat usage during the period of high population levels.

It seems unlikely that the broad trends of the last four decades, described above, are related to fluctuations in the seed crops of tree species. These occur on shorter time-scales and are often local; they are more likely to be the explanation for small, temporary fluctuations such as those shown in the CBC graphs. The seeds of the ash tree comprise one of the Bullfinch's more important natural food sources. Elm seeds are also significant, as are those of bramble and dock. It is when the supplies of these natural foods are insufficient to last through a winter that the birds turn to eating buds in orchards and thereby become pests (Newton 1968, 1972).

Regional variation

The pattern of variation is unclear, since regional indices for woodland and farmland are not in harmony. Farmland values show a downward trend in all regions, more marked in eastern and western England than elsewhere, while levels have held up fairly well in southern England. In woodland indices, the fall is more apparent in southern England and in Wales than elsewhere. In 1988, densities were highest in Northern Ireland in both habitat divisions.

Trends elsewhere in Europe

The subspecies *pileata* is endemic to Britain and Ireland. Few data are available for Continental populations. Swedish point counts fluctuated irregularly up to 1980, but there was then a very steep decline to a low point in 1984 (Hustings 1988). Index values were high in Denmark during 1976-1978, but fell by two-thirds by 1982 and have since made only a partial recovery (DOFF 1989). Dutch data indicate a small overall increase from 1984 (Hustings 1988).

Hawfinch *Coccothraustes coccothraustes*

Present population trend: no reliable information.
Percentages of plots occupied 1968/78/88: farmland 1/1/4; woodland 8/13/10.
Latest estimate of breeding population: 5000-10,000 pairs in Britain (Sharrock 1976).

The Hawfinch is not indexed by the CBC, for it is a scarce and elusive species and occurs on too few plots. The male's song is soft and quiet and little known, and the birds themselves are shy and unapproachable, slipping away through the woodland canopy when disturbed. Even the distribution is imperfectly known. Both the Breeding and Winter Atlases (Sharrock 1976, Lack 1986) acknowledge that their maps are probably incomplete.

CBC ubiquity figures are shown in the graph, but it is unclear to what extent the changes indicated are fluctuations in Hawfinch numbers rather than variations in detection rate. It appears, however, that the overall trend is of stability as a territory-holder, with some suggestion of increase in the percentage of plots to which Hawfinch is a visitor.

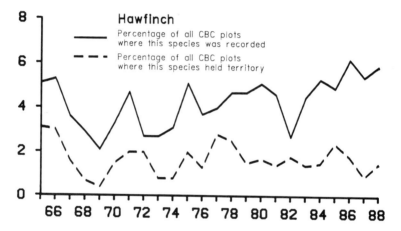

Hawfinch

— Percentage of all CBC plots where this species was recorded

– – – Percentage of all CBC plots where this species held territory

The view has been expressed that Hawfinches did not colonise England until the early 19th century and did not become at all widespread here until after 1850 (*e.g.* Parslow 1973). This is questionable, given the species' extreme secretiveness. The Hawfinch was certainly known to 17th- and 18th-century British writers, who seemed unsure of its status but whose reports included summer (cherry-time) observations. While contemporary ornithologists were confident that the species became less scarce during the second half of the 19th century, nevertheless the upsurge of breeding records after 1850 may owe a good deal to the widespread preoccupation with egg-collecting during that period.

Yet there are grounds for believing that Hawfinches did extend their range both westwards and northwards in the closing three or four decades of last century, while the first positive Scottish breeding record came as late as 1903 and the sole confirmed Irish nest was found in 1902. However, no major range changes are known to have occurred since 1950. Atlas registrations suggest that the species is most strongly represented southeast of a line from Hampshire northwards to the Chilterns and the Wash, though some breed as far north as Tayside.

Hawfinches frequent deciduous woodlands and timbered parklands, especially those containing such important food species as hornbeam, beech, wych elm, yew, sycamore and wild cherry. In Kent, and doubtless other fruit-growing regions, damson orchards are a frequently used winter habitat (J.J.M. Flegg, *in litt.*). Breeding numbers are thought to fluctuate, at least locally, and occupation of individual sites can be erratic, but there are no numerical data on national trends. Nor is year-to-year variation in the size of winter flocks a reliable guide to population change. Local distribution is dictated largely by food availability, depending on the distribution of favoured tree species and the quantity of the seed crops available at the time. Large winter flocks gather in some traditional localities when food is abundant there, but not otherwise.

For Britain, the standard source of information on Hawfinches is still Mountfort (1957), but breeding biology has been studied in the Netherlands by Bijlsma (1979), and winter ecology in Belgium by Desmet (1981).

Regional variation
Information is too sparse to allow comparisons of population trends or densities between regions.

Trends elsewhere in Europe
There is little information. Danish point counts suggest some increase since 1983 (DOFF 1989), while Dutch census data for 1984-1987 show fluctuations but no overall change (Hustings 1988).

Yellowhammer *Emberiza citrinella*

Present population trend: long-term overall stability.
Percentages of plots occupied 1968/78/88: farmland 86/84/87; woodland 51/58/49.
Latest estimate of breeding population: about 1½ million pairs in Britain (Hudson & Marchant 1984).
Regional density rankings 1988: farmland EE>W> SE>WE>S>NI>NE.

Typically, the Yellowhammer is a farmland bird in Britain, though breeding also on heaths and commons and in scrub and woodland edge. It has been suggested (Bell 1969) that Yellowhammers have been partly displaced from farmland into other habitats by an expansion of Reed Buntings into drier nesting sites. But more recent studies (Williamson & Batten 1976, O'Connor 1980a) have shown that the Yellowhammer's diversification of habitat use is due to overspill from the preferred farmland at times when its population level is high.

Prior to the establishment of the CBC in 1962 there was little evidence for any long-term change in Yellowhammer status, except that there was a decline, most noticeable in eastern England, in the late 1950s (Parslow 1973). This fall lasted in some regions until the mid-1960s and was most pronounced in predominantly cereal-growing counties. There can be little doubt that the underlying reason was the use then of organochlorines as seed dressings, the Yellowhammer being a granivorous bird. The severe winter of 1962/63 may have exacerbated the decrease. Nest record card analysis has shown that egg mortality rose sharply through the 1950s and early 1960s, but then fell in line with the implementation of 1966 restrictions on organochlorine pesticide usage (O'Connor & Pearman 1987).

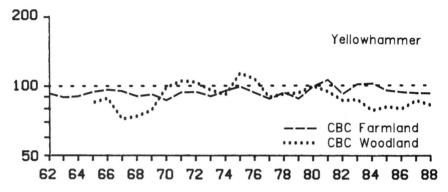

The farmland CBC shows no sign of any overall changes in numbers during the 1960s: indeed, the national farmland index values have been remarkably consistent right up to the present. Woodland values have shown more fluctuation, in keeping with the notion that this is suboptimal habitat; values were consistently higher in the 1970s, when there was a run of mild winters, than before or since. The higher population level in woodland in the 1970s represents an overflow from farmland. Nest record cards show that the recovery in population levels in the late 1960s has been associated with an increased diversity of nesting habitats. A positive correlation has been demonstrated between egg mortality and nest habitat diversity; this is a predictable consequence of population overflow from farmland into less favourable sites where breeding success is lower (O'Connor & Pearman 1987).

The seed-eating farmland passerines have been affected in different ways by modern farming changes. Those species having smaller body and bill sizes, such as Tree Sparrow and the cardueline finches, tend to specialise more on weed seeds. It is these birds which have declined in parallel with the recent spread of herbicide usage in weed control. In contrast, the larger granivores, such as the Chaffinch and Yellowhammer, exploit more the larger seeds such as cereal grain. Though there is less overwinter stubble nowadays, this is to some extent compensated for by increased cereal acreages, which mean more grain spillage overall. Hence the Yellowhammer has been able to maintain a stable population level.

Regional variation
O'Connor & Shrubb (1986a) reported the existence of local differences in trends. They claimed a tendency for numbers to fall in cereal-growing areas, where food resources are minimal in the difficult late winter period, but to be maintained in stock-rearing regions, where livestock food can be exploited by the birds in winter. However, the CBC regional indices indicate a marked farmland decline only in western England. The 1988 regional density rankings confirm a trend for high population levels in the east, with declining density towards the west and north. A decrease has been reported from Northern Ireland during the 1980s (Hutchinson 1989).

Trends elsewhere in Europe
No trends are known on the Continent; the species is apparently stable. Danish point-count data for 1976-1988 indicate some decline up to 1981 but a slow recovery

thereafter (DOFF 1989). Swedish mapping-census data show fluctuations but no overall trend between 1971 and 1984, though some slight increase subsequently (Hustings 1988). In Ireland there is some evidence of decrease and range contraction in recent decades (Hutchinson 1989).

Reed Bunting *Emberiza schoeniclus*

Present population trend: steep decline 1975-1983; now stable at lower level.
Percentages of plots occupied 1968/78/88: farmland 64/71/66; woodland 24/27/11; all WBS plots -/74/69.
Latest estimate of breeding population: about 400,000 pairs in Britain (Hudson & Marchant 1984).
Regional density rankings 1988: farmland NI>SE>W> EE>S>NE>WE.

Prior to 1950 there was no indication of any significant change in Reed Bunting status, except for some colonisation of Scottish islands at the very periphery of the British range. During the 1950s, however, it became evident that an increase was occurring in various parts of England and southern Scotland and that this was most evident through an ecological expansion into drier habitats, including farmland, more typical of Yellowhammers (*e.g.* Kent 1964, Bell 1969). In retrospect this change can be seen as overspill into suboptimal drier sites as a consequence of high population levels, following the run of generally mild winters which characterised the 1950s. The British population is mostly resident and, like those of northern and central Europe, its overall numbers are influenced by the severity of winter weather, especially in terms of snow cover since this is essentially a ground feeder (Prŷs-Jones 1984).

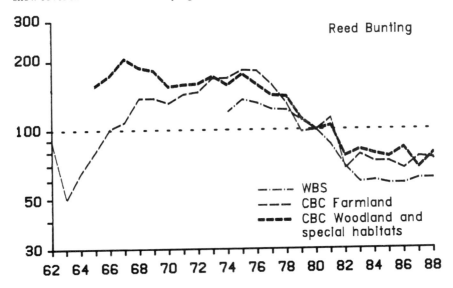

239

The first years of the CBC were influenced by the cold winters of 1961/62 and 1962/63, which severely depressed the Reed Bunting population. Thereafter there was a steady recovery, and high population levels were maintained until the mid-1970s in all CBC habitats, with the farmland increase being especially marked. A shallow decline began in 1976 or 1977, and this steepened through the adverse effects of the cold winters of 1978/79 and 1981/82, perhaps exacerbated on farmland by agricultural changes (see below). Farmland index values fell back to their level of the mid-1960s, and numbers in other habitats were halved. The WBS did not begin until 1974, at a time when Reed Bunting densities were certainly high. Thereafter, the WBS index values fell in line with those of the CBC, and have shown a parallel stability at a new, lower level since 1983. Recently, the two surveys both seem to have been monitoring essentially the population in waterway habitats, since most Reed Buntings on CBC sites are now in reed beds or along aquatic boundaries.

As already indicated, the high population levels prior to the mid-1970s were accompanied by increased habitat diversity through overspill. On farmland, Reed Buntings use weedy patches among crops and hedges with weedy bases, including neglected ditches. An Oxfordshire study (Gordon 1972) found that such territories were taken up later in the season than those in preferred wetland sites. Nest record data also show this trend towards nest habitat diversity increasing during the 1950s, but falling sharply in the 1960s because of cold winters and then a preference by survivors for wetland sites. Nest habitat diversity increased again in the late 1960s, as the population expanded once more, but declined after the mid-1970s for reasons that most probably include changes in farmland management (O'Connor & Pearman 1987). On farmland these birds probably use weedy areas in summer as much for nest sites as for food, though weeds become more important for food during the difficult winter period. Reed Bunting declines on farmland after the mid-1970s coincided with an increase in the use of herbicides for weed control (O'Connor & Shrubb 1986a). Though the species shows a strong association with oil-seed rape, the acreages of which are increasing (P.C. Lack, *in litt.*), this food source is not available in winter. Yet farmland changes can only be part of the answer, for there was contemporary decline on waterways also. The return to colder winters (on average) after 1978/79 will also have been an important factor in the recent downward trend. Thompson (1988) noted a big increase from 1978/79 onwards in the numbers of Reed Buntings visiting feeding stations in suburban gardens in midwinter.

Regional variation

The farmland indices have fallen in all regions except for Wales where, however, CBC samples are small. The 1988 density rankings on farmland do not show a clear pattern.

Trends elsewhere in Europe

In both Denmark and Sweden, census returns indicated a population trough in 1979, but subsequently a return to previous levels (DOFF 1989, Hustings 1988). In the Netherlands there has been a small downward trend since 1984 (Hustings 1988). Reed Buntings are increasing long-term in Ireland (Hutchinson 1989).

Corn Bunting *Miliaria calandra*

Present population trend: decline since the early 1970s, much steeper since 1981.
Percentages of plots occupied 1968/78/88: farmland 35/33/26; woodland 4/3/2.
Latest estimate of breeding population: about 30,000 pairs in Britain and Ireland (Sharrock 1976); 95% of occupied squares were then in Britain.
Regional density rankings 1988: all CBC habitats EE> NE>SE.

Long-term oscillations in the fortunes of the Corn Bunting have been linked to the state of arable farming in this country. Following the agricultural revolution, completed early last century, this became a common bird in cultivated districts "though somewhat capricious in its choice of localities" (Morris 1863). A decline in arable farming began towards the end of the 19th century, reaching its nadir during the recession between the two world wars. This was accompanied by a national decline of Corn Buntings. By 1940 they had disappeared from large areas of the country, especially in the north and west. Following agricultural revival during the Second World War, the species expanded again and continued to increase until the 1960s.

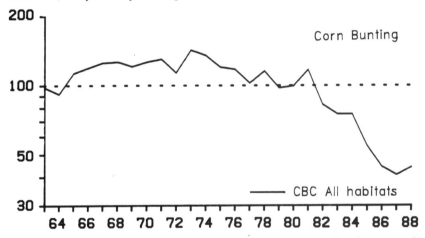

The CBC index is derived from plots of all habitats; in practice, however, the farmland contribution is much the largest. The early years of the CBC reflected the later stages of the post-1940s increase, with a high point being reached in the early 1970s. Since then Corn Buntings have again been in steady decline, despite temporary fluctuations, and the index is now at one-third the level which applied 20 years ago. The Breeding Atlas estimate of 30,000 pairs (Sharrock 1976) was surely too low a figure for 1968-72, but may now be approximately correct.

The Corn Bunting's name is derived from its long-appreciated association with cereal crops. More recently it has been realised that its distribution is linked especially to that of barley. In the western Midlands, Harrison *et al* (1982) demonstrated the close link since the 1930s between Corn Bunting numbers and the availability of barley, with barley acreage reaching a peak in the mid-1960s. This association was confirmed by O'Connor & Shrubb (1986*a*) who found it at all levels, from national statistics even down to individual farms. Hence the Corn Bunting decline since the early 1970s seems to be linked to reduced acreages of barley, for wheat has become the dominant cereal crop. Thompson & Gribbin (1986) studied a population of Corn Buntings in Lancashire, where barley comprised 41% of their crop area but held 60% of Corn Bunting territories and 79% of their polygynous matings (males paired to more than one female). These authors suggested that, since polygyny seems to be less frequent in other crops, the progressive reduction in barley acreages will result in reduced overall breeding productivity which will itself contribute to the decline in Corn Buntings. However, there is no evidence that individual females raise more young in polygynous than in monogamous matings: indeed, the reverse may be true (D. Harper, pers. comm.). A further possible contributory reason which has been advanced (Macdonald 1965, Terry 1986) is that the late breeding season of this species, with peak activity in July, renders it more susceptible to nest loss through the earlier cropping which occurs under modern farming regimes.

Regional variation

The recent decline has included contraction of range, such that Corn Buntings have virtually disappeared from Wales and southwestern England, and in Scotland occur now mainly in eastern coastal counties, though an isolated population still persists in the Western Isles. Evans & Flower (1967) suggested that higher rainfall in the west may restrict distribution there. Elsewhere, CBC regional indices show the steepest decline in eastern England, where wheat-growing predominates, as compared with only a small suggestion of decline in northern England. Scottish data are too few for separate analysis; latterly, no Corn Buntings have been present on Scottish CBC plots.

Trends elsewhere in Europe

There are trends towards reduction in northwestern Europe, possibly related to pesticide usage (Yeatman 1971), and strong decrease over much of central Europe (G. Rheinwald, pers. comm.). Danish point counts indicated a decrease of more than one-half between 1981 and 1988 (DOFF 1989). Corn Buntings have been in decline in Ireland throughout this century, and the species is now rare and localised there (Hutchinson 1989).

Additional species

As explained earlier, the species treated at length in this book are those for which CBC, WBS or other BTO census data are available. The following briefer entries for an additional 59 species are included in order to provide more comprehensive coverage. With their inclusion, the book discusses population trends in all terrestrial and freshwater species which have a current British breeding population of at least 50 pairs. Seabirds are omitted because a detailed treatment of these has been prepared elsewhere (Lloyd *et al*, in press); for practical reasons the seabird exclusions extend to inland colonies of gulls and terns. Those species with fewer than 50 breeding pairs in Britain (except for a few incipient ferals) are monitored by the Rare Breeding Birds Panel, and their population trends are already documented in the RBBP annual reports in *British Birds*. Another reason for excluding the rarities is that the available information concerning some of them is known to be incomplete.

Population size estimates of all British breeding species, including both seabirds and rare breeders, are given in Appendix 4.

Red-throated Diver *Gavia stellata*

Believed to be increasing, though the higher numbers reported recently are due in part to surveys being more thorough. In particular, the Shetland total has been revised upwards to 700 pairs (Gomersall *et al* 1984), while there are now thought to be at least 100 pairs in Orkney and 40-50 pairs in the Western Isles. With the breeding range also covering the northern and western Highlands and the Inner Hebrides, for which only some local figures are available, the current Scottish population is probably in the region of 1200-1500 pairs (Stroud *et al* 1989). Whereas the Black-throated Diver requires large lochs where it can feed as well as breed, the Red-throated breeds on the much more numerous small hill lochs and *dubh-lochain* and often feeds at sea (Bundy 1976, Merrie 1978).

Black-throated Diver *Gavia arctica*

Either stable or in gradual decline. Black-throated Divers are practically confined as breeding birds to the northern and western Highlands and the Western Isles. They breed on large oligotrophic lochs which contain islands and shallow water for fishing. Both Parslow (1973) and Sharrock (1976) estimated that the population numbered about 150 pairs. Subsequent detailed surveys indicated 151 territorial pairs in 1985 (Campbell & Talbot 1987) and 154 breeding pairs in 1986-1988 (Stroud *et al* 1989). Because the data are reliable only for recent years, the population trend is uncertain. However, breeding success in Scotland is consistently poor and below the level indicated by a Scandinavian study as necessary for a stable population (see Stroud *et al* 1989), at least without immigration for which there is no evidence in Scotland. The main causes of nest failure have been egg predation and water-level fluctuations (Campbell & Mudge 1989).

Slavonian Grebe *Podiceps auritus*

Increasing slowly. Since the first case of proven breeding in Inverness-shire in 1908, a small but growing population has built up in the Highlands, mainly in the original county. There, they prefer shallow mesotrophic lochs, larger than those used elsewhere by Black-necked Grebes and often with less emergent vegetation (Sharrock 1976). Apparently no more than 20 pairs were known in Scotland in 1958 (Bannerman 1959); but there were 48-51 pairs present in 1972, 58-77 pairs in 1979 and 68-87 pairs in

1986 (Sharrock 1976, Spencer et al 1989). Human disturbance and fluctuating water levels seem to be the main limiting factors.

Greylag Goose *Anser anser*

Increasing due to growth of feral stocks. The indigenous British stock has declined over the last two centuries, and is now confined to the northwest Scottish Highlands and Western Isles; it now numbers 500-700 pairs in total (Thom 1986), with 300 pairs or more in the Uists where there has been a recent increase (Patterson 1987). Feral populations arose in the 1930s and have increased subsequently, in England as well as in south and central Scotland. Major increase dates from the 1970s, when wildfowling organisations founded many new feral groups; the population grew from 1700 birds in the late 1960s to an estimated 13,000-14,000 birds by 1985-1986 (Owen & Salmon 1988). The steepest growth has been in central and southern England, where gravel-pit complexes provide suitable habitat, despite the presence there already of Canada Geese. There are large non-breeding components in goose populations, but there must now be in excess of 2000 breeding pairs of Greylags in Britain.

Egyptian Goose *Alopochen aegyptiacus*

Stable or increasing slightly. The feral population is based on Norfolk with, until recently, only scattered pairs elsewhere. There were estimated to be 300-400 birds in the 1960s and 1970s (Sharrock 1976). No major change is known since then, but nor has there been a comprehensive survey. This species' habit of nesting in early spring, when weather is often cold and wet, is likely to prevent it from ever becoming numerous here (Owen et al 1986). Nevertheless, there has been a distinct spread into northern Suffolk during the last ten years, in the coastal fringe as well as in the Brecks (*Suffolk Bird Repts.*).

Wigeon *Anas penelope*

Perhaps stable in recent decades, but has increased this century. The population was estimated stable at 350 pairs by Yarker & Atkinson-Willes (1971) and at 300-500 pairs by Sharrock (1976), and is not known to have changed since (Thom 1986). British breeding Wigeon are found mainly on moorland pools and lochs along the upland spine of the country, from northernmost Highland to the northern Pennines. Recent local assessments have been made for Badenoch and Strathspey (up to 50 pairs: Dennis 1984), Loch Leven (35-46 pairs: Wright 1986) and Ettrick Forest (30-39 pairs: Thomson & Dougall 1988), all of importance for holding 10% or more of the British population.

Gadwall *Anas strepera*

Continuing increase of the essentially feral British population. Gadwall have been breeding in England since 1850; initial releases and population growth were in East Anglia, from which the species has spread with the aid of further liberations at other, widely scattered sites. The much smaller numbers breeding in Scotland since 1909 are of uncertain origin, but a feral source is possible for these also (Fox 1988). By 1983 the British population had risen to about 600 pairs. There were signs then that stability had been reached in eastern England, though increase was still occurring in the southeast and southwest, at 9-10% per annum in September counts (Fox 1988). Breeding is also regular now in Lancashire, Cheshire and Anglesey. Supplementary liberations must have had a significant impact while the population was relatively small; but these releases have been phased out in the 1980s, and recent expansion is

244

due to this species' ability to exploit such man-made habitats as reservoirs and gravel pits (Fox & Salmon 1989).

Garganey *Anas querquedula*
Some long-term decline has occurred through habitat loss, but numbers fluctuate. Breeding Garganey often select rushy marshland, wet meadows, and rough grasslands intersected with ditches or dykes; but the availability of habitats such as these has been reduced by drainage and other agricultural improvements. Parslow (1973) thought that British breeding numbers were below 100 pairs in the 1960s, while Sharrock (1976) estimated 50-70 pairs in the period 1968-1972. Records submitted to the RBBP since 1980 indicate that Garganey numbers fluctuate, generally in the range 40-60 pairs, but rising to 90 pairs or more in occasional years of peak spring influx such as 1982 (Spencer *et al* 1989). East Anglia and southeast England are the principal regions for them.

Shoveler *Anas clypeata*
Major increase this century, probably still continuing but more slowly. This trend has been in line with population growth in western Europe generally (Voous 1960, Parslow 1973). The Breeding Atlas estimated a population of about 1000 pairs in the years around 1970 (Sharrock 1976); and September counts in the 1980s suggested breeding numbers around 1000-1500 pairs (Owen *et al* 1986). Most are in eastern and southeastern England, but there are scattered pairs as far north and west as Orkney and the Western Isles.

Pochard *Aythya ferina*
Increase and northward spread over the last 100 years, perhaps continuing more slowly. Pochard breed relatively seldom on man-made waters such as reservoirs or gravel pits, and so have not increased to anything like the degree shown by the Tufted Duck. Yarker & Atkinson-Willes (1971) estimated the British breeding population at 200 pairs; but Sharrock (1976) thought it higher, possibly as high as 400 pairs, since confirmed or probable breeding was reported from 257 10-km squares during the Breeding Atlas and some of these had several pairs. However, the Breeding Atlas records were a composite of five years of fieldwork, and breeding is sporadic at some sites. Far more Pochard nest in the south of Britain than in the north: of 173 pairs known to the RBBP in 1987, an incomplete total since no count had been received from the important county of Norfolk, 62% were in southeastern England (including Suffolk and Hampshire) and only 5% in Scotland (Spencer *et al* 1989).

Eider *Somateria mollissima*
Considerable increase and spread since about 1850, though it is uncertain whether this is continuing other than locally. The Breeding Atlas estimated 15,000-25,000 pairs in Britain and Ireland, with the Irish contribution being small (Sharrock 1976). Winter counts suggest an overall increase of 30-40% since the 1960s (Owen *et al* 1986). Breeding numbers are still increasing locally in eastern and southwestern Scotland (Thom 1986); but in Shetland there was a fall of 25-30% between 1977 and 1984 in the size of moulting flocks, following abnormal mortality there in 1979 and 1980 (Heubeck 1987).

Common Scoter *Melanitta nigra*

Population trend is uncertain. The British breeding stock is small, and for the most part confined to moorland lochs in northern and western Scotland, where pairs preferentially select water-bodies of lowest acidity (Fox *et al* 1989). Because of the remoteness of many nesting sites, there has been doubt about the numbers involved (Thom 1986). However, recent work has ascertained that there are 100-115 pairs, with at least 50 pairs in Sutherland and Caithness and 30 pairs in Inverness-shire (Stroud *et al* 1989, Fox *et al* 1989). Because this clarification is so recent the population trend is uncertain, except that there have been some declines at peripheral sites in the southwest. In Northern Ireland, on the other hand, there has been an obvious decline, with numbers in Co. Fermanagh having fallen from 140-150 pairs in the 1960s to only 7 pairs by 1988 (Partridge 1989).

Goldeneye *Bucephala clangula*

Increasing. The present population is the result of a colonisation which began in 1970 in Inverness-shire. Aided by large-scale provision of nestboxes, which most birds use, numbers of laying females rose to 12-15 in 1978, 27 in 1982, and 80 in 1987 (Dennis & Dow 1984, Spencer *et al* 1989). There were at least 87 occupied nests in 1988 (Stroud *et al* 1989). So far, population growth has been concentrated in the original county, with little sign of expansion. The birds breed in coniferous forests close to water. Nestbox provision has been the key to their success, for there are shortages of natural nesting holes in these areas since forests are not allowed to mature (Dennis & Dow 1984, Stroud *et al* 1989).

Red-breasted Merganser *Mergus serrator*

Much *increase and range expansion* occurred during the first half of this century, and this still continues in Wales and northern England. In Scotland, which retains much the largest numbers, the species is now stable or increasing only slightly, with spread towards the southeast but some decline in the northeast where it is persecuted on salmon rivers (Thom 1986). Atkinson-Willes (1970) estimated 2000 pairs in Britain; while Sharrock (1976) suggested 2000-3000 pairs in Britain and Ireland together, of which the British portion, based on numbers of occupied 10-km squares, would be 1500-2200 pairs. These numbers are compatible with those derived from autumn and winter duck counts (Owen *et al* 1986).

Goosander *Mergus merganser*

Substantial *increase and spread* since initial colonisation, and this still continues locally. After colonising central Scotland in the 1870s, breeding Goosanders spread over the Highland counties and then, in the 1920s and 1930s, southwards into the Southern Uplands. In the 1940s they reached northern England, and since 1972 they have been moving into the uplands of Wales. Surveys by Meek & Little (1977) and Lovegrove (1978) indicated a total of 925-1250 pairs: 735-950 in Scotland, 180-290 in northern England, and 10 in Wales. There are now thought to be about 100 pairs in Wales (Tyler 1986, RSPB unpubl.). Since 1980, 1-3 pairs have nested in Devon (Sitters 1988).

Ruddy Duck *Oxyura jamaicensis*

Approaching stability after earlier major increase. The British feral population dates from 1960, and arose from escapes from waterfowl collections. In the early years, breeding was centred on the small reedy meres of the English West Midlands, but pairs spread far beyond this, even into Scotland and Northern Ireland, as numbers increased. There were over 50 pairs in 1975, and probably 200-250 pairs by 1982 (Hudson 1976, Hudson & Marchant 1984). There is no later breeding estimate; but peak counts in winter, when these ducks are more concentrated on reservoirs, rose from 1400 birds in 1982/83 to 2400 in 1986/87 and the two subsequent winters. Recent stability of winter counts suggests that the phase of rapid increase has now passed.

Red Kite *Milvus milvus*

Increasing slowly. The Red Kite was persecuted to extinction in England and Scotland during the 19th century, and reduced to no more than 12 birds in Wales by 1905. There were no more than 10 pairs in any year up to 1939, but increase during the Second World War and its aftermath resulted in there being 15-18 pairs by 1954 (Salmon 1970). Following setbacks in the 1950s and 1960s, due to the effects of myxomatosis and organochlorine pesticides, numbers have been recovering slowly; there were 26 nests in 1972, 42 pairs with 30 nests built in 1980, and 57 pairs with 50 nests built in 1987 (Davis & Davis 1973, Spencer *et al* 1989). The age of first breeding varies between 2 and 7 years; pre-breeding pairs hold territory and often build a nest in the season prior to laying their first egg (Newton *et al* 1989). Human interference is still the main restriction on the rate of increase, though land-use changes in the Welsh uplands have not been helpful (Newton *et al* 1981). The population remains confined to Wales; but the NCC and RSPB are currently attempting reintroductions to other parts of Britain, using birds largely of Continental origin (Stroud *et al* 1989).

Marsh Harrier *Circus aeruginosus*

Increasing, especially in recent years. Marsh Harriers became extinct in Britain in the 19th century, due to wetland drainage and persecution, but recolonised in 1911. Initially, the increase was very slow, and there were only 15 nests by 1958; this was followed by a decline to only one nest in 1971 (Day 1984). Recovery then began, and increase has been marked since the mid-1970s, probably linked to high breeding numbers in the Netherlands (Spencer 1983). In Britain there were 20 nests in 1980, 32 in 1984, and at least 60 in 1989 (Spencer *et al* 1989, Glue 1989). However, further population growth is likely to be limited by the shortage of suitable *Phragmites* reed beds in Britain, even though some pairs now nest in arable crops (Everett 1989).

Hen Harrier *Circus cyaneus*

Perhaps now stable, but with some local declines, following earlier major increase. 19th-century persecution all but banished breeding Hen Harriers to Orkney and the Western Isles, where the only viable populations were retained. Reductions after the Second World War in the extent of gamekeeping and related amount of heather burning, together with increased afforestation of moorland, combined to allow these birds to recolonise the Scottish mainland in the 1950s; since then they have increased considerably. By the 1960s a few pairs were breeding in northern England and in Wales also, though there has not been a large spread in those regions; indeed, there now appears to be a decline due to persecution and habitat loss. By the mid-1980s there were thought to be about 450 breeding females in the United Kingdom (Cadbury *et al* 1988); the number of females is the appropriate measure because some males practise polygyny. Hen Harriers still suffer very considerably from persecution on grouse moors; and, though young plantation is good habitat for them, large blocks of maturing afforestation eventually reduce upland hunting ranges.

Goshawk *Accipiter gentilis*

Present feral population is *increasing slowly*. The original population of Scotland and northern England had become extinct by the 1880s as a result of persecution (Baxter & Rintoul 1953). The present stock is believed to be descended from falconers' escapes and releases. There is evidence for such pairs having been present in Sussex as early as the 1920s (Meinertzhagen 1950); but it was only during the Breeding Atlas years, 1968-1972, that there came realisation that breeding in Britain was occurring regularly in several areas, probably 10-30 pairs in all (Sharrock 1976). Knowledge grew during the 1970s, and Newton (1984) assessed the population size as about 70 pairs and still increasing. In one unidentified study area, comprising just 270 sq.kms of lowland mixed woodland and farmland, a local population of 15-20 pairs built up over the years 1979-1986 (Anon 1989). Reports submitted to the RBBP suggest that there could now be over 100 pairs in Britain, despite continuing persecution which is relentless in some counties (Lack 1986, Spencer *et al* 1989).

Golden Eagle *Aquila chrysaetos*

Probably stable now. Intense persecution in the 18th and 19th centuries eliminated Golden Eagles from Ireland, England and Wales, and greatly reduced the Scottish population. With numbers of hill shepherds and gamekeepers lower after the First World War, the species was able to increase again and even spread into areas formerly occupied by the White-tailed Eagle. Home ranges of the Golden Eagle have been remarkably constant this century, so one can estimate that there is room in Scotland for about 600 pairs (Dennis *et al* 1984). These authors checked these sites in 1982-1983 and found 511 occupied: 424 by pairs, and 87 by single birds. This exceeded earlier estimates of numbers of pairs, but the difference was probably due to improved methodology and coverage. In 1982-1983 the biggest regional proportions of vacant home ranges were in the eastern and far northwestern Highlands (22-24%), the lowest in the central and western Highlands (8-9%) (Dennis *et al* 1984). Winter food supplies (carrion) are higher in the west, while summer food supplies and related breeding success are higher in the east (Watson *et al* 1987, 1989); but in the eastern Highlands there is much more persecution, especially on sporting estates. Watson *et al* (1987) predict some decline in certain areas as the hunting grounds at middle altitudes are lost to growing conifer plantations. There has been one breeding pair in the English Lake District since 1969.

Osprey *Pandion haliaetus*

Increasing after modern colonisation. Scottish Ospreys declined through persecution in the 18th and 19th centuries, and breeding ceased in 1916, until recolonisation began in 1954 (Sandeman 1957). After a slow start, due to various setbacks, numbers rose to 7 pairs in 1968, 25 pairs (of which 20 laid eggs) in 1980, and 51 pairs (of which 44 laid eggs) in 1987 (Spencer *et al* 1989). The increase is continuing, and there are probably more Ospreys breeding in Scotland now than at any time since the 1840s. The productivity of Scottish pairs is similar to that of healthy populations abroad (Dennis 1983), but the rapid population growth may have been aided by immigration of Scandinavian birds. The building of artificial nest foundations in selected trees has encouraged the settlement of new pairs, and enabled some young pairs to begin breeding a year earlier than they would otherwise have done – since their first season together is normally occupied with nest construction.

Merlin *Falco columbarius*

Long-term decline. Widespread decreases have been noted this century, with the rate of decline having accelerated since the 1950s. Other raptors also declined then, due to organochlorine pesticides, but the Merlin alone failed to recover after restrictions were placed on the most persistent of these agrochemicals in the 1960s. Newton *et al* (1982) found that the predominantly ground-nesting British Merlins have a lower breeding success than do more northerly populations which frequently nest in trees; hence even small reductions in breeding success here, through pesticides (still present at reduced levels), habitat loss and disturbance, can tip the balance into population decline. Bibby & Nattrass (1986) estimated the British population at 550-650 pairs. Decline is still continuing in some areas, such as Orkney (Meek 1988), but in others there seems to have been something of a recent revival, as in Northumberland where birds seem to be nesting increasingly on trees at the edges of plantations (B. Little, pers. comm.).

Peregrine *Falco peregrinus*

Continuing slow increase: the species has recovered well from the pesticide-induced population collapse in the late 1950s. About 850 territories were known in Britain during the 1930s, but Peregrine numbers were reduced by culling in the Second World War to protect homing pigeons in military use. There was partial recovery, but then even more serious losses in the late 1950s and early 1960s that were due to organochlorine pesticides. By 1962, only about 360 pairs remained and many of these were failing to breed (Ratcliffe 1963). A recovery began when restrictions were placed on the use of the more persistent of these compounds, and by 1981 the British population had doubled to about 700-750 pairs (Ratcliffe 1984). Recovery was uneven, however; in North Wales, northern England and the Scottish Southern Uplands the densities were the highest ever recorded, though Peregrines remained absent from many former territories on coastal cliffs in southern England. There could now be around 1000 pairs in the United Kingdom (Cadbury *et al* 1988).

Red Grouse *Lagopus lagopus*

Long-term overall decline, but major cyclical fluctuations occur in some areas. Spring densities range from 2-3 pairs per sq.km on wet and acidic ground to 100 pairs per sq.km on prime sporting estates, where the substrate is base-rich and where heather quality is managed through rotational burning. Such management techniques maintain populations at levels probably higher than they would be otherwise or in a natural situation. Red Grouse have declined markedly during the last 50 years, for various reasons which may include reduced habitat management, less gamekeeping and predator control, outbreaks of parasitic and parasite-borne diseases, local overgrazing by sheep and red deer, and loss of moorland to forestry and agriculture (Watson & Miller 1976, Potts *et al* 1984, Hudson 1986). Annual shooting bags averaged 2½ million birds in Britain in the years preceding the First World War, but have varied recently between 260,000 and 660,000 (Harradine 1983). Further decline in Scotland during 1976-1982 was linked to some poor breeding seasons and to high predation levels during snowy winters; there was improvement there in 1987 and 1988, after two mild winters (Hudson *et al* 1989). There is no reliable estimate of the size of the British population, though it is assumed to be below 500,000 pairs (Sharrock 1976), and probably now well below that figure.

Ptarmigan *Lagopus mutus*

Some local declines, but population levels fluctuate. There seem to be natural cycles of abundance in Scottish Ptarmigan, with a periodicity of about ten years; spring densities range from zero on some hills in trough years to 65 pairs per sq.km on the richest ground in peak years (Watson 1965). In winters following peak years the Scottish population may number 10,000-15,000 birds (Lack 1986). There have been some long-term peripheral range contractions, in the Hebrides and Southern Uplands, but not within the main range. There have, however, been local declines in the vicinity of Cairngorm ski-lifts, due to nest predation from corvids attracted by waste food dropped by visitors and to the Ptarmigan themselves colliding with ski-lift wires (Watson 1982, Thom 1986).

Black Grouse *Tetrao tetrix*

Long-term decline. Black Grouse have disappeared in historical times from large areas of England, most recently from Exmoor, and are still declining over most of their current British range (Lack 1986, Hudson 1989). Following particularly steep falls between the two world wars, shooting bags are now barely one-fifth of what they were in the early years of this century (Tapper & Clements 1987). These changes in Britain are paralleled by decreases and range contractions over much of temperate Europe (Hudson 1989). Habitat changes, in particular the loss of habitat mosaics, seem to be at the root of Black Grouse declines. These birds prefer sparse birch and pine woodland near to moorland and insect-rich bogs; but this mosaic is disturbed or destroyed by burning, which lets in bracken, by overgrazing, since sheep compete for food plants and destroy nesting cover, by new plantings of conifers, which are suitable for grouse only in their early stages, and by modernisation of traditional low-intensity agriculture (Lovenbury *et al* 1978, Grove *et al* 1988, Hudson 1989). No reliable estimate of the British population is possible, but numbers must be nearer to 10,000 than to 100,000 birds (Lack 1986).

Capercaillie *Tetrao urogallus*

Fluctuates irregularly; currently in decline. Following 19th-century reintroductions, Capercaillies spread along east Highland valleys to occupy most suitable woodlands. Open woodlands of Scots pine, with an abundant field layer, hold more birds and produce more young than do planted conifers (Moss *et al* 1979). Population densities were unusually high around 1970, at the time of the Breeding Atlas, so that shooting became more commercial and a source of income to many estates. This may have contributed to the recent decline, for in some places shooting continued after the birds had become scarce (R. Moss, in Lack 1986). A questionnaire survey of Forestry Commission personnel in 1986 found that numbers had fallen over the previous five years in 80% of woods which had previously held the species; it was suspected that the Scottish population had dropped to 1000-2000 birds (Stroud *et al* 1989).

Golden Pheasant *Chrysolophus pictus*

Stable or decreasing locally. There are small feral populations in Galloway, the East Anglian Brecks, and on the South Downs in Hampshire and West Sussex, plus scattered pairs elsewhere derived from independent escapes or releases. Most nest in young conifer plantations, not yet thinned or brashed, or in mature woodlands with a dense rhododendron understorey; yew woods are also favoured. Sharrock (1976) offered an estimate of 500-1000 pairs in total; no later figures are available. There has been a decline in Galloway in the 1980s (Thom 1986), though trends elsewhere are unclear. This species is unlikely ever to become widespread here, due to the fragmented nature of suitable habitat in lowland Britain (Lack 1986).

Lady Amherst's Pheasant *Chrysolophus amherstiae*

Decreasing. A feral population in Bedfordshire and neighbouring parts of Buckinghamshire and Hertfordshire was estimated at 100-200 pairs by Sharrock (1976). Declines have occurred in the 1980s at some of its former strongholds, due to habitat changes, cold winters and wet springs (*Bedfordshire Nat*. 42, 1988), while there have been few recent sightings from the Buckinghamshire/Hertfordshire border. Like the Golden Pheasant, this species occupies young conifer woodland, at the stage where undergrowth has died back following canopy closure, but before the growing trees have thinned out enough to let ground vegetation emerge again (Lack 1986). It also occurs in mature woodlands where a dense understorey of rhododendron provides suitable cover.

Water Rail *Rallus aquaticus*

Population trend unknown. Sharrock (1976) suggested that there were between 2000 and 4000 pairs in Britain and Ireland together; 70% of occupied squares were then in Britain. No later figure is available. With its dense marshland habitat, and tendency in the breeding season to be silent during the day, this is an extremely difficult species to survey or census. Mortality certainly rises in severe winters when shallow waters and mud margins are frozen, so it is quite possible that Water Rail numbers have been affected by the several cold winters in the last ten years.

Corncrake *Crex crex*

Major long-term decline. Decrease and range contraction date at least from the 1880s, and breeding Corncrakes had virtually disappeared from England and Wales by the 1960s (Parslow 1973, Sharrock 1976). A national census in 1978-1979 found 700-746 calling birds, of which all but 12 were in Scotland, and 71% of the total were on the islands of the Scottish west coast (Cadbury 1980). A repeat survey in 1988 found 551-596 calling birds, all but 5 in Scotland and 90% on the Inner Hebrides and Western Isles (Hudson *et al*, in press). This represented an overall decline of 15-26% between the two censuses and further concentration into the Hebridean islands. Assessment of habitat requirements indicates that earlier and more mechanised mowing of hayfields (Norris 1947*b*) is not the sole reason for the decline. Agricultural improvements have reduced the diversity of plant species in grasslands, and presumably the invertebrate fauna also. Moreover, tall and rank vegetation is required by the birds when they arrive in spring, and this has become scarce except in remoter areas where traditional farming methods are still practised (Cadbury 1980).

Avocet *Recurvirostra avosetta*

Increasing after modern recolonisation. A former breeding population in coastal east and southeast England had dwindled and disappeared before 1850. Recolonisation attempts began in the early 1940s, when much of the east coast was closed off by wartime defences. Two small colonies were located in Suffolk in 1947 and, aided by protective measures, the numbers there continued to grow. In more recent years, Avocets have also bred regularly in Norfolk, Essex and Kent. Numbers have been increasing since about 1930 in northwest Europe generally, and especially in Denmark, West Germany and the Netherlands; recolonisation of England can be seen as part of that same pattern of population growth. The new British population exceeded 100 pairs for the first time in 1968 (Cadbury & Olney 1978), and by 1988 it totalled 385 pairs (Stroud *et al* 1989). Hill (1988) and Cadbury *et al* (1989) have discussed population growth in relation to conservation measures and the dynamics of existing colonies.

Stone-curlew *Burhinus oedicnemus*

Long-term decline and range contraction. Though formerly widespread over open country – wolds, heaths and downs – in eastern and southern England, some contraction of breeding range has been evident since the mid-19th century. There were local increases during the 1920s and 1930s, however, when agriculture was in recession. But since the 1940s Stone-curlews have been affected progressively by increased cultivation of marginal land, by conversions of grassland to arable and of root crops to cereals, by scrub growth after myxomatosis depressed rabbit numbers, and by afforestation of heathland. The primary requirement of these birds is bare ground or sparse vegetation kept short by grazing pressure. The British population may have numbered 1000-2000 pairs in the 1930s; but by the mid-1980s it was reduced to 135-155 pairs, almost all in the East Anglian Brecks or on Wiltshire/Hampshire downland (Green 1988*b*, Stroud *et al* 1989).

Little Ringed Plover *Charadrius dubius*

Still increasing. Following a colonisation which began in 1938, British breeding totals increased to 157 pairs by 1962, 467-477 pairs by 1973, and 608-630 pairs by 1984 (Parrinder & Parrinder 1969, 1975; Parrinder 1989). Little Ringed Plovers prefer to nest by unvegetated aquatic margins, and the sites most commonly occupied are sand and gravel pits and reservoirs. Such habitats are best represented in southern, eastern and central England, and this is reflected in the species' British distribution. Between the 1973 and 1984 surveys, however, most of the increase occurred in the west and north, which suggests that saturation is being reached in the south and east (Parrinder 1989). While the growth of the sand and gravel extraction industries has greatly assisted this plover's increase within Britain, this did not trigger the colonisation process. Rather, the species' spread into Britain has been part of a pattern of population growth since the 1930s over western Europe as a whole (Cramp & Simmons 1983).

Dotterel *Charadrius morinellus*

Believed to be increasing, though recent high figures owe much to surveys being more thorough. Nethersole-Thompson (1973) considered that British Dotterels declined during the long period of climatic warming around 1890-1940; numbers were at their lowest in the 1930s, when there may have been no more than 50 pairs on Scottish hills and breeding in the English Lake District, previously regular, had ceased. With a reversal of the climatic amelioration since the 1940s, Dotterels have increased again. Surprisingly high numbers have been estimated from recent large-scale sample surveys. Watson & Rae (1987) considered that the Scottish population was closer to 600 pairs in the 1980s. A survey by the NCC in 1987 produced an estimate of at least 520 pairs that year (Spencer *et al* 1989). The British population is now considered to be at least 860 pairs, with 355 pairs located during sample surveys (D.B.A. Thompson, pers. comm.); all but five pairs are in Scotland.

Golden Plover *Pluvialis apricaria*

Some decline due to habitat loss. Ratcliffe (1976) estimated nearly 30,000 pairs breeding in Britain, with 21,400 in Scotland and 8500 in England and Wales, and suspected that the overall trend was downwards. Golden Plovers breed in a range of upland habitats, from submontane grasslands to blanket bogs, and have been affected by such land-use changes as agricultural improvement and, especially, upland afforestation. Breeding areas are known to have been lost to conifer planting in Wales, the North Yorkshire Moors, Cheviots, Scottish Southern Uplands, eastern Highlands, and the Caithness/Sutherland flows; and the British breeding population may now be closer to 23,000 pairs (Stroud *et al* 1989). In the southern Pennines there have also been adverse effects from disturbance by hikers and ramblers, which have led to redistribution of Golden Plover pairs (Yalden & Yalden 1989).

Dunlin *Calidris alpina*

Some decline is probable, owing to continuing habitat loss. The British breeding population has been estimated at 9900 pairs (Stroud *et al* 1987). These are widely distributed in Welsh, English and Scottish uplands, but the main concentrations are on the peatlands of Caithness and Sutherland, and in the Western Isles on the peatlands of Lewis and the *machair* of the Uists. The *machair* probably holds 25-30% of the British population, making the conservation of this habitat of particular importance for Dunlin as well as other waders (Fuller *et al* 1986). Losses of wet moorland due to blanket conifer planting on the Scottish mainland, especially over the last decade, have certainly destroyed some tracts of former Dunlin breeding habitat. An estimated 17% of Dunlin habitat has been lost to afforestation in the Flow Country alone (Stroud *et al* 1987).

Black-tailed Godwit *Limosa limosa*

Fluctuates considerably, according to water levels at the more important breeding sites in spring. After becoming extinct as a British breeding species in the 1840s, this godwit began nesting sporadically in the Fens of Cambridgeshire and Norfolk in the late 1930s. Breeding has been regular there at least since 1952, with the Ouse Washes as the main site (Cottier & Lea 1969). Breeding has also occurred since the 1940s at a good many other British localities, mainly coastal, and as far north as Shetland, though occupancy of individual sites has usually been temporary. Breeding records in Shetland (only) refer to the race *islandica*. This recolonisation followed increase in Iceland and other parts of northwestern Europe, and the regular occurrence of higher passage numbers in Britain. British breeding numbers currently fluctuate around 50 pairs, with up to 80 pairs (55 proved breeding) in 1984 but only half those figures in 1987 (Stroud *et al* 1989, Spencer *et al* 1989).

Whimbrel *Numenius phaeopus*

Increasing since the 1950s. As a British breeding bird, the Whimbrel has always been restricted to northern Scotland. Numbers declined during the first half of this century, coincident with a warmer climatic period which ended in the 1940s. Recovery has been taking place since the 1950s, and there are now thought to be about 465 pairs in Scotland. The majority are in Shetland, with smaller numbers in Orkney, the Western Isles and on the northern mainland (Stroud *et al* 1989). Whimbrels are vulnerable to land-use changes, of which agricultural intensification is more relevant to this species than is afforestation. Tracts of moorland in Shetland are being enclosed and allocated to crofters, for reseeding as grassland (Thom 1986).

Greenshank *Tringa nebularia*

The overall trend is unclear. The Scottish population was estimated at 800-900 pairs by Nethersole-Thompson & Nethersole-Thompson (1979); this figure was revised upwards, after further surveys, to about 1550 pairs (Piersma 1986, Stroud *et al* 1989). Greenshanks had been spreading in the Western Isles since the 1950s and had colonised Shetland from 1980 (Thom 1986). The new figures suggest an increase, but it is known that the species has declined in recent years in parts of Sutherland and Caithness, due to blanket afforestation of traditional breeding areas there (Stroud *et al* 1987). Numbers fluctuate, and in one study area of 15.4 sq.km the population varied between 7 and 23 breeding pairs during 1964-1989 (P.S. Thompson, pers. comm.). In this study, population size was found to be correlated positively with mild weather conditions around the time of hatching in the previous two years (Thompson *et al* 1986).

Rock Dove *Columba livia*

Population trend is unknown. The many forms of the Feral Pigeon, subjected by man to different degrees of selective breeding, are conspecific with the wild-type Rock Dove which is still to be found in the remotest parts of northwest Britain. Despite this relationship, attitudes vary as to whether the Feral Pigeon should be considered as relevant to lists and summaries of British birds, and it has received rather little attention in regional avifaunas (Hastings 1988). Arguments about what constitutes a "Rock Dove" are to a large extent semantic; both coastal and inland populations are subject to selection pressures which have produced birds best fitted to occupy their respective niches (Petersen & Williamson 1949, Murton & Clarke 1968). There has never been a reliable estimate of British numbers, in part because there is the additional problem of separating truly feral individuals from domestic ones still in semicaptivity (Lack 1986). It has been greatly under-recorded on CBC plots over the years, and in any case the urban habitat, in which Feral Pigeons reach their highest densities, is not monitored. Sharrock (1976) guessed that there must be in excess of 100,000 pairs in Britain and Ireland; 78% of occupied squares were then in Britain.

Ring-necked Parakeet *Psittacula krameri*

Perhaps now stable or still increasing slowly. The small British feral population dates from 1969 and arose from avicultural escapes and releases. The species was added to the official British list in 1983, when there were thought to be about 500-1000 birds living wild, mainly in Kent and the Thames valley (*Ibis* 126: 441, 1984; see also Lack 1986). There are no later census figures. Records submitted to county bird reports do not indicate any general diminution in numbers after recent cold winters; indeed, slow increase seems to have been maintained around London at least. In part, the recent success of these birds may be attributed to their habit of entering gardens to feed on supplementary foods provided for them.

Long-eared Owl *Asio otus*

No population change is known, nor has there been any attempt to assess breeding numbers since Sharrock (1976) suggested that there were between 3000 and 10,000 pairs in Britain and Ireland together; 63% of occupied squares were then in Britain. The Long-eared Owl's patchy distribution here and its predominant use of conifer woodland (in contrast to the situation in Ireland where all types of woodland are used) have led to suggestions that its present British pattern of occurrence is a consequence of competition from the Tawny Owl, which has increased this century (Sharrock 1976,

Lack 1986). Yet a Scottish study found that the two species used different ages of plantation there (Petty 1985), while work in the Peak District has revealed considerable dietary differences between them (Yalden 1985).

Short-eared Owl *Asio flammeus*

No long-term changes are known, though this is a species which benefits during the early stages of upland afforestation; it is prone to large fluctuations that are related to cycles of prey abundance. Short-eared Owls occupy open country, especially moorland, heathland and rough grazing. It has long been known that the low densities at which they normally occur increase markedly during peaks in vole numbers, the latter being especially a feature of northern Britain (*e.g.* Lockie 1955). Hence, it has been suggested that Britain may hold as few as 1000 pairs in poor vole years, but possibly up to 10,000 pairs in peak ones (Parslow 1973, Sharrock 1976).

Nightjar *Caprimulgus europaeus*

In long-term decline, since 1930 or earlier, and more steeply since the 1950s. During the five years of the Breeding Atlas, 1968-1972, Nightjars were reported from 656 10-km squares in Britain and Ireland; not all of these were occupied annually, and the population was considered to be around 3000 pairs (Sharrock 1976). A BTO survey in 1981 found Nightjars at 764 sites in 241 10-km squares; 1784 churring males were counted, and the population was thought not to exceed 2100 pairs (Gribble 1983). The reduction between these two surveys was unexpectedly large, and had been accompanied by obvious range contraction in the north (Scotland and northern England) and west (especially Ireland and Wales). Part of the decline may have been due to continuing fragmentation of heathland and downland Nightjar habitat, through scrub invasion, forestry planting and reclamation for agriculture; plantations provide good Nightjar habitat only while young or when eventually clear-felled (Gribble 1983, Ravenscroft 1989). However, climatic trends are probably implicated also. Spring arrivals have averaged later since the 1920s (Kemp 1983), and an East Anglian study showed that proportionately fewer second broods were being reared compared to the figures for the same region 50 years previously (Berry & Bibby 1981).

Swift *Apus apus*

No population change is known. It is an abundant and widespread bird, seen in 1988 on at least 58% of farmland and 17% of woodland CBC plots. However, most of the records are of feeding birds; index samples over the years have never exceeded 12 plots, even combining all habitats, far too few from which to build a reliable index. The great majority of Swifts breed in towns and villages, a habitat which the CBC does not in any case cover. Furthermore, it is a species which has proved very difficult to census, owing to its semicolonial habit and particularly to the frequent but unpredictable presence of non-breeding immature birds. No reliable information on population trends is available from any other source. Subjective opinion is that the British status of the Swift has changed little this century, if at all (Parslow 1973). Sharrock (1976) suggested that there might be around 100,000 pairs in Britain and Ireland; judged from the distribution of occupied 10-km squares, over 70% would have been in Britain.

Woodlark *Lullula arborea*

Numbers fluctuate, but the recent trend has been downwards. After a low point at the beginning of this century, both numbers and range increased again from the 1920s up to a peak in the early 1950s; but by the mid-1960s the species was again at a low ebb (Parslow 1973). This timing corresponded with climatic amelioration and its subsequent reversal. The Breeding Atlas found Woodlarks in 188 10-km squares in 1968-1972, and population size was estimated at 200-450 pairs (Sharrock 1976). Using data from county bird reports, Sitters (1986) estimated that there were 400-430 pairs in 1981 but, after the cold winter of 1981/82, only 210-230 pairs in 1983. A BTO survey in 1986, supplemented by RBBP records, found a maximum of 228 pairs that year (H.P. Sitters, pers. comm.; Spencer *et al* 1988). Habitat preference is likely to be involved in the recent pattern of distribution. In the early 1980s the main concentrations were on heathland (especially burnt areas), commercial tree nurseries, and clear-felled areas of conifer woodland, notably in East Anglia and southern England (Sitters 1986).

Rock Pipit *Anthus petrosus*

Stable, so far as is known. British Rock Pipits breed on rocky coasts and islands, and find little suitable habitat on the mainly soft eastern and southeastern shores between the Humber and the Solent. No modern changes to the species' status or distribution are known, except for small-scale colonisation or recolonisation of chalk cliffs in East Sussex and east Kent. Sharrock (1976) suggested that the British and Irish population was in excess of 50,000 pairs. Based on the distribution of occupied 10-km squares, and assuming similar densities in each country, the British portion of this total may have been 35,000-40,000 pairs or more. No improved figure is available.

Redwing *Turdus iliacus*

Stable or fluctuating after earlier increase. Redwings were first confirmed breeding in Britain in 1925, in Sutherland; nesting was sporadic in the early years but became more regular in the 1950s. There was a noticeable upsurge in breeding records in the 1960s, and some 50 territories were located in Scotland in both 1971 and 1972 (Sharrock 1976). Since then there has been much annual variation in the numbers recorded, but this has probably been due in part to varying levels of fieldwork and reporting. In 1979 only 9 singing birds or pairs (2 confirmed breeding) were recorded, while in 1984 the corresponding figures were 78 and 31 (Spencer *et al* 1988). In 1986 about 70 territorial males were located in the Highland Region; about half of these certainly or probably nested, the status of the others being uncertain (Hogg 1987). Lower figures in 1987 were certainly due to some key areas not being visited that year (Hogg 1988).

Cetti's Warbler *Cettia cetti*

Now stable after cold-weather declines, or beginning to increase again. This modern colonist increased rapidly until checked by colder winters in the 1980s. Originally a Mediterranean species, the Cetti's Warbler has been spreading northwards in Europe since the 1920s. Following a small influx into southern England in 1971, breeding occurred in Kent in 1972 (Bonham & Robertson 1975). With rapid growth in numbers, aided by continuing immigration, British totals of singing males reached 153 in 1977 and a peak of 316 in 1984 (Spencer *et al* 1988). Initial settlements were mainly in East Anglia and southeast England, especially Kent, with subsequent westward spread. By 1984, however, the centre of abundance had moved to the west, following declines in the east that were probably related to the bigger impacts there of recent cold winters.

The latter are responsible for reductions in overall numbers since 1984. In 1987, the latest year for which figures are available, 187 singing males were reported of which almost 85% were in South Wales and southwest England, including Hampshire (Spencer *et al* 1989).

Dartford Warbler *Sylvia undata*

Fluctuates markedly according to winter weather conditions, while there has been a progressive long-term reduction in the extent of gorse-clad heath, the favoured habitat of this species. Hampshire (especially the New Forest) is the British stronghold of the Dartford Warbler, followed in importance by the Dorset heathlands. Counties further west (Cornwall, Devon) and east (Surrey, Sussex), where habitat is more fragmented, may be deserted when the national population is low after a severe winter. A British total of 460 pairs in 1961 was reduced to 10-12 pairs in 1963, following two consecutive cold winters (Tubbs 1963, 1967), but recovery over a series of mild seasons brought the total up to 560 pairs by 1974 (Bibby & Tubbs 1975). Numbers fell again after the hard winter of 1978/79, and remained somewhat reduced in the early to mid-1980s (Robins & Bibby 1985) when winters averaged colder. In 1988, however, 454 territories were mapped in the New Forest, and the English population was then estimated at 600 pairs (Westerhoff 1989).

Firecrest *Regulus ignicapillus*

Now fluctuating after initial phase of increase. The Firecrest was first found holding territory, then breeding, in the New Forest in 1961-1962. For some years this remained the only known breeding area (Adams 1966), but territories were located in seven other counties during Breeding Atlas fieldwork in 1968-1972 (Batten 1973*b*). Subsequently, singing males have been found in one year or another in most English counties, with a small-scale presence in Wales also. Numbers fluctuate markedly, both nationally and at individual sites: in a study area of 100 ha in Buckinghamshire, numbers of territories varied between 5 (1986) and 16 (1987) during 1981-1989, but 1975 was the peak year in this locality (J.H. Marchant). During 1980-1987, national annual totals of singing males varied between 29 and 102, except in 1983 when there were an exceptional 175. The latest, 1987, figure was 82 (Spencer *et al* 1989). Lowland conifer woodlands (particularly Norway spruce and other plantations) comprise the habitat most frequently used for breeding.

Bearded Tit *Panurus biarmicus*

Probably stable: higher levels are being maintained, after earlier increase. British Bearded Tits were almost exterminated by the severe winter of 1946/47, with only 2-5 pairs known to have survived it; subsequent recovery was slow, with the population not reaching 100 pairs until 1957. Yet the species was affected much less by the equally severe winter of 1962/63, and those losses were made good by 1965 (Axell 1966). Substantial increases during the mild seasons which followed, and an intensified scale of eruptive behaviour in autumn, led to colonisation of a good many additional sites well away from the traditional East Anglian strongholds; by 1974 the British population had risen to about 590 pairs (O'Sullivan 1976). Present numbers are probably slightly higher than this, for recent cold winters have had only temporary effects (Bibby & Lunn 1982, Lack 1986).

Crested Tit *Parus cristatus*

Stable or increasing locally. In Britain, the Crested Tit is confined to the Scottish Highlands, centred especially on the Spey valley. Natural Scots pine woodlands within the old Caledonian Forest comprise the traditional habitat, though the species has spread into some commercial pine plantations and thereby increased its distribution somewhat. Cook (1982) estimated that the population size was 900 pairs in years when the previous winter was not unusually severe. Numbers can be reduced seriously by hard weather, but when stocks are high birds can be found in fair numbers even in the stunted pines at the uppermost fringes of the forests (Grant 1984).

Chough *Pyrrhocorax pyrrhocorax*

Now stable at reduced levels, or increasing locally, after earlier range contraction. The final pair of Choughs in southwest England survived until 1967 (Penhallurick 1978). British Choughs were censused in 1963 (Rolfe 1966) and 1982 (Bullock *et al* 1983). There was a large apparent increase between these surveys, but 1963 totals had probably been depressed by severe weather the previous winter, while in 1982 coverage was more complete. An update of Scottish numbers was made in 1986 (Monaghan *et al* 1989). Combining Welsh and Manx figures for 1982 with Scottish results for 1986, the British population comprised about 300 breeding pairs plus 280-300 immature birds. In Scotland, there had been a significant increase between 1982 and 1986, from 61-72 to 105 pairs, though the range was still restricted to the Inner Hebrides (Monaghan *et al* 1989); and this Scottish increase appears to be continuing (Bignal & Curtis 1989). The British distribution remains an essentially coastal one; only in North Wales and Islay are there significant numbers inland.

Twite *Carduelis flavirostris*

Population trend is uncertain, but it may be downward overall in view of the losses of its upland habitats to agricultural intensification and afforestation. Sharrock (1976) estimated the British and Irish breeding population at 20,000-40,000 pairs; based on the distribution of occupied 10-km squares, some 85% of these were probably in Britain. Davies (1988) has stressed the conservation importance of these populations in a European context. However, the only detailed studies so far have concerned the isolated Pennine birds, whose distribution and ecology were described by Orford (1973). These winter around southern North Sea coasts, especially on the Wash in Lincolnshire and Norfolk where transect surveys indicated that 17,000 birds were present in February 1986 (Davies 1988).

Scottish Crossbill *Loxia scotica*

Numbers fluctuate with the size of annual cone crop, as in other crossbills. However, this species is not known to erupt beyond the Scottish Highlands, though it seems that its range there expands temporarily when numbers are high, for example into Sutherland, Ross-shire and Aberdeenshire. Nethersole-Thompson (1975) considered that Scottish Crossbills may have numbered 100 pairs or fewer during poor years in the 1960s, but 300 or more pairs during 1970-1974. Thom (1986) thought that this population probably numbered 300-400 pairs in the 1980s. This form has only recently been elevated to species rank (Knox 1975, Voous 1978).

Cirl Bunting *Emberiza cirlus*

Long-term decline. Cirl Buntings were most numerous and widespread in the decades up to the 1930s, during the long period of climatic warming, but this climatic trend was reversed in the 1940s. Since about 1950 their British breeding range has been contracting, and the rate of decrease has accelerated during the last 20 years. Numbers of pairs and territorial males fell from 210-240 in 1973-1976 to a maximum of 167 in 1982 (Sitters 1982, 1985), and to about 60 in 1986-1987 when the distribution had become concentrated even more into Devon (Spencer *et al* 1988, 1989). Comparable declines have occurred in Belgium and northern France, and it is suspected that climatic deterioration has had an important influence on the species' status.

References cited in the text

Adams, M.C. 1966. Firecrests breeding in Hampshire. *Brit. Birds* 59: 240-246.

Aebischer, N.J., & G.R. Potts. 1989. Towards a more exact ecology: control of population size in birds. In: P.J. Grubb & J.B. Whittaker (eds.), *Towards a More Exact Ecology*. Oxford (Blackwell: BES Symposium).

Alatalo, R.V., L. Gustafsson, M. Linden & A. Lundberg. 1985. Interspecific competition and niche shifts in tits and the Goldcrest: an experiment. *J. Anim. Ecol.* 54: 977-984.

Alexander, W.B. 1945-1947. The Woodcock in the British Isles. *Ibis* 87: 512-550; 88: 1-24, 159-179, 271-286, 427-444; 89: 1-28.

Alexander, W.B., & D. Lack. 1944. Changes in status among British breeding birds. *Brit. Birds* 38: 42-45, 62-69, 82-88.

Alsop, D. 1975. The Ring Ouzel (*Turdus torquatus*) in Derbyshire. *Derbyshire Bird Rept.* 1974: 10-14.

Anon. 1968. *Common Birds Census Instructions*. Tring (BTO).

Anon. 1989. Goshawk breeding habitat in lowland Britain. *Brit. Birds* 82: 56-67.

Antikainen, E., U. Skaren, J. Toivanen & M. Ukkonen. 1980. (The nomadic breeding of the Redpoll *Acanthis flammea* in North Savo, Finland.) *Ornis Fenn.* 57: 124-131. (In Finnish, with English summary.)

Arnold, G.W. 1983. The influence of ditch and hedgerow structure, length of hedgerows, and area of woodland and garden on bird numbers on farmland. *J. appl. Ecol.* 20: 731-750.

Asbirk, S., & T. Dybbro. 1978. (Population size and habitat selection of the Great Crested Grebe *Podiceps cristatus* in Denmark, 1975.) *Dansk Orn. Foren. Tidsskr.* 72: 1-13. (In Danish, with English summary.)

Atkinson-Willes, G.L. 1963. *Wildfowl in Great Britain*. London (NC Monograph 3).

Atkinson-Willes, G.L. 1970. Wildfowl conservation in England, Scotland and Wales. *Proc. Int. Reg. Meet. Conserv. Wildfowl Resources (Leningrad, 1968)*: 101-107.

Axell, H.E. 1966. Eruptions of Bearded Tits during 1959-65. *Brit. Birds* 59: 513-543.

Bacon, P.J. 1980. Status and dynamics of a Mute Swan population near Oxford between 1976 and 1978. *Wildfowl* 31: 35-50.

Baillie, S.R. (in press, *a*). Integrated population monitoring of breeding birds in Britain and Ireland. *Ibis*.

Baillie, S.R. (in press, *b*). Monitoring terrestrial breeding bird populations. In: F.B. Goldsmith (ed.), *Monitoring for Conservation and Ecology*. London (Chapman & Hall).

Bannerman, D.A. 1959. *The Birds of the British Isles*. Edinburgh and London (Oliver & Boyd). Vol. 8.

Bastian, H.V. 1987. Zur Habitatswahl des Braunkehlchens (*Saxicola rubetra*) in einer südwestdeutschen Kulturlandschaft. *Ökol. der Vögel* 9: 107-112.

Bastian, H.V. 1989. Are corvids able to exterminate populations of Whinchats (*Saxicola rubetra*)? *Vogelwelt* 110: 150-156.

Batten, L.A. 1973*a*. Population dynamics of suburban Blackbirds. *Bird Study* 20: 251-258.

Batten, L.A. 1973*b*. The colonisation of England by the Firecrest. *Brit. Birds* 66: 159-166.

Batten, L.A. 1977. Studies on the population dynamics and energetics of Blackbirds, *Turdus merula* L. Ph.D. thesis, University of London.

Baxter, E.V., & L.J. Rintoul. 1953. *The Birds of Scotland*. Edinburgh and London (Oliver & Boyd). 2 vols.

Beintema, A.J., R.J. Beintema-Hietbrink & G.J.D.M. Müskens. 1985. A shift in the timing of breeding in meadow-birds. *Ardea* 73: 83-89.

Bejer, B., & M. Rudemo. 1985. Fluctuations of tits (Paridae) in Denmark and their relation to winter food and climate. *Ornis Scand.* 16: 29-37.

Bell, B.D. 1969. Some thoughts on the apparent ecological expansion of the Reed Bunting. *Brit. Birds* 62: 209-218.

Bell, B.D., C.K. Catchpole & K.J. Corbett. 1968. Problems of censusing Reed Buntings, Sedge Warblers and Reed Warblers. *Bird Study* 15: 16-21.

Bell, B.D., C.K. Catchpole, K.J. Corbett & R.J. Hornby. 1973. The relationship between census results and breeding populations of some marshland passerines. *Bird Study* 20: 127-140.

Bennett, J.W., & E.G. Bolen. 1978. Stress response in wintering Green-winged Teal. *J. Wildl. Manage.* 42: 81-86.

Benson, G.B.G., & K. Williamson. 1972. Breeding birds of a mixed farm in Suffolk. *Bird Study* 19: 34-50.

Berry, R., & C. Bibby. 1981. A breeding study of Nightjars. *Brit. Birds* 74: 161-169.

Berthold, P. 1974. Die gegenwärtige Bestandsentwicklung der Dorngrasmucke (*Sylvia communis*) und anderer Singvögelarten im westlichen Europa bis 1973. *Vogelwelt* 95: 170-183.

Berthold, P., G. Fliege, U. Querner & H. Winkler. 1986. Die Bestandsentwicklung von Kleinvögeln in Mitteleuropa: analyse von fangzahlen. *J. Orn.* 127: 397-437.

Best, L.B. 1975. Interpretational errors in the "mapping method" as a census technique. *Auk* 92: 452-460.

Bibby, C.J. 1989. A survey of breeding Wood Warblers *Phylloscopus sibilatrix* in Britain, 1984-1985. *Bird Study* 36: 56-72.

Bibby, C.J., C.G. Bain & D.J. Burgess. 1989. Bird communities of highland birchwoods. *Bird Study* 36: 123-133.

Bibby, C.J., & J. Lunn. 1982. Conservation of reed beds and their avifauna in England and Wales. *Biol. Conserv.* 23: 167-186.

Bibby, C.J., & M. Nattrass. 1986. Breeding status of the Merlin in Britain. *Brit. Birds* 79: 170-185.

Bibby, C.J., & D.K. Thomas. 1985. Breeding and diets of the Reed Warbler at a rich and a poor site. *Bird Study* 32: 19-31.

Bibby, C.J., & C.R. Tubbs. 1975. Status, habitats and conservation of the Dartford Warbler in England. *Brit. Birds* 68: 177-195.

Bignal, E., & D.J. Curtis (eds.). 1989. *Choughs and land-use in Europe. Proceedings of an International Workshop on the Conservation of the Chough in the EC.* Peterborough (NCC) and Tarbert (Scottish Chough Study Group).

Bijlsma, R. 1979. (The ecology of the Hawfinch *Coccothraustes coccothraustes* on the Zuidwest-Veluwe, with special reference to the breeding biology.) *Limosa* 52: 53-71. (In Dutch, with English summary.)

Bijlsma, R.G. 1989. Goshawk *Accipiter gentilis* and Sparrowhawk *A. nisus* in the Netherlands during the 20th century. Pp. 67-89 in: J.T. Lumeij, W.P.F. Huyskens & N. Croin Michielsen (eds.), *Valkerij in Perspectief.* Monnickendam (Valkeniersverbond "Adriaan Mollen").

Birkhead, M.E. 1982. Causes of mortality in the Mute Swan *Cygnus olor* on the River Thames. *J. Zool. Lond.* 198: 15-25.

Birkhead, M., & C. Perrins. 1986. *The Mute Swan.* London (Croom Helm).

Blackett, A., & W. Ord. 1962. Lesser Whitethroats breeding in Northumberland. *Brit. Birds* 55: 445.

Blaedel, N. (ed.). 1963. *Nordens Fugle i Farver.* Copenhagen (Munksgaard). Vol. 1.

Blaker, G.B. 1934. *The Barn Owl in England and Wales.* London (RSPB).

Blok, A.A., & A.L. Spaans. 1962. (On the occurrence of the Redpoll *Carduelis flammea* as a breeding bird in the Netherlands.) *Limosa* 35: 4-15. (In Dutch, with English summary.)

Blurton-Jones, N.G. 1956. Census of breeding Canada Geese 1953. *Bird Study* 3: 153-170.

Boddy, M. 1984. Body weights of adult and juvenile Lesser Redpolls in central and southern England. *Ring. & Migr.* 5: 91-100.

Boddy, M., & R.M. Sellers. 1983. Oriented movements by Greenfinches in southern Britain. *Ring. & Migr.* 4: 129-138.

Bonham, P.F., & J.C.M. Robertson. 1975. The spread of Cetti's Warbler in north-west Europe. *Brit. Birds* 68: 393-408.

Bossema, L. 1979. Jays and oaks: eco-ethological study of a symbiosis. *Behaviour* 70: 1-117.

Bouldin, L.E. 1968. The population of the House Martin *Delichon urbica* in East Lancashire. *Bird Study* 15: 135-146.

Bourgaize, T.J. 1982. Ornithological report for 1981. *Rept. Trans. Soc. Guernes.* 21: 23-29.

Braae, L., H. Nøhr & B.S. Petersen. 1988. (*Bird faunas in conventionally and organically farmed areas.*) Miljøprojekt 102. Copenhagen (Ornis Consult ApS). (In Danish, with English summary.)

Braaksma, S. 1960. (The spread of the Curlew *Numenius arquata* as a breeding bird.) *Ardea* 48: 65-90. (In Dutch, with English summary.)

Brenchley, A. 1984. The use of birds as indicators of change in agriculture. Pp. 123-128 in: D. Jenkins (ed.), *Agriculture and the Environment*. ITE symp. 13. Cambridge (ITE/NERC).

Brenchley, A. 1986. The breeding distribution and abundance of the Rook (*Corvus frugilegus*) in Great Britain since the 1920s. *J. Zool. Lond.* (A) 210: 261-278.

Briggs, K.B. 1983. The distribution and reproduction of Ringed Plovers breeding coastally and inland in north-west England. *Bird Study* 30: 222-228.

Briggs, K.B. 1984. The breeding ecology of coastal and inland Oystercatchers in north Lancashire. *Bird Study* 31: 141-147.

Brooke, M. de L., & N.B. Davies. 1987. Recent changes in host usage by Cuckoos *Cuculus canorus* in Britain. *J. Anim. Ecol.* 56: 873-883.

Brooker, M.P., & D.L. Morris. 1980. A survey of the macroinvertebrate riffle fauna of the River Wye. *Freshwat. Biol.* 10: 437-458.

Brown, P.E. 1957. The rarer birds of prey: their present status in the British Isles. Hobby. *Brit. Birds* 50: 149.

Bruderer, B., & W. Hirschi. 1984. Langfristige Bestandsentwicklung von Gartenrotel *Phoenicurus phoenicurus* und Trauerschnäpper *Ficedula hypoleuca* nach schweizerischen Beringungszahlen und Nisthohlenkontrollen. *Orn. Beob.* 81: 285-302.

Bryant, D.M. 1978. Moulting Shelducks on the Forth estuary. *Bird Study* 25: 103-108.

Bryant, D.M. 1981. Moulting Shelducks on the Wash. *Bird Study* 28: 157-158.

Bullock, I.D., D.R. Drewett & S.P. Mickleburgh. 1983. The Chough in Britain and Ireland. *Brit. Birds* 76: 377-401.

Bunce, R.G.H., C.J. Barr & H.A. Whittaker. 1981*a*. An integrated system of land classification. *Ann. Rep. Inst. of Terrestrial Ecology* 1980: 28-33.

Bunce, R.G.H., C.J. Barr & H.A. Whittaker. 1981*b*. *Land classes in Great Britain: preliminary descriptions for users of the Merlewood method of land classification*. ITE, Merlewood Res. Devel. Pap. 86.

Bundy, G. 1976. Breeding biology of the Red-throated Diver. *Bird Study* 23: 249-256.

Bunn, D.S., A.B. Warburton & R.D.S. Wilson. 1982. *The Barn Owl*. Calton (Poyser).

Burton, J.F. 1956. Report on the national census of heronries, 1954. *Bird Study* 3: 42-73.

Burton, P., & P. Osborne. 1980. Woodman – spare that tree! *Birds (RSPB)* 8: 35-37.

Buxton, E.J.M. 1962. The inland breeding of the Oystercatcher in Great Britain, 1958-59. *Bird Study* 8: 194-209.

Buxton, J. 1950. *The Redstart*. London (Collins, New Naturalist).

Buxton, N.E. 1975. The feeding behaviour and food supply of the Common Shelduck (*Tadorna tadorna*) on the Ythan estuary, Aberdeenshire. Unpublished Ph.D. thesis, University of Aberdeen.

Cadbury, C.J. 1980. The status and habitats of the Corncrake in Britain 1978-79. *Bird Study* 27: 203-218.

Cadbury, C.J., G. Elliott & P. Harbard. 1988. Birds of prey conservation in the UK. *RSPB Conserv. Rev.* 2: 9-16.

Cadbury, C.J., D. Hill, J. Partridge & J. Sorensen. 1989. The history of the Avocet population and its management in England since recolonisation. *RSPB Conserv. Rev.* 3: 9-13.

Cadbury, C.J., & P.J.S. Olney. 1978. Avocet population dynamics in England. *Brit. Birds* 71: 102-121.

Cameron, R.A.D. 1969. Predation by Song Thrushes *Turdus ericetorum* on the snails *Cepaea hortensis* and *Arianta arbustorum* near Rickmansworth. *J. Anim. Ecol.* 38: 547-553.

Campbell, B. 1954-55. The breeding distribution and habitats of the Pied Flycatcher (*Muscicapa hypoleuca*) in Britain. *Bird Study* 1: 81-101; 2: 24-32, 179-191.

Campbell, B. 1960. The Mute Swan census in England and Wales 1955-56. *Bird Study* 7: 208-223.

Campbell, B. 1965. The British breeding distribution of the Pied Flycatcher, 1953-62. *Bird Study* 12: 305-318.

Campbell, B., & I.J. Ferguson-Lees. 1972. *A Field Guide to Birds' Nests*. London (Constable).

Campbell, L.H. 1988. The impact of river engineering on water birds on an English lowland river. *Bird Study* 35: 91-96.

Campbell, L.H., & G.P. Mudge. 1989. Conservation of Black-throated Divers in Scotland. *RSPB Conserv. Rev.* 3: 72-74.

Campbell, L.H., & T.R. Talbot. 1987. Breeding status of Black-throated Divers in Scotland. *Brit. Birds* 80: 1-8.

Carter, S.P. 1989*a*. Heronries census – preliminary report for 1986-88 for England and Wales. *BTO News* 162: 13.

Carter, S.P. 1989*b*. The Waterways Bird Survey of the British Trust for Ornithology: an overview. *Regulated Rivers: Research & Management* 4: 191-197.

Carter, S.P. 1989*c*. Waterways Bird Survey…1987-88 population changes. *BTO News* 161: 10-11.

Catley, G.P., & D. Hursthouse. 1985. Parrot Crossbills in Britain. *Brit. Birds* 78: 482-505.

Cawthorne, R.A., & J.H. Marchant. 1980. The effects of the 1978/79 winter on British bird populations. *Bird Study* 27: 163-172.

Clark, F., & D.A.C. McNeil. 1980. Cliff-nesting colonies of House Martins *Delichon urbica* in Great Britain. *Ibis* 122: 27-42.

Clarkson, K., & T. Birkhead. 1987. Magpies in Sheffield – a recipe for success. *BTO News* 151: 8-9.

Cody, M.L. 1978. Habitat selection and interspecific territoriality among the sylviid warblers of England and Sweden. *Ecol. Monogr.* 48: 351-396.

Conder, P. 1989. *The Wheatear*. London (Christopher Helm).

Cook, A. 1975. Changes in the Carrion/Hooded Crow hybrid zone and the possible importance of climate. *Bird Study* 22: 165-168.

Cook, M.J.H. 1982. Breeding status of the Crested Tit. *Scot. Birds* 12: 97-106.

Cooke, A.S. 1979. Population declines of the Magpie *Pica pica* in Huntingdonshire and other parts of eastern England. *Biol. Conserv.* 15: 317-324.

Cooper, J.E.S. 1985. Spring migration of Siskins in north Sussex during 1984. *Ring. & Migr.* 6: 61-65.

Cottier, E.J., & D. Lea. 1969. Black-tailed Godwits, Ruffs and Black Terns breeding on the Ouse Washes. *Brit. Birds* 62: 259-270.

Cowley, E. 1979. Sand Martin population trends in Britain, 1965-1978. *Bird Study* 26: 113-116.

Cowley, E. 1983. Multi-brooding and mate infidelity in the Sand Martin. *Bird Study* 30: 1-7.

Cox, S. 1984. *A New Guide to the Birds of Essex*. Ipswich (Essex Bird Watch. & Pres. Society).

Cramp, S., & J. Gooders. 1967. The return of the House Martin. *London Bird Rept.* 31: 93-98.

Cramp, S., & P.J.S. Olney. 1967. *The sixth report of the joint committee of the British Trust for Ornithology and the Royal Society for the Protection of Birds on toxic chemicals*. Tring (BTO).

Cramp, S., & K.E.L. Simmons (eds.). 1977-88. *The Birds of the Western Palearctic*. Vol. 1, 1977; vol. 2, 1980; vol. 3, 1983; vol. 4, 1985; vol. 5, 1988. Oxford (Oxford University Press).

Cramp, S., & A.D. Tomlins. 1966. The birds of Inner London 1951-65. *Brit. Birds* 59: 209-233.

Cryer, M., N.W. Linley, R.M. Ward, J.O. Stratford & P.F. Randerson. 1987. Disturbance of overwintering wildfowl by anglers at two reservoir sites in South Wales. *Bird Study* 34: 191-199.

Cvitanic, A. 1986. (The spreading of nesting areas for some species of Fringillidae along the Middle Dalmatian coast.) *Larus* 36-37: 239-243. (In Croatian, with English summary.)

da Prato, S.R.D. 1980. How many Lesser Whitethroats breed in the Lothians? *Scot. Birds* 11: 108-112.

Darby, K.V. 1985. Migration counts and local weather at British bird observatories – an examination by linear discriminant analysis. Pp. 37-64 in: B.J.T. Morgan & P.M. North (eds.), *Statistics in Ornithology*. New York (Springer Verlag).

Dare, P.J. 1986. Raven *Corvus corax* populations in two upland regions of north Wales. *Bird Study* 33: 179-189.

Davidson, N.C., & N.A. Clark. 1985. The effects of severe weather in January and February 1985 on waders in Britain. *Bull. Wader Study Group* 44: 10-16.

Davies, A.K. 1985. The British Mandarins – outstripping their ancestors. *BTO News* 136: 12.

Davies, A.K. 1988. The distribution and status of the Mandarin Duck *Aix galericulata* in Britain. *Bird Study* 35: 203-208.

Davies, A.K., & G.K. Baggott. 1989. Clutch size and nesting sites of the Mandarin Duck *Aix galericulata*. *Bird Study* 36: 32-36.

Davies, M. 1988. The importance of Britain's Twites. *RSPB Conserv. Rev.* 2: 91-94.

Davies, N.B. 1987. Studies of West Palearctic birds: 188. Dunnock. *Brit. Birds* 80: 604-624.

Davis, P., C. Erard, N.O. Preuss, M. Tekke & J. Tricot. 1966. Invasion de Cailles (*Coturnix coturnix*) en Europe durant l'année 1964. *Aves (Belgium)* 3: 65-97.

Davis, P.G. 1982. Nightingales in Britain in 1980. *Bird Study* 29: 73-79.

Davis, P.W., & P.E. Davis. 1973. The ecology and conservation of the Red Kite in Wales. *Brit. Birds* 66: 183-224, 241-270.

Day, J.C.U. 1984. Population and breeding biology of Marsh Harriers in Britain since 1900. *J. appl. Ecol.* 21: 773-787.

Dennis, R.H. 1964. Capture of moulting Canada Geese in the Beauly Firth. *Wildfowl Trust Ann. Rept.* 15: 71-74.

Dennis, R.H. 1983. Population studies and conservation of Ospreys in Scotland. Pp. 207-214 in: D.M. Bird (ed.), *Biology and Management of Bald Eagles and Ospreys*. Montreal, Quebec (Harpell Press).

Dennis, R.H. 1984. *A Status and Guide to the Birds of Badenoch and Strathspey*. North Kessock (author).

Dennis, R.H., & H. Dow. 1984. The establishment of a population of Goldeneyes *Bucephala clangula* breeding in Scotland. *Bird Study* 31: 217-222.

Dennis, R.H., P.M. Ellis, R.A. Broad & D.R. Langslow. 1984. The status of the Golden Eagle in Britain. *Brit. Birds* 77: 592-607.

Desmet, J. 1981. (Occurrence and winter ecology of the Hawfinch *Coccothraustes coccothraustes* at Sint-Michiels, Bruges.) *Gerfaut* 71: 627-657. (In Dutch, with English summary.)

Dhondt, A.A. 1989. Ecological and evolutionary effects of interspecific competition in tits. *Wilson Bull.* 101: 198-216.

Dobbs, A. (ed.). 1975. *The Birds of Nottinghamshire Past and Present*. Newton Abbot (David & Charles).

Dobinson, H.M., & A.J. Richards. 1964. The effects of the severe winter of 1962/63 on birds in Britain. *Brit. Birds* 57: 373-434.

DOFF. 1989. *Ynglefuglerapport 1988*. Copenhagen (Dansk Ornitologisk Forenings Fugleregistreringsgruppe). (In Danish, with English summary.)

Dougall, T.W., & P.M. North. 1983. Problems of censusing Long-tailed Tits (*Aegithalos caudatus*) by the mapping method. *The Ring (Wrocław)* 10 (114-115): 88-97.

Durman, R.F. 1978. Ring Ouzels in the Pentlands. *Edinburgh Ring. Group Rept.* 5: 24-27.

Easy, G.M.S. 1964. A report on the birds of Breckland. *Cambridge Bird Club Rept.* 37 (1963): 39-42.

Eden, S.F. 1985. The comparative breeding biology of Magpies *Pica pica* in an urban and a rural habitat. *J. Zool. Lond.* (A) 205: 325-334.

Edington, J.M., & M.A. Edington. 1972. Spatial patterns and habitat partition in the breeding birds of an upland wood. *J. Anim. Ecol.* 41: 331-357.

Elkins, N. 1983. *Weather and Bird Behaviour*. Calton (Poyser).

Eltringham, S.K. 1963. The British population of the Mute Swan. *Bird Study* 10: 10-28.

Eltringham, S.K., & H. Boyd. 1960. The Shelduck population in the Bridgwater Bay moulting area. *Wildfowl Trust Ann. Rept.* 11: 107-117.

Enemar, A. 1959. On the determination of the size and composition of a passerine bird population during the breeding season. *Vår Fågelvärld* 18: supp. 2.

Enemar, A., & B. Nystrom. 1981. (Population fluctuations, food and breeding of the Redpoll *Carduelis flammea* in a mountain birch forest, Swedish Lapland.) *Vår Fågelvärld* 40: 409-426. (In Swedish, with English summary.)

Enoksson, B., & S.G. Nilsson. 1983. Territory size and population density in relation to food supply in the Nuthatch *Sitta europaea*. *J. Anim. Ecol.* 52: 927-935.

Eriksson, M.O.G. 1985. Acidification of lakes: effects on waterbirds in Sweden. *Ambio* 13: 260-262.

Ernst, S. 1988. (The spread of the Lesser Redpoll, *Carduelis flammea cabaret* P.L.S. Müller, in Europe until 1986.) *Mitt. Zool. Mus. Berl.* 64, Suppl. Ann. Orn. 12: 3-50. (In German, with English summary.)

Evans, P.R. 1966. Autumn movements, moult and measurements of the Lesser Redpoll *Carduelis flammea cabaret*. *Ibis* 108: 183-216.

Evans, P.R. 1969. Ecological aspects of migration, and pre-migratory fat deposition in the Lesser Redpoll *Carduelis flammea cabaret*. *Condor* 71: 316-330.

Evans, P.R., & W.U. Flower. 1967. The birds of the Small Isles. *Scot. Birds* 4: 404-445.

Evans, P.R., & M.W. Pienkowski. 1982. Behaviour of Shelducks *Tadorna tadorna* in a winter flock: does regulation occur? *J. Anim. Ecol.* 51: 241-262.

Evans, P.R., & M.W. Pienkowski. 1984. Population dynamics of shorebirds. Pp. 83-123 in: J. Burger & B.L. Olla (eds.), *Behavior of Marine Animals*. New York (Plenum).

Everett, M.J. 1989. Reedbeds – a scarce habitat. *RSPB Conserv. Rev.* 3: 14-19.

Ewins, P.J., J.N. Dymond & M. Marquiss. 1986. The distribution, breeding and diet of Ravens *Corvus corax* in Shetland. *Bird Study* 33: 110-116.

Feare, C. 1984. *The Starling*. Oxford (Oxford University Press).

Ferns, P.N. (ed.). 1977. *The Birds of Gwent*. Pontypool (Gwent Orn. Soc.).

Fisher, J. 1947. Rook Investigation. *BTO Ann. Rept.* 13: 3-5.

Fitter, R.S.R. 1959. *The Ark in our Midst*. London (Collins).

Fitter, R.S.R. 1971. Black Redstarts breeding in Britain in 1964-68. *Brit. Birds* 64: 117-124.

Fitter, R.S.R. 1976. Black Redstarts breeding in Britain in 1969-73. *Brit. Birds* 69: 9-15.

Fiuczynski, D. 1978. Zur Populationsökologie des Baumfalken (*Falco subbuteo*). *Zool. Jb. Syst.* 105: 193-257.

Fiuczynski, D. 1987. *Der Baumfalke*. Neue Brehm Bucherei 575. Wittenberg-Lutherstadt (A. Ziemsen Verlag).

Fiuczynski, D., & D. Nethersole-Thompson. 1980. Hobby studies in England and Germany. *Brit. Birds* 73: 275-295.

Flegg, J.J.M. 1973. A study of Treecreepers. *Bird Study* 20: 287-302.

Flegg, J.J.M., & T.J. Bennett. 1974. The birds of oak woodlands. Pp. 324-340 in: M.G. Morris & F.H. Perring (eds.), *The British Oak*. Faringdon.

Flegg, J.J.M., & D.E. Glue. 1975. The nesting of the Ring Ouzel. *Bird Study* 22: 1-8.

Fox, A.D. 1986. The breeding Teal (*Anas crecca*) of a coastal raised mire in central West Wales. *Bird Study* 33: 18-23.

Fox, A.D. 1988. Breeding status of the Gadwall in Britain and Ireland. *Brit. Birds* 81: 51-66.

Fox, A.D., N. Jarrett, H. Gitay & D. Paynter. 1989. Late summer habitat selection by breeding waterfowl in northern Scotland. *Wildfowl* 40: 106-114.

Fox, A.D., & D.G. Salmon. 1989. The winter status and distribution of Gadwall in Britain and Ireland. *Bird Study* 36: 37-44.

Frost, R.A. 1978. *Birds of Derbyshire*. Hartington, Buxton (Moorland Publ. Co.).

Fuller, P. 1988. A study of the Mandarin (*Aix galericulata*) in Bedfordshire. *Bedford. Nat.* (1987): 51-54.

Fuller, R.J. 1982. *Bird Habitats in Britain*. Calton (Poyser).

Fuller, R.J. 1984. The distribution and feeding behaviour of breeding songbirds on cereal farmland at Manydown Farm, Hampshire, in 1984. *BTO Research Rept.* 16.

Fuller, R.J., J.K. Baker, R.A. Morgan, R. Scroggs & M. Wright. 1985. Breeding populations of the Hobby *Falco subbuteo* on farmland in the southern midlands of England. *Ibis* 127: 510-516.

Fuller, R.J., & D.E. Glue. 1977. The breeding biology of the Stonechat and Whinchat. *Bird Study* 24: 215-228.

Fuller, R.J., & J.H. Marchant. 1985. Species-specific problems of cluster analysis in British mapping censuses. Pp. 83-86 in: K. Taylor, R.J. Fuller & P.C. Lack (eds.), *Bird Census and Atlas Studies*. Tring (BTO).

Fuller, R.J., J.H. Marchant & R.A. Morgan. 1985. How representative of agricultural practice in Britain are Common Birds Census farmland plots? *Bird Study* 32: 56-70.

Fuller, R.J., T.M. Reed, N.E. Buxton, A. Webb, T.D. Williams & M.W. Pienkowski. 1986. Populations of breeding waders *Charadrii* and their habitats on the crofting lands of the Outer Hebrides, Scotland. *Biol. Conserv.* 37: 333-361.

Fuller, R.J., & M.S. Warren (in press). *Coppiced woodlands: their management for wildlife*. Peterborough (NCC).

Fuller, R.J., & P.A. Whittington. 1987. Breeding bird distribution within Lincolnshire ash-lime woodlands: the influence of rides and the woodland edge. *Acta Oecologica* 8: 259-268.

Galbraith, H. 1988. Effects of agriculture on the breeding ecology of Lapwings *Vanellus vanellus*. *J. appl. Ecol.* 25: 487-503.

Galbraith, H., R.W. Furness & R.J. Fuller. 1984. Habitats and distribution of waders breeding on Scottish agricultural land. *Scot. Birds* 13: 98-107.

Garcia, E.F.J. 1983. An experimental test of competition for space between Blackcaps *Sylvia atricapilla* and Garden Warblers *Sylvia borin* in the breeding season. *J. Anim. Ecol.* 52: 795-805.

Geissler, P.H., & B.R. Noon. 1981. Estimates of avian population trends from the North American Breeding Bird Survey. *Stud. Avian Biol.* 6: 42-51.

Gibbons, D.W. 1987. Juvenile helping in the Moorhen *Gallinula chloropus*. *Anim. Behav.* 35: 170-181.

Ginn, H.B. 1969. The use of annual ringing and nest record card totals as indicators of bird population trends. *Bird Study* 16: 210-248.

Gladwin, T., & B. Sage. 1986. *The Birds of Hertfordshire*. Ware (Castlemead Publications).

Glas, P. 1960. Factors governing density in the Chaffinch (*Fringilla coelebs*) in different types of wood. *Arch. Néerl. Zool.* 13: 466-472.

Glen, N.W., & C.M. Perrins. 1988. Co-operative breeding by Long-tailed Tits. *Brit. Birds* 81: 630-641.

Glück, E.E. 1985. Seed preference and energy intake of Goldfinches *Carduelis carduelis* in the breeding season. *Ibis* 127: 421-429.

Glue, D.E. 1982. *The Garden Bird Book*. London (Macmillan).

Glue, D. 1989. The 1989 breeding season. *BTO News* 165: 5.

Glue, D.E., & D. Scott. 1980. Breeding biology of the Little Owl. *Brit. Birds* 73: 167-180.

Glutz von Blotzheim, U.N. (ed.). 1977-1988. *Handbuch der Vögel Mitteleuropas*. Band 7, 1977; Band 9, 1980; Band 10, 1985; Band 11, 1988. Wiesbaden (AULA-Verlag).

Gomersall, C.H., J.S. Morton & R.M. Wynde. 1984. Status of breeding Red-throated Divers in Shetland, 1983. *Bird Study* 31: 223-229.

Gooch, S., S.R. Baillie & T.R. Birkhead (in prep.). The impact of Magpies *Pica pica* on songbird populations. Retrospective investigation of trends in population density and breeding success.

Goodfellow, P. 1986. The Wood Warbler Survey 1984-85. *Devon Birds* 39: 87-92.

Goodhart, C.B. 1958. Thrush predation on the snail *Cepaea hortensis*. *J. Anim. Ecol.* 27: 47-57.

Goodwin, D. 1987. Decline of the Turtle Dove. *Brit. Birds* 80: 637-638.

Gordon, M. 1972. Reed Buntings on an Oxfordshire farm. *Bird Study* 19: 81-90.

Gosler, A.G. 1988. Wing-length variation and flock relationships in the Long-tailed Tit *Aegithalos caudatus*. *Ring. & Migr.* 9: 68-70.

Gotmark, F. 1981. (The Redpoll *C. f. cabaret* colonising south Sweden: results from a census in 1978.) *Vår Fågelvärld* 40: 47-56. (In Swedish, with English summary.)

Grant of Rothiemurchus, J.P. 1984. Crested Tits on Deeside. *Scot. Birds* 13: 54-55.

Green, R.E. 1978. Factors affecting the diet of farmland Skylarks *Alauda arvensis*. *J. Anim. Ecol.* 47: 913-928.

Green, R.E. 1980. Food selection in Skylarks: the effects of a pesticide on grazing preferences. Pp. 180-187 in: E.N. Wright, I.R. Inglis & C.J. Feare (eds.), *Bird Problems in Agriculture*. Croydon (British Crop Protection Council).

Green, R.E. 1981. Double nesting in Red-legged Partridges. *Game Conserv. Ann. Rev.* (1980) 12: 35-38.

Green, R.E. 1983. Spring dispersal and agonistic behaviour of the Red-legged Partridge (*Alectoris rufa*). *J. Zool. Lond.* 201: 541-555.

Green, R.E. 1984. The feeding ecology and survival of partridge chicks (*Alectoris rufa* and *Perdix perdix*) on arable farmland in East Anglia. *J. appl. Ecol.* 21: 817-830.

Green, R.E. 1985. Estimating the abundance of breeding Snipe. *Bird Study* 32: 141-149.

Green, R.E. 1988a. Effects of environmental factors on the timing and success of breeding of Common Snipe *Gallinago gallinago* (Aves: Scolopacidae). *J. appl. Ecol.* 25: 79-93.

Green, R.E. 1988b. Stone-curlew conservation. *RSPB Conserv. Rev.* 2: 30-33.

Grenquist, P. 1970. Status of the species of wildfowl occurring in Finland. Pp. 83-87 in: Y.A. Isakov (ed.), *Proc. Int. Reg. Meet. Conserv. Wildfowl Resources (Leningrad 1968)*. Moscow.

Gribble, F.C. 1983. Nightjars in Britain and Ireland in 1981. *Bird Study* 30: 165-176.

Grimmett, R. 1987. *A review of the problems affecting Palearctic migratory birds in Africa*. Cambridge (ICBP Study Rept. 22).

Grove, S.J., P. Hope Jones, A.R. Malkinson, D.H. Thomas & I. Williams. 1988. Black Grouse in Wales, spring 1986. *Brit. Birds* 81: 2-9.

Gudmundsson, F. 1951. The effects of the recent climatic changes on the bird life of Iceland. *Proc. Int. Orn. Congr.* 10: 502-514.

Haftorn, S. 1971. *Norges Fugler*. Oslo (Scand. Univ. Books).

Hald-Mortensen, P. 1970. (Lesser Redpoll *Carduelis flammea cabaret* as a breeding bird in Denmark.) *Dansk Orn. Foren. Tidsskr.* 64: 163-193. (In Danish, with English summary.)

Hardman, J.A., & D.R. Cooper. 1980. Mute Swans on the Warwickshire Avon - a study of a decline. *Wildfowl* 31: 29-36.

Harradine, J. 1983. Sport-shooting in the United Kingdom: some facts and figures. Pp. 63-83 in: F.J. Leeuwenberg & I.R. Hepburn (eds.), *Proc. 2nd Meet. Working Group on Game Statistics, Int. Union Game Biol.* Zoetermeer, Netherlands.

Harradine, J. 1985. Duck shooting in the United Kingdom. *Wildfowl* 36: 81-94.

Harriman, R., & B.R.S. Morrison. 1982. Ecology of streams draining forested and non-forested catchments in an area of central Scotland subject to acid precipitation. *Hydrobiologia* 88: 251-263.

Harrison, C.J.O. 1988. *The History of the Birds of Britain*. London (Collins).

Harrison, G.R., A.R. Dean, A.J. Richards & D. Smallshire. 1982. *The Birds of the West Midlands*. Studley (West Midlands Bird Club).

Harrison, J., & J. Wardell. 1970. WAGBI duck to supplement wild populations. Pp. 195-209 in: N.M. Sedgwick, N.M.P. Whitaker & J. Harrison (eds.), *The New Wildfowler in the 1970s*. London (Barrie & Jenkins).

Harrisson, T.H., & P.A.D. Hollom. 1932. The Great Crested Grebe enquiry, 1931. *Brit. Birds* 26: 62-92, 102-131, 142-155, 174-195.

Hartert, E. 1898. A hitherto overlooked British bird. *Zoologist* (4) 2: 116-118.

Harvey, H.J. 1979. Great Crested Grebes breeding on rivers. *Brit. Birds* 71: 385-386.

Harvie-Brown, J.A. 1908. The Great Spotted Woodpecker's resuscitation in Scotland since 1841 or 1851. *Ann. Scott. Nat. Hist.* 1908: 210-216.

Hastings, R.P. 1988. The Feral Rock Dove. *Brit. Birds* 81: 652.

HCC. 1987. *Report of the Hertfordshire pond survey 1986*. Hertfordshire County Council.

Henderson, I. (ed.) 1989. *Slugs and Snails in World Agriculture*. British Crop Protection Council, monograph 41.

Heppleston, P.B. 1972. The comparative breeding ecology of Oystercatchers (*Haematopus ostralegus* L.) in inland and coastal habitats. *J. Anim. Ecol.* 41: 23-51.

Herrera, C.M. 1978. On the breeding distribution pattern of European migrant birds: MacArthur's theme re-examined. *Auk* 95: 496-509.

Heubeck, M. 1987. Changes in the status of the Common Eider in Shetland, 1977-84. *Scot. Birds* 14: 146-152.

Hibbert-Ware, A. 1937. Report of the Little Owl food inquiry, 1936-37. *Brit. Birds* 31: 162-187, 205-229, 249-264.

Hildén, O. 1979. (Effects of the advances in field ornithology on bird censuses.) *Lintumies* 14: 9-14. (In Finnish, with English summary.)

Hildén, O. 1981. Sources of error involved in the Finnish line-transect method. *Stud. Avian Biol.* 6: 152-159.

Hildén, O. 1989. The effects of severe winters on the bird fauna of Finland. *Memoranda Soc. Fauna Flora Fennica* 65: 59-66.

Hildén, O., & J.T.R. Sharrock. 1982. (Recent changes in the status of European birds.) *Lintumies* 17: 150-160. (In Finnish, with English summary.)

Hildén, O., & J.T.R. Sharrock. 1985. A summary of recent avian range changes in Europe. *Proc. Int. Orn. Congr.* 18: 716-736.

267

Hill, D.A. 1984. Population regulation in Mallard (*Anas platyrhynchos*). *J. Anim. Ecol.* 53: 191-202.
Hill, D.A. 1988. Population dynamics of the Avocet *Recurvirostra avosetta* breeding in Britain. *J. Anim. Ecol.* 57: 669-683.
Hill, D., & P. Robertson. 1988. *The Pheasant: ecology, management and conservation.* Oxford (Blackwell).
Hirons, G. 1980. The significance of roding by Woodcocks *Scolopax rusticola*: an alternative explanation based on observations of marked birds. *Ibis* 122: 350-354.
Hirons, G. 1982. Conclusion of the studies on Woodcock. *Game Conserv. Ann. Rev.* (1981) 13: 35-42.
Hirons, G., A. Hardy & P. Stanley. 1979. Starvation in young Tawny Owls. *Bird Study* 26: 59-63.
Hogg, A. (ed.). 1987. Scottish bird report 1986. *Scot. Birds* 14: 219-260.
Hogg, A. (ed.). 1988. Scottish bird report 1987. *Scot. Birds*, suppl.: 1-55.
Hogstad, O. 1984. Variation in numbers, territoriality and flock size of a Goldcrest *Regulus regulus* population in winter. *Ibis* 126: 296-306.
Hogstad, O., & A. Moksnes. 1986. Expansion and present status of the Wood Warbler *Phylloscopus sibilatrix* in Central Norway. *Fauna Norveg., Ser. C. (Cinclus)* 9: 49-54.
Holland, P.K., J.E. Robson & D.W. Yalden. 1982a. The breeding biology of the Common Sandpiper *Actitis hypoleucos* in the Peak District. *Bird Study* 29: 99-110.
Holland, P.K., J.E. Robson & D.W. Yalden. 1982b. The status and distribution of the Common Sandpiper (*Actitis hypoleucos*) in the Peak District. *Naturalist* 107: 77-86.
Holland, P., I. Spence & T. Sutton. 1984. *Breeding Birds in Greater Manchester.* Manchester Orn. Soc.
Hollom, P.A.D. 1936. Report on Great Crested Grebe sample count 1935. *Brit. Birds* 30: 138-158.
Hollom, P.A.D. 1951. Great Crested Grebe sample census: report to end of 1950. *Brit. Birds* 44: 361-369.
Hollom, P.A.D. 1959. The Great Crested Grebe sample census: 1946-55. *Bird Study* 6: 1-7.
Homes, R.C. (ed.). 1957. *The Birds of the London Area since 1900.* London (Collins, New Naturalist).
Homes, R.C., B.L. Sage & R. Spencer. 1960. Breeding populations of Lapwings, Coot and Meadow Pipits. *London Bird Rept.* 23: 54-61.
Hornbuckle, J., & D. Herringshaw. 1985. *Birds of the Sheffield Area including the north-east Peak District.* Sheffield (City Libraries).
Horváth, R. 1988. Angaben über die Wasseramsel (*Cinclus cinclus*) in Ungarn. *Egretta* 31: 12-17.
Howells, G. 1962. The status of the Red-legged Partridge in Britain. *Game Research Assoc. Ann. Rept.* 2: 46-51.
Hudson, A., T.J. Stowe & S.J. Aspinall (in press). The status and distribution of Corncrakes in Britain in 1988. *Brit. Birds.*
Hudson, P. 1986. *The Red Grouse. The biology and management of a wild gamebird.* Fordingbridge (Game Conservancy Trust).
Hudson, P. 1989. Black Grouse in Britain. *Game Conserv. Rev.* 20: 119-124.
Hudson, P., J. Renton & G. Dalby. 1989. Winter losses and grouse predation in the Highlands of Scotland. *Game Conserv. Rev.* 20: 127-130.
Hudson, R. 1965. The spread of the Collared Dove in Britain and Ireland. *Brit. Birds* 58: 105-139.
Hudson, R. 1972. Collared Doves in Britain and Ireland during 1965-70. *Brit. Birds* 65: 139-155.
Hudson, R. 1976. Ruddy Ducks in Britain. *Brit. Birds* 69: 132-143.
Hudson, R. 1979. Nightingales in Britain in 1976. *Bird Study* 26: 204-212.
Hudson, R. 1988. Bird territories in relation to habitat features in CBC farmland data. *BTO Research Rept.* 33.
Hudson, R., & J.H. Marchant. 1984. Population estimates for British breeding birds. *BTO Research Rept.* 13.
Hughes, S.W.M. 1972. The breeding distribution and status of the Tree Pipit in Sussex. *Sussex Bird Rept.* 24: 68-79.

Hughes, S.W.M., P. Bacon & J.J.M. Flegg. 1979. The 1975 census of the Great Crested Grebe in Britain. *Bird Study* 26: 213-226.

Hustings, F. 1986. (Population changes in the Stonechat *Saxicola torquata* during 1970-84.) *Limosa* 59: 153-162. (In Dutch, with English summary.)

Hustings, F. 1988. *European Monitoring Studies of Breeding Birds*. Beek, Netherlands (SOVON).

Hutcheson, M. 1986. *Cumbrian Birds: a review of status and distribution 1964-1984*. Kendal (F. Peters).

Hutchinson, C. 1979. *Ireland's Wetlands and their Birds*. Dublin (Irish Wildbird Conservancy).

Hutchinson, C.D. 1989. *Birds in Ireland*. Calton (Poyser).

Hutchinson, J. 1840. Birds of Durham. Unpublished ms. quoted by Temperley & Blezard (1951), *q.v.*

Inglis, I.R., A.J. Isaacson & R.J.P. Thearle (in press). The effects of changing agricultural practices upon Woodpigeon (*Columba palumbus*) numbers. *Ibis*.

International Bird Census Committee. 1969. Recommendations for an international standard for a mapping method in bird census work. *Bird Study* 16: 248-255.

Isenmann, P. 1987. L'évolution récente de la distribution du Pipit farlouse (*Anthus pratensis*) en France. *Oiseau & RFO* 57: 52-55.

Jepson, P.C., & R.E. Green. 1983. Prospects for improving control strategies for sugar-beet pests in England. *Advances in Applied Biology* 7: 175-250.

John, A.W.G., & J. Roskell. 1985. Jay movements in autumn 1983. *Brit. Birds* 78: 611-637.

Johnson, E.D.H. 1971. Observations on a resident population of Stonechats in Jersey. *Brit. Birds* 64: 201-213, 267-279.

Jones, G. 1987. Selection against large size in the Sand Martin *Riparia riparia* during a dramatic population crash. *Ibis* 129: 274-280.

Jourdain, F.C.R., & H.F. Witherby. 1918. The effect of the winter of 1916-1917 on our resident birds. *Brit. Birds* 11: 266-271; 12: 26-35.

Joyce, B., G. Williams & A. Woods. 1988. Hedgerows: still a cause for concern. *RSPB Conserv. Rev.* 2: 34-37.

Juillard, M. 1989. The decline of the Little Owl *Athene noctua* in Switzerland. Pp. 435-439 in: B.-U. Meyburg & R.D. Chancellor (eds.), *Raptors in the Modern World*. Berlin, London and Paris (WWGBP).

Kaiser, A. 1985. Zur Verbreitung und Bestandssituation der Wasseramsel (*Cinclus c. aquaticus*) in Rheinhessen, Rheingau und östlichen Hunsrück. *Ökol. der Vögel* 7: 185-196.

Kemp, M.S. 1983. The Nightjar in Avon. *Avon Bird Rept.* 1982: 49-66.

Kent, A.K. 1964. The breeding habitats of the Reed Bunting and Yellowhammer in Nottinghamshire. *Bird Study* 11: 123-127.

Kerney, M.P., & B.S. Morton. 1970. The distribution of *Dreissena polymorpha* (Pallas) in Britain. *J. Conch.* 27: 97-100.

Kjellen, N. 1986. (Census of Collared Doves *Streptopelia decaocto* in Scania in January 1985.) *Anser* 25: 127-130. (In Swedish, with English summary.)

Klomp, H. 1981. Fluctuations and stability in a Great Tit population. *Ardea* 68: 205-224.

Knox, A.G. 1975. Crossbill taxonomy. Pp. 191-201 in: D. Nethersole-Thompson, *Pine Crossbills*. Berkhamsted (Poyser).

Krebs, J.R. 1971. Territory and breeding density in the Great Tit *Parus major*. *Ecology* 52: 1-22.

Lack, D. 1966. *Population Studies of Birds*. Oxford (Clarendon Press).

Lack, D. 1971. *Ecological Isolation in Birds*. Oxford (Blackwell).

Lack, P. 1986. *The Atlas of Wintering Birds in Britain and Ireland*. Calton (Poyser).

Lack, P.C. 1989. Overall and regional trends in warbler populations of British farmland over 25 years. *Ann. Zool. Fennici* 26: 219-225.

Lack, P.C. (in prep.). *Birds and Farmland Management*.

Lamb, P.J. 1982. Persistence of Subsaharan drought. *Nature (Lond.)* 299: 46-47.

Langslow, D.R. 1978. Recent increases of Blackcaps at bird observatories. *Brit. Birds* 71: 345-354.

Leach, I.H. 1981. Wintering Blackcaps in Britain and Ireland. *Bird Study* 28: 5-14.

Lever, C. 1977. *The Naturalized Animals of the British Isles*. London (Hutchinson).

Lever, C. 1984. The Little Owl in Britain. *Hawk Trust Ann. Rept.* 14: 12-14.

Lewis, G., & G. Williams. 1984. *Rivers and Wildlife Handbook: a guide to practices which further the conservation of wildlife on rivers*. Sandy (RSPB/RSNC).

Lister, M.D. 1964. The Lapwing Habitat Enquiry 1960-61. *Bird Study* 11: 128-147.

Lloyd, C.S., M.L. Tasker & K.E. Partridge (in press). *Status of Seabirds in Britain and Ireland*.

Locke, G.M.L. 1987. Census of woodlands and trees 1979-82. *Forestry Commission Bulletin* 63. HMSO.

Lockie, J.D. 1955. The breeding habits of Short-eared Owls after a vole plague. *Bird Study* 2: 53-69.

Lovegrove, R. 1978. Breeding status of Goosanders in Wales. *Brit. Birds* 71: 214-216.

Lovenbury, G.A., M. Waterhouse & D.W. Yalden. 1978. The status of Black Grouse in the Peak District. *Naturalist* 103: 3-14.

Macdonald, D. 1965. Notes on the Corn Bunting in Sutherland. *Scot. Birds* 3: 235-246.

MAFF. 1988. *Set-aside*. Ministry of Agriculture, Fisheries and Food.

Magee, J.D. 1965. The breeding distribution of the Stonechat in Britain and the causes of its decline. *Bird Study* 12: 83-89.

Magnusson, K.G. 1986. (Chaffinch *Fringilla coelebs* nesting in Iceland.) *Bliki* 5: 1-2. (In Icelandic, with English summary.)

Marchant, J.H. 1980. Recent trends in Sparrowhawk numbers in Britain. *Bird Study* 27: 152-154.

Marchant, J.H. 1981. Residual edge effects with the mapping bird census method. *Stud. Avian Biol.* 6: 488-491.

Marchant, J.H. 1983*a*. Bird population changes for the years 1981-1982. *Bird Study* 30: 127-133.

Marchant, J.H. 1983*b*. *BTO Common Birds Census instructions*. Tring (BTO).

Marchant, J.H. (in press). A review of long-term population trends in common British breeding birds. *Proc. XI Int. Conf. Bird Census and Atlas Work*. Prague.

Marchant, J.H., & S.P. Carter (in prep.). *Bibliographies of the CBC and WBS*.

Marchant, J.H., & P.A. Hyde. 1979. Population changes for waterways birds, 1974-78. *Bird Study* 26: 227-238.

Marchant, J.H., & P.A. Hyde. 1980*a*. Population changes for waterways birds, 1978-79. *Bird Study* 27: 179-182.

Marchant, J.H., & P.A. Hyde. 1980*b*. Aspects of the distribution of riparian birds on waterways in Britain and Ireland. *Bird Study* 27: 183-202.

Marchant, J.H., & P.C. Lack. 1984. Recommended letter-code abbreviations for British birds. *Brit. Birds* 77: 570-571.

Marchant, J.H., & P.A. Whittington. 1989. 1987-88 CBC index report. *BTO News* 162: 9-12.

Marquiss, M. 1989. Grey Herons *Ardea cinerea* breeding in Scotland: numbers, distribution, and census techniques. *Bird Study* 36: 181-191.

Mason, B.J. 1979. The distinction between weather and climate. *Met. Mag.* 108: 211-212.

Mason, C.F. 1976. Breeding biology of the *Sylvia* warblers. *Bird Study* 23: 213-232.

Mason, C.F., & A. Hussey. 1984. Bird population trends as shown by chick ringing data. *Ring. & Migr.* 5: 113-120.

Mason, C.F., & S.M. Macdonald. 1976. Aspects of the breeding biology of the Snipe. *Bird Study* 23: 33-38.

Mather, J.R. 1986. *The Birds of Yorkshire*. London (Croom Helm).

Mawson, G.P., & A. Crabtree. 1981. House Martins in the Sheffield area, 1977. *Magpie* 2: 26-33.

Mead, C.J. 1970. The winter quarters of British Swallows. *Bird Study* 17: 229-240.

Mead, C.J. 1974. *Bird Ringing*. BTO Guide 16.

Mead, C.J. 1979*a*. Colony fidelity and interchange in the Sand Martin. *Bird Study* 26: 99-106.

Mead, C.J. 1979*b*. Mortality and causes of death in British Sand Martins. *Bird Study* 26: 107-112.

Mead, C.J. 1984. Sand Martins slump. *BTO News* 133: 1.

Mead, C.J., & R. Hudson. 1985. Report on bird-ringing for 1984. *Ring. & Migr.* 6: 125-172.

Mead, C.J., P.M. North & B.R. Watmough. 1979. The mortality of British Grey Herons. *Bird Study* 26: 13-22.

Meadows, B.S. 1972*a*. The recovery of the Kingfisher in London after the 1962/63 hard winter. *London Bird Rept.* 36 (1971): 60-66.

Meadows, B.S. 1972*b*. Kingfisher numbers and stream pollution. *Ibis* 114: 443.

Mearns, R. 1983. The status of the Raven in southern Scotland and Northumbria. *Scot. Birds* 12: 211-218.
Meek, E.R. 1988. The breeding ecology and decline of the Merlin *Falco columbarius* in Orkney. *Bird Study* 35: 209-218.
Meek, E.R., & B. Little. 1977. The spread of the Goosander in Britain and Ireland. *Brit. Birds* 70: 229-237.
Meiklejohn, M.F.M., & J.K. Stanford. 1954. June notes on the birds of Islay. *Scot. Nat.* 66: 129-145.
Meinertzhagen, R. 1950. The Goshawk in Great Britain. *Bull. Brit. Orn. Club* 70: 46-49.
Meltofte, H. 1987. (The occurrence of staging waders at the Tipperne Reserve, western Denmark, 1928-1982.) *Dansk Orn. Foren. Tidsskr.* 81: 1-108. (In Danish, with English summary.)
Merrie, T.D.H. 1978. Relationship between spatial distribution of breeding divers and the availability of fishing waters. *Bird Study* 25: 119-122.
Milbled, T. 1979. Extension de l'aire nidifaction de sizerin flammé cabaret (*A. f. cabaret*) dans le Pas-de-Calais. *Héron* 1979: 48-53.
Milsom, T.P. 1982. Edge effect in breeding Reed Warblers in North Humberside. *Bird Study* 29: 167-168.
Møller, A.P. 1979. (Population changes among passerines in north Jutland, Denmark, 1960-1976.) *Dansk Orn. Foren. Tidsskr.* 73: 233-243. (In Danish, with English summary.)
Møller, A.P. 1980. (The impact of changes in agricultural use on the fauna of breeding birds.) *Dansk Orn. Foren. Tidsskr.* 74: 27-34. (In Danish, with English summary.)
Møller, A.P. 1983. Breeding habitat selection in the Swallow *Hirundo rustica*. *Bird Study* 30: 134-142.
Møller, A.P. 1989. Population dynamics of a declining Swallow *Hirundo rustica* population. *J. Anim. Ecol.* 58: 1051-1063.
Monaghan, P., E. Bignal, S. Bignal, N. Easterbee & C.R. McKay. 1989. The distribution and status of the Chough in Scotland in 1986. *Scot. Birds* 15: 114-118.
Montier, D. (ed.). 1977. *Atlas of Breeding Birds of the London Area*. London (Batsford).
Moore, N.W. 1957. The past and present status of the Buzzard in the British Isles. *Brit. Birds* 50: 173-197.
Moore, N.W., & M.D. Hooper. 1975. On the number of bird species in British woods. *Biol. Conserv.* 8: 239-250.
More, A.G. 1865. On the distribution of birds in Great Britain during the nesting season. *Ibis* (2) 1: 1-27, 119-142, 425-458.
Moreau, R.E. 1951. The British status of the Quail and some problems of its biology. *Brit. Birds* 44: 257-276.
Moreau, R.E. 1956. Quail in the British Isles, 1950-53. *Brit. Birds* 49: 161-166.
Moreau, R.E. 1961. Problems of Mediterranean-Saharan migration. *Ibis* 103a: 373-427, 580-623.
Morgan, R.A. 1982. Breeding seasons of some British waders. *BTO Research Rept.* 7.
Morgan, R.A., & P.G. Davis. 1977. The number of broods reared by Stonechats in Surrey. *Bird Study* 24: 229-232.
Morgan, R., & D. Glue. 1977. Breeding, mortality and movements of Kingfishers. *Bird Study* 24: 15-24.
Morgan, R.A., & D.E. Glue. 1981. Breeding survey of Black Redstarts in Britain, 1977. *Bird Study* 28: 163-168.
Morgan, R.A., & M. Shorten. 1974. Breeding of the Woodcock in Britain. *Bird Study* 21: 193-199.
Moritz, D. 1981. Abnahme des Feldsperlings *Passer montanus* auch als Durchzugler auf Helgoland. *Vogelwelt* 102: 215-219.
Morris, F.O. 1863. *A History of British Birds*. London (Groomebridge).
Moss, D. 1985. Some statistical checks on the BTO Common Birds Census index – 20 years on. Pp. 175-179 in: K. Taylor, R.J. Fuller & P.C. Lack (eds.), *Bird Census and Atlas Studies*. Tring (BTO).
Moss, D., P.N. Taylor & N. Easterbee. 1979. The effects on songbird populations of upland afforestation with spruce. *Forestry* 52: 129-150.

Moss, R., D. Weir & A.M. Jones. 1979. Capercaillie management in Scotland. Pp. 140-155 in: T.W.I. Lovel (ed.), *Woodland Grouse Symposium*. Bures, Suffolk (World Pheasant Association).

Mountford, M.D. 1982. Estimation of population fluctuations with application to the Common Birds Census. *Appl. Statist.* 31: 135-143.

Mountford, M.D. 1985. An index of population change with application to the Common Birds Census. Pp. 121-132 in: B.J.T. Morgan & P.M. North (eds.), *Statistics in Ornithology*. Berlin (Springer-Verlag).

Mountfort, G. 1957. *The Hawfinch*. London (Collins, New Naturalist).

Mudge, G. 1981. *The incidence and significance of ingested lead pellet poisoning in British wildfowl*. Report to BASC, RSPB and Wildfowl Trust.

Munro, C.A. 1984. Roof nesting Oystercatchers. *Bird Study* 31: 148.

Murton, R.K. 1965. *The Woodpigeon*. London (Collins, New Naturalist).

Murton, R.K., & S.P. Clarke. 1968. Breeding biology of Rock Doves. *Brit. Birds* 61: 429-448.

Murton, R.K., N.J. Westwood & A.J. Isaacson. 1964. The feeding habits of the Woodpigeon *Columba palumbus*, Stock Dove *C. oenas* and Turtle Dove *Streptopelia turtur*. *Ibis* 106: 174-188.

Murton, R.K., N.J. Westwood & A.J. Isaacson. 1974. A study of Wood-pigeon shooting: the exploitation of a natural animal population. *J. appl. Ecol.* 11: 61-82.

NCC. 1981. *Report of the Nature Conservancy Council's Working Group on Lead Poisoning in Swans*. London (Nature Conservancy Council).

NCC. 1984. *Nature conservation in Great Britain*. Peterborough (Nature Conservancy Council).

NCC. 1986. *Nature conservation and afforestation in Britain*. Peterborough (Nature Conservancy Council).

NCC. 1987. *Conversion and extensification of production: implications and opportunities for nature conservation*. Peterborough (Nature Conservancy Council).

Nethersole-Thompson, D. 1973. *The Dotterel*. London (Collins).

Nethersole-Thompson, D. 1975. *Pine Crossbills: a Scottish contribution*. Berkhamsted (Poyser).

Nethersole-Thompson, D., & M. Nethersole-Thompson. 1979. *Greenshanks*. Berkhamsted (Poyser).

Nethersole-Thompson, D., & M. Nethersole-Thompson. 1986. *Waders: their Breeding, Haunts and Watchers*. Calton (Poyser).

Nethersole-Thompson, D., & A. Watson. 1974. *The Cairngorms: their natural history and scenery*. London (Collins).

Newton, A. 1896. *A Dictionary of Birds*. London (Black).

Newton, I. 1968. Bullfinches and fruit buds. Pp. 199-209 in: R.K. Murton & E.N. Wright (eds.), *The Problems of Birds as Pests*. London (Academic Press).

Newton, I. 1972. *Finches*. London (Collins, New Naturalist).

Newton, I. 1979. *Population Ecology of Raptors*. Berkhamsted (Poyser).

Newton, I. 1983. Birds and forestry. Pp. 21-30 in: E.H.M. Harris (ed.), *Forestry and Conservation*. Tring (Royal Forestry Society).

Newton, I. 1984. Raptors in Britain – a review of the last 150 years. *BTO News* 131: 6-7.

Newton, I. 1986. *The Sparrowhawk*. Calton (Poyser).

Newton, I., J. Bogan, E.R. Meek & B. Little. 1982. Organo-chlorine compounds and shell-thinning in British Merlins. *Ibis* 124: 328-335.

Newton, I., P.E. Davis & J.E. Davis. 1982. Ravens and Buzzards in relation to sheep farming and forestry in Wales. *J. appl. Ecol.* 19: 681-706.

Newton, I., P.E. Davis & J.E. Davis. 1989. Age of first breeding, dispersal and survival of Red Kites *Milvus milvus* in Wales. *Ibis* 131: 16-21.

Newton, I., P.E. Davis & D. Moss. 1981. Distribution and breeding of Red Kites in relation to land-use in Wales. *J. appl. Ecol.* 18: 173-186.

Newton, I., & M.B. Haas. 1984. The return of the Sparrowhawk. *Brit. Birds* 77: 47-70.

Newton, I., & M.B. Haas. 1988. Pollutants in Merlin eggs and their effects on breeding. *Brit. Birds* 81: 258-269.

Nicholson, E.M. 1929. Report on the *British Birds* census of heronries, 1928. *Brit. Birds* 22: 270-323, 334-372.

Nicholson, E.M. 1938. Report on the Lapwing Habitat Enquiry, 1937. *Brit. Birds* 32: 170-191, 207-229, 255-259.
Nilsson, S.G. 1976. Habitat, territory size, and reproductive success in the Nuthatch *Sitta europaea*. *Ornis Scand.* 7: 179-184.
Nisbet, I.C.T., & A.E. Vine. 1955. Regular inland breeding of Shelducks in the fens. *Brit. Birds* 48: 362-363.
Noble, H. 1906. Birds of Berkshire. Pp. 140-166 in: P.H. Ditchfield & W. Page (eds.), *A History of Berkshire*. London (Constable, Victoria History series).
Nøhr, H. 1989. Organic farming benefits birds. *BTO News* 163: 4-5.
Nøhr, H., & L. Braae. 1984. (How are things with woodland birds?) *Fugle* 4: 22-23. (In Danish.)
Norris, C.A. 1947*a*. *Notes on the Birds of Warwickshire*. Birmingham (Cornish Bros.).
Norris, C.A. 1947*b*. Report on the distribution and status of the Corn Crake. *Brit. Birds* 40: 226-244.
North, P.M. 1979. Relating Grey Heron survival rates to winter weather conditions. *Bird Study* 26: 23-28.
Oakes, C. 1953. *The Birds of Lancashire*. Edinburgh and London (Oliver & Boyd).
O'Connor, R.J. 1980*a*. Population regulation in the Yellowhammer *Emberiza citrinella* in Britain. Pp. 190-200 in: H. Oelke (ed.), *Bird Census Work and Nature Conservation*. Proc. VI Int. Conf. Bird Census Work. Lengede (Dachverbandes Deutscher Avifaunisten).
O'Connor, R.J. 1980*b*. Pattern and process in Great Tit *Parus major* populations in Britain. *Ardea* 68: 165-183.
O'Connor, R.J. 1981. Comparisons between migrant and non-migrant birds in Britain. Pp. 167-195 in: D.J. Aidley (ed.), *Animal Migration*. Soc. for Experimental Biology, Seminar 13. Cambridge (Cambridge University Press).
O'Connor, R.J. 1982. Habitat occupancy and regulation of clutch size in the European Kestrel *Falco tinnunculus*. *Bird Study* 29: 17-26.
O'Connor, R.J., R.A. Cawthorne & C.J. Mead. 1982. The effects of severe winter weather on British bird populations. *BTO Research Rept.* 8.
O'Connor, R.J., & R.J. Fuller (eds.). 1984. A re-evaluation of the aims and methods of the Common Birds Census. *BTO Research Rept.* 15.
O'Connor, R.J., & J.H. Marchant. 1981. A field validation of some Common Birds Census techniques. *BTO Research Rept.* 4.
O'Connor, R.J., & C.J. Mead. 1981. Population level and nesting biology of the Stock Dove *Columba oenas* in Great Britain, 1930-1980. *BTO Research Rept.* 5.
O'Connor, R.J., & C.J. Mead. 1984. The Stock Dove in Britain, 1930-80. *Brit. Birds* 77: 181-201.
O'Connor, R.J., & R.A. Morgan. 1982. Some effects of weather conditions on the breeding of the Spotted Flycatcher *Muscicapa striata* in Britain. *Bird Study* 29: 41-48.
O'Connor, R.J., & D.N. Pearman. 1987. Long-term trends in breeding success of some British birds. *BTO Research Rept.* 23.
O'Connor, R.J., & M. Shrubb. 1986*a*. *Farming and Birds*. Cambridge (Cambridge University Press).
O'Connor, R.J., & M. Shrubb. 1986*b*. Recent changes in bird populations in relation to farming practices in England and Wales. *J. Roy. Agric. Soc. England* 147: 132-141.
Ogilvie, M.A. 1967. Population changes and mortality of the Mute Swan in Britain. *Wildfowl Trust Ann. Rept.* 18: 64-73.
Ogilvie, M.A. 1969. The status of the Canada Goose in Britain 1967-69. *Wildfowl* 20: 79-85.
Ogilvie, M.A. 1977. The numbers of Canada Geese in Britain 1976. *Wildfowl* 28: 27-34.
Ogilvie, M.A. 1981. The Mute Swan in Britain, 1978. *Bird Study* 28: 87-106.
Ogilvie, M.A. 1983. A migration study of the Teal (*Anas crecca*) in Europe using ringing recoveries. Unpubl. PhD. thesis, University of Bristol.
Ogilvie, M.A. 1986. The Mute Swan *Cygnus olor* in Britain, 1983. *Bird Study* 33: 121-137.
Olney, P.J.S. 1963. The food and feeding habits of Tufted Duck *Aythya fuligula*. *Ibis* 105: 55-62.
Orell, M., & M. Ojanen. 1980. Zur Abnahme des Stars (*Sturnus vulgaris*) in Skandinavien. *J. Orn.* 121: 397-401.
Orford, N. 1973. Breeding distribution of the Twite in central Britain. *Bird Study* 20: 51-62, 121-126.

Ormerod, S.J., N. Allinson, D. Hudson & S.J. Tyler. 1986. The distribution of breeding Dippers (*Cinclus cinclus*: Aves) in relation to stream acidity in upland Wales. *Freshwater Biology* 16: 501-507.

Ormerod, S.J., M.A. Boilstone & S.J. Tyler. 1985*a*. Factors influencing the abundance of breeding Dippers *Cinclus cinclus* in the catchment of the River Wye, mid-Wales. *Ibis* 127: 332-340.

Ormerod, S.J., & S.J. Tyler. 1987*a*. Aspects of the breeding ecology of Welsh Grey Wagtails *Motacilla cinerea*. *Bird Study* 34: 43-51.

Ormerod, S.J., & S.J. Tyler. 1987*b*. Dippers (*Cinclus cinclus*) and Grey Wagtails (*Motacilla cinerea*) as indicators of stream acidity in upland Wales. *ICBP Technical Publication* 6: 191-208.

Ormerod, S.J., S.J. Tyler & J.M.S. Lewis. 1985*b*. Is the breeding distribution of Dippers influenced by stream acidity? *Bird Study* 32: 32-39.

Osborne, P. 1982. Some effects of Dutch elm disease on nesting farmland birds. *Bird Study* 29: 2-16.

Osborne, P. 1983. The influence of Dutch elm disease on bird population trends. *Bird Study* 30: 27-38.

Osborne, P. 1985. Some effects of Dutch elm disease on the birds of a Dorset dairy farm. *J. appl. Ecol.* 22: 681-691.

Österlöf, S., & B.O. Stolt. 1982. Population trends indicated by birds ringed in Sweden. *Ornis Scand.* 13: 135-140.

O'Sullivan, J.M. 1976. Bearded Tits in Britain and Ireland, 1966-74. *Brit. Birds* 69: 473-489.

Owen, M. 1977. *Wildfowl in Europe*. London (Macmillan).

Owen, M., G.L. Atkinson-Willes & D.G. Salmon. 1986. *Wildfowl in Great Britain*. Cambridge (Cambridge University Press). 2nd edition.

Owen, M., & D.G. Salmon. 1988. Feral Greylag Geese *Anser anser* in Britain and Ireland, 1960-86. *Bird Study* 35: 37-46.

Palmer, K.H. 1983. The breeding season status of the Grey Wagtail in the London area, 1979-1981. *London Bird Rept.* 47 (1982): 106-122.

Parmenter, T.W. 1982. The Grasshopper Warbler in Sussex: the results of a breeding survey during 1977-80. *Sussex Bird Rept.* 34 (1981): 79-82.

Parr, R. 1979. Sequential breeding by Golden Plovers. *Brit. Birds* 72: 499-503.

Parr, S.J. 1985. The breeding ecology and diet of the Hobby *Falco subbuteo* in southern England. *Ibis* 127: 60-73.

Parrinder, E.D. 1989. Little Ringed Plovers *Charadrius dubius* in Britain in 1984. *Bird Study* 36: 147-153.

Parrinder, E.R., & E.D. Parrinder. 1969. Little Ringed Plovers in Britain in 1963-67. *Brit. Birds* 62: 219-223.

Parrinder, E.R., & E.D. Parrinder. 1975. Little Ringed Plovers in Britain in 1968-73. *Brit. Birds* 68: 359-368.

Parslow, J.L.F. 1973. *Breeding Birds of Britain and Ireland*. Berkhamsted (Poyser).

Partridge, J.K. 1989. Lower Lough Erne's Common Scoters. *RSPB Conserv. Rev.* 3: 25-28.

Patterson, I.J. 1982. *The Shelduck: a study in behavioural ecology*. Cambridge (Cambridge University Press).

Patterson, I.W. 1987. The status and distribution of Greylag Geese *Anser anser* in the Uists, Scotland. *Bird Study* 34: 235-238.

Penhallurick, R.D. 1978. *The Birds of Cornwall and the Isles of Scilly*. Penzance (Headland Publications).

Pennie, I.D. 1962. A century of bird-watching in Sutherland. *Scot. Birds* 2: 167-192.

Perrins, C.M. 1966. The effect of beech crops on Great Tit populations and movements. *Brit. Birds* 59: 419-432.

Perrins, C. 1979. *British Tits*. London (Collins, New Naturalist).

Perry, K. 1986. *The Irish Dipper*. Belfast (author).

Persson, C. 1987. Age structure, sex ratios and survival rates in a south Swedish Sand martin (*Riparia riparia*) population, 1964 to 1984. *J. Zool. Lond.* (B) 1: 639-670.

274

Petersen, N.F., & K. Williamson. 1949. Polymorphism and breeding of the Rock Dove in the Faeroe Islands. *Ibis* 91: 17-23.

Petty, S. 1985. A study of Tawny Owls in commercial spruce forests in the uplands. *Argyll Bird Rept.* 2: 70-71.

Peus, F. 1951. Nüchterne Analyse der Massenvermehrung der Misteldrossel (*Turdus viscivorus* L.) in Nordwesteuropa. *Bonn. Zool. Beitr.* 2: 55-82.

Phillips, J.S. 1973. Stonechats in young forestry plantations. *Bird Study* 20: 82-84.

Pienkowski, M.W. 1984. Behaviour of young Ringed Plovers *Charadrius hiaticula* and its relation to growth and survival to reproductive age. *Ibis* 126: 133-155.

Pienkowski, M.W., & P.R. Evans. 1979. The origins of Shelducks moulting on the Forth. *Bird Study* 26: 195-196.

Pienkowski, M.W., & P.R. Evans. 1982a. Breeding behaviour, productivity and survival of colonial and non-colonial Shelducks *Tadorna tadorna*. *Ornis Scand.* 13: 101-116.

Pienkowski, M.W., & P.R. Evans. 1982b. Clutch parasitism and nesting interference between Shelducks at Aberlady Bay. *Wildfowl* 33: 159-163.

Piersma, T. 1986. Breeding waders in Europe. A review of population size estimates and a bibliography of information sources. *Bull. Wader Study Group* 48, suppl.: 1-116.

Pollard, E., M.D. Hooper & N.W. Moore. 1974. *Hedges*. London (Collins).

Potts, G.R. 1967. Urban Starling roosts in the British Isles. *Bird Study* 14: 35-42.

Potts, G.R. 1980. The effects of modern agriculture, nest predation and game management on the population ecology of partridges (*Perdix perdix* and *Alectoris rufa*). *Advances Ecol. Research* 11: 1-82.

Potts, G.R. 1981. Fewer Woodpigeons? *Game Conserv. Ann. Rev.* 12 (1980): 83-87.

Potts, G.R. 1984. Grey Partridges: how a computer model can help to solve practical game management questions. *Game Conserv. Ann. Rev.* 15 (1983): 56-59.

Potts, G.R. 1986. *The Partridge*. London (Collins).

Potts, G.R. 1989. The impact of releasing hybrid partridges on wild Red-legged populations. *Game Conserv. Ann. Rev.* 20: 81-85.

Potts, G.R., S.C. Tapper & P.J. Hudson. 1984. Population fluctuations in Red Grouse: analysis of bag records and a simulation model. *J. Anim. Ecol.* 53: 21-36.

Poxton, I.R. 1986. Breeding Ring Ouzels in the Pentland Hills. *Scot. Birds* 14: 44-48.

Poxton, I.R. 1987. Breeding status of the Ring Ouzel in southeast Scotland 1985-86. *Scot. Birds* 14: 205-208.

Prater, A.J. 1976. Breeding population of the Ringed Plover in Britain. *Bird Study* 23: 155-161.

Prater, A.J. 1981. *Estuary Birds of Britain and Ireland*. Calton (Poyser).

Prater, A.J. 1988. The breeding population of Reed and Sedge Warblers in Sussex. *Sussex Bird Rept.* 40 (1987): 81-96.

Prater, A.J. 1989. Ringed Plover *Charadrius hiaticula* breeding population of the United Kingdom in 1984. *Bird Study* 36: 154-159.

Preston, K. 1976. Census of Great Crested Grebes, summer 1975. *Irish Bird Rept.* 23 (1975): 38-43.

Prestt, I. 1965. An enquiry into the recent breeding status of some of the smaller birds of prey and crows in Britain. *Bird Study* 12: 196-221.

Prestt, I. 1970. Organochlorine pollution of rivers and the Heron *Ardea cinerea*. *Pap. Proc. Tech. Meet. Int. Union Conserv. Nat. Resour., 11th (New Delhi 1969)* 1: 95-102. Morges.

Prestt, I., & D.H. Mills. 1966. A census of the Great Crested Grebe in Britain, 1965. *Bird Study* 13: 163-203.

Prŷs-Jones, R.P. 1984. Migration patterns of the Reed Bunting, *Emberiza schoeniclus schoeniclus*, and the dependence of wintering distribution on environmental conditions. *Gerfaut* 74: 15-37.

Pulliainen, E. 1980. The history and spread of the Moorhen *Gallinula chloropus* in Finland. *Ornis Fenn.* 57: 117-123.

Purroy, F.J., M. Rodero & L. Tomialojć. 1984. The ecology of Woodpigeons *Columba palumbus* wintering on the Iberian Peninsula. *Acta Ornithol.* 20: 111-146.

Rackham, O. 1986. *The History of the Countryside*. Dent.

Rands, M.R.W. 1985. Pesticide use on cereals and the survival of Grey Partridge chicks: a field experiment. *J. appl. Ecol.* 22: 49-54.

Rands, M., & S. Tapper. 1986. The national game census: 1985/86 season. *Game Conserv. Ann. Rev.* 17: 145-150.

Ratcliffe, D.A. 1962. Breeding density in the Peregrine *Falco peregrinus* and Raven *Corvus corax*. *Ibis* 104: 13-39.

Ratcliffe, D.A. 1963. The status of the Peregrine in Great Britain. *Bird Study* 10: 56-90.

Ratcliffe, D.A. 1976. Observations on the breeding of Golden Plover in Great Britain. *Bird Study* 23: 63-116.

Ratcliffe, D.A. 1977. Uplands and birds – an outline. *Bird Study* 24: 140-158.

Ratcliffe, D.A. 1984. The Peregrine breeding population of the United Kingdom in 1981. *Bird Study* 31: 1-18.

Raven, P. 1986. Changes in the breeding bird population of a small clay river following flood alleviation works. *Bird Study* 33: 24-35.

Ravenscroft, N.O.M. 1989. The status and habitat of the Nightjar *Caprimulgus europaeus* in coastal Suffolk. *Bird Study* 36: 161-169.

Redfern, C.P.F. 1982. Lapwing nest sites and chick mobility in relation to habitat. *Bird Study* 29: 201-208.

Reed, T. 1985. Estimates of British breeding wader populations. *Bull. Wader Study Group* 45: 11-12.

Reinikainen, A. 1937. The irregular migrations of the Crossbill *L. c. curvirostra* and their relation to the cone crop of the conifers. *Ornis Fenn.* 14: 55-64.

Rettig, K. 1985. Brutvorkommen des Birkenzeisigs (*Carduelis flammea cabaret*) in Emden. *Beitr. Naturk. Niedersachs.* 38: 222-223.

Reynolds, C.M. 1979. The heronries census: 1972-1977 population changes and a review. *Bird Study* 26: 7-12.

Riddiford, N. 1983. Recent declines of Grasshopper Warblers *Locustella naevia* at British bird observatories. *Bird Study* 30: 143-148.

Riddiford, N. 1986. Why do Cuckoos *Cuculus canorus* use so many species of hosts? *Bird Study* 33: 1-5.

Robbins, C.S., D. Bystrak & P.H. Geissler. 1983. Monitoring bird population trends in North America. Pp. 180-183 in: F.J. Purroy (ed.), *Bird census and mediterranean landscape. Proc. 7th Int. Conf. Bird Census Work.* León, Spain.

Robertson, P.A. 1988. Hand-rearing and the size of the national Pheasant bag. *Game Conserv. Ann. Rev.* 19: 166-170.

Robins, M., & C.J. Bibby. 1985. Dartford Warblers in 1984 Britain. *Brit. Birds* 78: 269-280.

Rolfe, R. 1966. The status of the Chough in the British Isles. *Bird Study* 13: 221-236.

Rose, L.N. 1982. Breeding ecology of British pipits and their Cuckoo parasite. *Bird Study* 29: 27-40.

Round, P.D., & M. Moss. 1984. The waterbird populations of three Welsh rivers. *Bird Study* 31: 61-68.

Rüger, A., C. Prentice & M. Owen. 1986. *Results of the IWRB International Waterfowl Census 1967-1983.* Slimbridge (IWRB Special Publ. 6).

Rutschke, E. (ed.). 1983. *Die Vogelwelt Brandenburgs.* Jena.

Ruttledge, R.F. 1966. *Ireland's Birds: their distributions and migrations.* London (Witherby).

Ruttledge, R.F. 1968. The Kingfisher population. *Irish Bird Rept.* 15 (1967): 11-14.

Safriel, U.N. 1985. "Diet dimorphism" within an Oystercatcher *Haematopus ostralegus* population – adaptive significance and effects on recent distribution dynamics. *Ibis* 127: 278-305.

Sage, B.L. 1959. *A History of the Birds of Hertfordshire.* London (Barrie & Rockliff).

Sage, B., & J.D.R. Vernon. 1978. The 1975 national survey of rookeries. *Bird Study* 25: 64-86.

Sage, B., & P.A. Whittington. 1985. The 1980 sample survey of rookeries. *Bird Study* 32: 77-81.

Salmon, D.G., R.P. Prŷs-Jones & J.S. Kirby. 1988. *Wildfowl and Wader Counts 1987-88. The results of the National Wildfowl Counts and Birds of Estuaries Enquiry.* Slimbridge (Wildfowl Trust).

Salmon, H.M. 1970. The Red Kites in Wales: the story of their preservation. Pp. 67-79 in: W.S. Lacey (ed.), *Welsh Wildlife in Trust.* Bangor (N. Wales Nat. Trust).

Sandeman, P.W. 1957. The rarer birds of prey: their present status in the British Isles. Osprey. *Brit. Birds* 50: 147-149.

Schläpfer, A. 1988. Populationsökologie der Feldlerche *Alauda arvensis* in der intensiv genutzten Agrarlandschaft. *Orn. Beob.* 85: 309-371.

Sears, J. 1988. *A report on lead poisoning in Mute Swans in the Thames area during 1987.* Report to NCC.

Seel, D.C., & K.C. Walton. 1979. Numbers of Meadow Pipits *Anthus pratensis* on mountain farm grassland in North Wales in the breeding season. *Ibis* 121: 147-164.

Seel, D.C., K.C. Walton & I. Wyllie. 1981. Age of first breeding in the Cuckoo. *Bird Study* 28: 211-214.

Sellers, R.M. 1984. Movements of Coal, Marsh and Willow Tits in Britain. *Ring. & Migr.* 5: 79-89.

Sellers, R.M. 1986. Biometrics of the Siskin *Carduelis spinus. Ring. & Migr.* 7: 99-111.

Sellin, D. 1987. Zu Bestand, Ökologie und Ethologie des Kolkraben (*Corvus corax*) in Nordösten des Bezirkes Rostock. *Vogelwelt* 108: 13-27.

Sells, J.D. 1984. Marsh Tits and the Batsford nest-box scheme. *Gloucs. Nat.* 1: 26.

Sharrock, J.T.R. 1969. Grey Wagtail passage and population fluctuations in 1956-67. *Bird Study* 16: 17-34.

Sharrock, J.T.R. 1976. *The Atlas of Breeding Birds in Britain and Ireland.* Tring (BTO) and Berkhamsted (Poyser).

Sharrock, J.T.R., & O. Hildén. 1983. Survey of some of Europe's breeding birds. *Brit. Birds* 76: 118-123.

Shawyer, C.R. 1987. *The Barn Owl in the British Isles: its past, present and future.* London (Hawk Trust).

Shooter, P. 1970. The Dipper population of Derbyshire 1958-68. *Brit. Birds* 63: 158-163.

Shrubb, M. 1985. Breeding Sparrowhawks *Accipiter nisus* and organo-chlorine pesticides in Sussex and Kent. *Bird Study* 32: 155-163.

Shrubb, M., & P.C. Lack (in press). The numbers and distribution of Lapwings (*Vanellus vanellus*) nesting in England and Wales in 1987. *Bird Study.*

Simms, E. 1985. *British Warblers.* London (Collins, New Naturalist).

Sitters, H.P. 1982. The decline of the Cirl Bunting in Britain, 1968-80. *Brit. Birds* 75: 105-108.

Sitters, H.P. 1985. Cirl Buntings in Britain in 1982. *Bird Study* 32: 1-10.

Sitters, H.P. 1986. Woodlarks in Britain, 1968-83. *Brit. Birds* 79: 105-116.

Sitters, H.P. (ed.). 1988. *Tetrad Atlas of the Breeding Birds of Devon.* Yelverton (Devon Bird Watch. & Pres. Society).

Smart, N., & J. Andrews. 1985. *Birds and Broadleaves Handbook.* Sandy (RSPB).

Smith, A.E. 1975. The impacts of lowland river management. *Bird Study* 22: 249-254.

Smith, K.W. 1983. The status and distribution of waders breeding on wet lowland grasslands in England and Wales. *Bird Study* 30: 177-192.

Smith, S. 1950. *The Yellow Wagtail.* London (Collins, New Naturalist).

Snow, B.K., & D.W. Snow. 1984. Long-term defence of fruit by Mistle Thrushes *Turdus viscivorus. Ibis* 126: 39-49.

Snow, D.W. 1965. The relationship between census results and the breeding population of birds on farmland. *Bird Study* 12: 287-304.

Snow, D.W. 1966. Population dynamics of the Blackbird. *Nature (Lond.)* 211: 1231-1233.

Snow, D.W. 1968. Movements and mortality of British Kestrels. *Bird Study* 15: 65-83.

Snow, D.W. 1969. Some vital statistics of British Mistle Thrushes. *Bird Study* 16: 34-44.

Solonen, T. 1979. Population dynamics of the Garden Warbler *Sylvia borin* in southern Finland. *Ornis Fenn.* 56: 3-12.

Southern, H.N. 1970. Natural control of a population of Tawny Owls. *J. Zool. Lond.* 162: 197-285.

Southern, H.N., & A. Morley. 1950. Marsh Tit territories over six years. *Brit. Birds* 43: 33-47.

SOVON. 1987. *Atlas van de Nederlandse Vogels.* Arnhem (SOVON).

Spencer, R. 1983. Our changing avifauna. Pp. 93-128 in: R. Hickling (ed.), *Enjoying Ornithology. Fifty years of the British Trust for Ornithology*. Calton (Poyser).

Spencer, R., & G.H. Gush. 1973. Siskins feeding in gardens. *Brit. Birds* 66: 91-99.

Spencer, R., & the Rare Breeding Birds Panel. 1988. Rare breeding birds in the United Kingdom in 1986. *Brit. Birds* 81: 417-444.

Spencer, R., & the Rare Breeding Birds Panel. 1989. Rare breeding birds in the United Kingdom in 1987. *Brit. Birds* 82: 477-504.

Stafford, J. 1971. The Heron population of England and Wales, 1928-1970. *Bird Study* 18: 218-221.

Stafford, J. 1979. The national census of heronries in England and Wales in 1964. *Bird Study* 26: 3-6.

Stanford, J.K. 1955. The Common Curlew as a Wiltshire breeding bird. *Wiltshire Arch. Nat. Hist. Mag.* 56: 30-34.

Stenning, M.J., P.H. Harvey & B. Campbell. 1988. Searching for density-dependent regulation in a population of Pied Flycatchers *Ficedula hypoleuca*. *J. Anim. Ecol.* 57: 307-317.

Steventon, D.J. 1985. Breeding Ringed Plover survey 1984. *Hampshire Bird Rept.* (1984): 81-84.

Stresemann, E., & E. Nowak. 1958. Die Ausbreitung der Türkentaube in Asien und Europa. *J. Orn.* 99: 243-296.

Stroud, D.A., M.W. Pienkowski & G.P. Mudge. 1989. *Review of the protection afforded to bird species by the network of proposed and designated Special Protection Areas in Great Britain*. Peterborough (NCC).

Stroud, D.A., T.M. Reed, M.W. Pienkowski & R.A. Lindsay. 1987. *Birds, Bogs and Forestry: the peatlands of Caithness and Sutherland*. Peterborough (NCC).

Summers-Smith, J.D. 1988. *The Sparrows*. Calton (Poyser).

Summers-Smith, J.D. 1989. A history of the status of the Tree Sparrow *Passer montanus* in the British Isles. *Bird Study* 36: 23-31.

Svensson, S. 1974. Interpersonal variation in species map evaluation in bird census work with the mapping method. *Acta Ornithol.* 14: 322-338.

Tamisier, A. 1974. Etho-ecological studies of Teal wintering in the Camargue (Rhône delta, France). *Wildfowl* 25: 123-133.

Tapper, S. 1981. The effects of farming and Dutch elm disease on corvids. *Game Conserv. Ann. Rev.* 12: 98-101.

Tapper, S., & A. Clements. 1987. A longer view of game bag records. *Game Conserv. Ann. Rev.* 18: 58-64.

Tasker, M.L. 1982. Moulting Shelducks on the Humber. *Bird Study* 29: 164-166.

Tatner, P. 1978. A review of House Martins (*Delichon urbica*) in part of South Manchester, 1975. *Naturalist* 103: 59-68.

Tatner, P. 1982. Factors influencing the distribution of Magpies *Pica pica* in an urban environment. *Bird Study* 29: 227-234.

Tatner, P. 1983. The diet of urban Magpies *Pica pica*. *Ibis* 125: 90-107.

Taylor, D.W., D.L. Davenport & J.J.M. Flegg. 1981. *The Birds of Kent: a review of their status and distribution*. Meopham (Kent Orn. Soc.).

Taylor, I.R., A. Dowell, T. Irving, I.K. Langford & G. Shaw. 1988. The distribution and abundance of the Barn Owl *Tyto alba* in south-west Scotland. *Scot. Birds* 15: 40-43.

Taylor, K. 1982. *BTO Waterways Bird Survey instructions*. Tring (BTO).

Taylor, K. 1984. The influence of watercourse management on Moorhen breeding biology. *Brit. Birds* 77: 141-148.

Taylor, K., R. Hudson & G. Horne. 1988. Buzzard breeding distribution and abundance in Britain and Northern Ireland in 1983. *Bird Study* 35: 109-118.

Taylor, S.M. 1965. The Common Birds Census – some statistical aspects. *Bird Study* 12: 268-286.

Temperley, G.W. 1951. *A History of the Birds of Durham*. Newcastle-on-Tyne (Northumberland & Durham N.H.S., *Trans.* vol. 9).

Temperley, G.W., & E. Blezard. 1951. Status of Green Woodpecker in northern England. *Brit. Birds* 44: 24-26.

Temrin, H. 1984. Why are some Wood Warbler (*Phylloscopus sibilatrix*) males polyterritorial? *Ann. Zool. Fennici* 21: 243-247.

Terborgh, J. 1989. *Where have all the birds gone?* Princeton, New Jersey (Princeton University Press).

Terry, J.H. 1986. Corn Bunting in Hertfordshire. *Trans. Hertford. Nat. Hist. Soc.* 29: 303-312.

Thom, V.M. 1986. *Birds in Scotland*. Calton (Poyser).

Thomas, D.K. 1984. Aspects of habitat selection in the Sedge Warbler *Acrocephalus schoenobaenus*. *Bird Study* 31: 187-194.

Thomas, J.F. 1942. Report on the Redshank Inquiry, 1939-40. *Brit. Birds* 36: 5-14, 22-34.

Thompson, D.B.A., & S. Gribbin. 1986. Ecology of Corn Buntings (*Miliaria calandra*) in NW. England. *Bull. Brit. Ecol. Soc.* 17: 69-75.

Thompson, D.B.A., P.S. Thompson & D. Nethersole-Thompson. 1986. Timing of breeding and breeding performance in a population of Greenshanks (*Tringa nebularia*). *J. Anim. Ecol.* 55: 181-199.

Thompson, P.S. 1988. Long-term trends in the use of gardens by birds. *BTO Research Rept.* 32.

Thomson, D.L., & T.W. Dougall. 1988. The status of breeding Wigeon in Ettrick Forest. *Scot. Birds* 15: 61-64.

Tiainen, J., I.K. Hanski & J. Mehtälä. 1983. Insulation of nests and the northern limits of the three *Phylloscopus* warblers in Finland. *Ornis Scand.* 14: 149-153.

Ticehurst, N.F., & P.H.T. Hartley. 1948. Report on the effect of the severe winter of 1946-1947 on bird-life. *Brit. Birds* 41: 322-334.

Ticehurst, N.F., & H.F. Witherby. 1940. Report on the effect of the severe winter of 1939-40 on bird-life in the British Isles. *Brit. Birds* 34: 118-132, 142-155.

Tomiałojć, L. 1976. The urban population of the Woodpigeon (*Columba palumbus* L.) in Europe – its origin, increase and distribution. *Acta Zool. Cracow.* 21: 585-631.

Tubbs, C.R. 1963. The significance of the New Forest to the status of the Dartford Warbler in England. *Brit. Birds* 56: 41-48.

Tubbs, C.R. 1967. Numbers of Dartford Warblers in England during 1962-66. *Brit. Birds* 60: 87-89.

Tubbs, C.R. 1974. *The Buzzard*. Newton Abbot (David & Charles).

Tucker, G.M. (in press). Farmland birds in winter: the design of intensive and extensive studies. *Proc. XI Int. Conf. Bird Census and Atlas Work*. Prague.

Turner, A.K. 1982. Counts of aerial-feeding birds in relation to pollution levels. *Bird Study* 29: 221-226.

Tye, A. 1980. The breeding biology and population size of the Wheatear (*Oenanthe oenanthe*) on the Breckland of East Anglia, with implications for its conservation. *Bull. Ecol.* 11: 559-569.

Tyler, S.J. 1986. *Goosanders on the Afon Tywi*. Newtown, Powys (RSPB).

Tyler, S., J. Lewis, A. Venables & J. Walton. 1987. *The Gwent Atlas of Breeding Birds*. Newport (Gwent Orn. Soc.).

Tyson, P.D. 1986. *Climatic Change and Variability in Southern Africa*. Cape Town (Oxford University Press).

Upton, R. 1962. *Great Spotted Woodpecker Enquiry 1959-60*. Chelmsford (author).

Väisänen, R.A., O. Hildén & E. Pulliainen. 1989. (Monitoring of Finnish land bird populations in 1979-88.) *Lintumies* 24: 60-67. (In Finnish, with English summary.)

Van Balen, J.H. 1980. Population fluctuations of the Great Tit and feeding conditions in winter. *Ardea* 68: 143-164.

Van Balen, J.H., C.J.H. Booy, J.A. van Franeker & E.R. Osieck. 1982. Studies on hole-nesting birds in natural nest sites. 1. Availability and occupation of natural nest sites. *Ardea* 70: 1-24.

Van Dijk, J. 1975. (The English Yellow Wagtail as a breeding bird in the Netherlands.) *Limosa* 48: 86-99. (In Dutch, with English summary.)

Veenhuizen, W.D. 1984. (Breeding results of House Martins around Eindhoven.) *Vogeljaar* 32: 88-90. (In Dutch.)

Vinicombe, K. 1982. Breeding and population fluctuations of the Little Grebe. *Brit. Birds* 75: 204-218.

Von Haartman, L. 1981. Co-evolution of the Cuckoo *Cuculus canorus* and a regular Cuckoo host. *Ornis Fenn.* 58: 1-10.

Voous, K.H. 1960. *Atlas of European Birds*. London (Nelson).

Voous, K.H. 1978. The Scottish Crossbill: *Loxia scotica*. *Brit. Birds* 71: 3-10.

Walker, A.F.G. 1970. The moult migration of Yorkshire Canada Geese. *Wildfowl* 21: 99-104.
Walker, I.M. 1955. An earlier report of nestling Shelducks in Berkshire. *Brit. Birds* 48: 277.
Wammes, D.F., G.C. Boere & S. Braaksma. 1983. (To what extent are changes in the abundance of passerines related to their patterns of migration?) *Limosa* 56: 231-242. (In Dutch, with English summary.)
Warren, M.S., & R.J. Fuller (in press). *Woodland rides and glades: their management for wildlife*. Peterborough (NCC).
Watson, A. 1965. Research on Scottish Ptarmigan. *Scot. Birds* 3: 331-349.
Watson, A. 1982. Effects of human impact on Ptarmigan and Red Grouse near ski lifts in Scotland. *Ann. Rept. Inst. Terrest. Ecol.* 1981: 51.
Watson, A., D.R. Langslow & S.R. Rae. 1987. *The impact of land-use changes on Golden Eagles in the Scottish Highlands*. CSD Rept. 720. Peterborough (NCC).
Watson, A., & G.R. Miller. 1976. *Grouse Management*. Fordingbridge (Game Conservancy).
Watson, A., S. Payne & R. Rae. 1989. Golden Eagles *Aquila chrysaetos*: land use and food in northeast Scotland. *Ibis* 131: 336-348.
Watson, A., & R. Rae. 1987. Dotterel numbers, habitat and breeding success in Scotland. *Scot. Birds* 14: 191-198.
Wells, J.H. 1978. Results of a census of Northern Ireland heronries in 1977. *Irish Birds* 1: 187-198.
Wesolowski, T. 1985. The breeding ecology of the Wood Warbler *Phylloscopus sibilatrix* in primaeval forest. *Ornis Scand.* 16: 49-60.
Westerhoff, D.V. 1989. Results of the 1988 survey of Dartford Warbler *Sylvia undata* in the New Forest. *Hampshire Bird Rept.* 1988: 77-78.
Wiens, J.A. 1981. Scale problems in avian censusing. *Stud. Avian Biol.* 6: 513-521.
Wilkinson, P. 1987. Red-legged impostors. *BTO News* 152: 1-2.
Williamson, K. 1967. The bird community of farmland. *Bird Study* 14: 210-226.
Williamson, K. 1969. Habitat preferences of the Wren on English farmland. *Bird Study* 16: 53-59.
Williamson, K. 1970. Birds and modern forestry. *Bird Study* 17: 167-176.
Williamson, K. 1971. A bird census study of a Dorset dairy farm. *Bird Study* 18: 80-96.
Williamson, K. 1975. Birds and climatic change. *Bird Study* 22: 143-164.
Williamson, K., R.S. Bailey & L.A. Batten. 1968. *Guiding principles for the analysis of Common Birds Census returns*. Tring (BTO).
Williamson, K., & L.A. Batten. 1976. Passerine population indices of the Common Birds Census. *Ibis* 118: 470-471.
Williamson, K., & L.A. Batten. 1977. Ecological implications of the Common Birds Census. *Pol. ecol. Stud.* 3: 237-244.
Williamson, K., & R.C. Homes. 1964. Methods and preliminary results of the Common Birds Census, 1962-63. *Bird Study* 11: 240-256.
Williamson, M. 1972. *The Analysis of Biological Populations*. London (Edward Arnold).
Wilson, J.R. 1978. Agricultural influences on waders nesting on the South Uist machair. *Bird Study* 25: 198-206.
Winstanley, D., R. Spencer & K. Williamson. 1974. Where have all the Whitethroats gone? *Bird Study* 21: 1-14.
Witherby, H.F., & F.C.R. Jourdain. 1929. Report on the effects of severe weather in 1929 on bird-life. *Brit. Birds* 23: 154-158.
Witherby, H.F., & E.M. Nicholson. 1937. On the distribution and status of the British Willow-Tit. *Brit. Birds* 30: 358-364.
Witherby, H.F., & N.F. Ticehurst. 1908. The spread of the Little Owl from the chief centres of its introduction. *Brit. Birds* 1: 335-342.
Wood, N.A. 1974. The breeding behaviour and biology of the Moorhen. *Brit. Birds* 67: 104-158.
Wright, G.A. 1986. Breeding wildfowl of Loch Leven NNR. *Scot. Birds* 14: 39-43.
Wyllie, I. 1981. *The Cuckoo*. London (Batsford).
Yalden, D.W. 1985. Dietary separation of owls in the Peak District. *Bird Study* 32: 122-131.
Yalden, D.W. 1986. The habitat and activity of Common Sandpipers *Actitis hypoleucos* breeding by upland rivers. *Bird Study* 33: 214-222.

Yalden, D.W., & P.E. Yalden. 1989. The sensitivity of breeding Golden Plovers *Pluvialis apricaria* to human intruders. *Bird Study* 36: 49-55.
Yapp, W.B. 1962. *Birds and Woods*. London (Oxford University Press).
Yapp, W.B. 1983. Game-birds in medieval England. *Ibis* 125: 218-221.
Yarker, B., & G.L. Atkinson-Willes. 1971. The numerical distribution of some British breeding ducks. *Wildfowl* 22: 63-70.
Yeatman, L.J. 1971. *Histoire des Oiseaux d'Europe*. Paris (Bordas).
Youngman, R.E. 1977. Great Crested Grebes breeding on rivers. *Brit. Birds* 70: 544-545.
Zucchini, W., & P.T. Adamson. 1984. *The Occurrence and Severity of Droughts in South Africa*. Stellenbosch (Water Res. Commiss. Rept. 91/1/84).
Zuckerbrot, Y.D., U.N. Safriel & U. Paz. 1980. Autumn migration of the Quail *Coturnix coturnix* at the north coast of the Sinai peninsula. *Ibis* 122: 1-14.

Appendix 1. Acknowledgements to contributors

The BTO's monitoring programmes could not operate without the support of the many birdwatchers and birdwatching groups who participate in censusing, and we are very grateful to all contributors. In attempting to list them all, we are conscious that not everybody who has helped with a CBC or WBS plot is mentioned individually: many names are subsumed under club titles or "*et al*". BTO staff are listed only if they have carried out censuses in their own time, but the distinction is not always clear and the number of plots given for each may include some performed purely during paid hours.

While the lists are long, it should be remembered that they are cumulative over many years. In any one season, there may be only 300 or so contributions of CBC and WBS censuses, and the individual value of each is more immediately apparent.

Contributors to the Common Birds Census, 1961-1988

M. Abbott, Aberdeen University Bird Club (5 plots), K. Adams, L.J. Adams, E.J. Adnams, K.G. Adsett, Dr N.E. Agar, Miss M. Ainsworth, R.C. Aitken, P.J. Alderman (2 plots), Dr J.B.J.F. Aldiss (2 plots), A.C. Aldridge, D.A. Alexander, Miss Alford, J. Allen (Hants) (2 plots), J. Allen (Kent) (3 plots), J. Allen (Somerset), S.J.H. Allen, Dr G. Allsop, Amersham & District Ornithological Society (2 plots), T.R. Ammonds, E.B. Anderson, Dr J. Anderson, A. Andrews, M. Andrews, W. Angell, G.F. Appleton, M.T. Archdale, G.J. Ariss, N. Arlott, D.W. Armstead, D.B.L. Arnold, G.A. & M.A. Arnold, R. Arnold, G. Atkin, K. Atkin (2 plots), D.R. Atkinson (2 plots), Dr E.R. Austin, M.J. Austin.

E.J. Babbs, J.C. Bacon (5 plots), D. Baggott, Mrs E. Bagshaw, Dr & Mrs A.B. Bailey (2 plots), C.W. Bailey (4 plots), Mrs H.M. Bailey, M. Bailey, Dr R.S. Bailey (3 plots), R. & Dr D. Baines (2 plots), J.P. Baker, Banbury Ornithological Society, P. Banks, S.W. Banyard, J. Barber, Bardsey Bird Observatory, Dr A. Barker, D. Barker, G.J. Barker, P. Barlow, L. Barnes, Dr S.F. Barstow, Mrs E. Bartlett (4 plots), Mrs G. Barton, P.R. Barwick, A. Basden, H.J.C. Bashford, C.G. Bass, D.J. Bates, Dr L.A. Batten *et al* (8 plots), G. Baxter, Miss B.E. Bayliss (2 plots), C. Bealey, Beccles Bird Club, G.K. Beck (2 plots), E. Belding, B.D. Bell, G. Bellamy, E.M. Bennett, J.S. Bennett, T.J. Bennett (3 plots), G.B.G. Benson, R.G. Bentall, Mrs J.M. Bentley-Taylor, Miss C. Bernrieder, J.A. Bertenshaw, K.F. Betton, M. Betts, Dr G. Beven *et al*, T.G. Beynon, L.H. Biggs, M. Biggs, A.E. Billett, D.F. Billett, A. Birkett, J.D. Blaxland, R.M. Blindell, S.S. Blythe, M. Boddy (4 plots), D. Bodenham, P. Bolson, D. Bolton, C.T. Bowker, P. Bowler, A.L. Bowley, P. Bowyer (2 plots), D.A. Boyd, W.R. Brackenridge (2 plots), Dr N.J.B.A. Branson, M.R. Branwhite, R.C. Branwhite (2 plots), D. Bremner, Dr A. Brenchley, Dr A. Brian, L.H. Bricknell, R.H. Bridson *et al* (2 plots), E.D. Britnell, C. Britton, Miss C. Brookfield, L.G. Broomfield, A.W. Brown, J.G. Brown, M. Brown (Berks), M. Brown (Kent), M.F. Brown, A. Brownett, A.A.S. Brunt, Bryanston School, M. Bryant, BTO Arriundle expedition (9 plots), BTO Glen Nant expedition (9 plots), BTO Greenfield expedition (5 plots), BTO Killarney expedition (8 plots), BTO Lincolnshire Limewoods expedition (8 plots), BTO Loch Lomond expedition (11 plots), BTO Malham expedition (3 plots), BTO Rhum expeditions (17 plots), BTO Surrey census courses (5 plots), BTO Wester Ross expedition (12 plots), BTO Wood of Cree expedition (6 plots), W.F.A. Buck, A.L. Bull, G. Bundy, J. Bundy, R. Bunten, Mrs J.A. Burn, K.F. Burn, P.F. Burns, R.T. Burrows, M. Burton, A.A.R. Butler, D.V. Butt, A.M.B. Butterworth, J.M. Butterworth (2 plots), J. Buxton.

Miss H.M. Caddick, T.A. Cadwallender, Mrs F.J. Cain, G. Caine, Miss T.S. Caine *et al*, Calf of Man Bird Observatory (2 plots), Cambridge Bird Club, Canford School, Cardiff Natural History Society, R. Carlisle, J. Carpenter, R.J. Carpenter (5 plots), T.D. Carruthers (2 plots), Mrs A. Carson, C. Carter, I. Castle, B.M. Cavanagh, B.T. Channon, I. Chapman, J. Chapman (2 plots), L. Charlton, Miss D.V. Chawner, R.G. Chaytor, B. Cheal, D.K. Chesterman, Dr C.S. Clapham, Dr D. Clare, G. Clark, M. Clark, S.P. Clark, A.J. Clarke, Mrs R. Clarke, J. Clayton, J. Clegg (3 plots), P. Cliffe (3 plots), T. Clifford, P. Cobb, B.W. Coburn, S. Cochrane, Col. J.C. Cockburn, D.R. Coda, D.A. Cohen (2 plots), E. Cohen, D.G. Coker, K. Colcomb-Heiliger, J.C. Coleman, E. Coles (3 plots), B. Constable (2 plots), J.G. Cook, M.J.H. Cook, Mrs R. Cook, J.D. Copp, K.J. Corbett *et al*, P.McM. Corbett, J. Corfield, K. Costar *et al* (3 plots), N.W. Cottle, R.T. Cottrill (2 plots), E.P. Coulston, Major D.J.R. Counsell, Coventry RSPB Group, Mrs S. Cowdy MBE (2 plots), M.J. Cowlard, J.A. Cowlin (2 plots), F. Cox, J.R. Cox, C.W. Craig, Mr & Mrs B. Crathorne, Mrs G. Craw, Dr A.R. Crawford, G.M. Crighton, Miss H.S. Crippin, Col. C. Crosbie-Smith, D.V. Crosland, A.P. Cross, G.G. Cross, Mr & Mrs M. Cross, J. Crudass, D. Cummings, G.C. Cundale, C.R. Cuthbert, H.M. Cutler.

Rev J. Dalby, Mr & Mrs A.J. Dallimore, Dr O. Dansie, M. Davenport (2 plots), J.R. Davidson, B.J. Davies, G.P. Davies *et al*, P.A. Davies, Miss Davis, P.E. Davis, P.G. Davis, B. Dawson, Mrs D. Dawson, J.P. Dawson, T. Dawson, C. Day, H. Dean, T. Dean, L.J. Degnan, Mr & Mrs A. Denison, M.K. Dennis, R.H. Dennis, Dr K.J. Derrett, L. Derrick, R. Devlin, R.A. Dewey, A.W. Diamond *et al* (3 plots), G. Dick, R.E. Dimsdale, A. Dobbs, H.M. Dobinson (2 plots), Mrs B. Dobson (2 plots), R.H. Dobson, J. Doe, T.A. Doe, T.W. Dougall (5 plots), J.W. Douglas, C.G. Douglas, T. Down, R.J. & J.P. Dowsett, R.R. Drew, C. Dring, J. Driver (2 plots), W. Duckworth, A.G. Duff, B.S. Duffin *et al* (3 plots), P.B. Duncan (2 plots), Dungeness Bird Observatory (2 plots), J. Dunn, P. Dunne, C.W. Dunster, R.F. Durman, R.C. Dye, A.R. Dykes, P.H. Dymott.

R.A. Eades, A. Eaves, R.D.M. Edgar, Mr & Mrs C. Edwards, P.J. Edwards *et al* (Berks/Bucks) (2 plots), P.J. Edwards *et al* (London) (2 plots), P.N. Edwards (2 plots), R. Edwards, T. Edwards, T.W. Edwards, I.D. Elder, N. Elkins, D. Elliott, D. Ellis, N. Ellis, R.J. Ellis (2 plots), I.R. English, R. Essery, A.W. Evans (2 plots), Mr & Mrs E.O. Evans, Miss F. Evans, G.C. Evans, H.W. Evans, M.C.W. Evans, N. Evans (2 plots), P.J. Evans, R. Evans, J.M. Ewer, F. Eyre, J.C. Eyre-Dickinson.

Fair Isle Bird Observatory, Dr Ferguson, I.J. Ferguson-Lees, J.E. Ferrar, J. Field, R.W. Field, J.L. Figueiras, Mrs Y. Filbey, Miss M. Fillingham, J. Filowiat, F. Fincher, I.H. Findlay, T. Finnemore, Dr G.H. Fisher, P. Fisher, M.B. Fitch (4 plots), B. & D. Flack (2 plots), Dr J.J.M. Flegg, J. Fleming (2 plots), D.M. Fletcher, J.D. Fletcher, J. Flood-Page, G.W. Follows (2 plots), H.A. Ford (2 plots), I. Ford, K.H. Forder, R.H.B. Forster, J. Forsyth (4 plots), H.B. Fossey, T.J. Foster, W.J. Foster, C. Fowler, R.J. Fox, I. Francis (2 plots), R.E. Franco, R.E. Freeman, T.T. Freeston, O.B.J. French, R.A. Frost, N.R. Fuggles-Couchman (2 plots), S. Fulford, Dr R.J. Fuller (4 plots), D. Fulton.

Dr H. Galbraith, D.J.S. Gamble, N.E. Gammon (4 plots), D.M. Garner, Mrs J. Garrington, J. Garstang, G.T. Gartside, A.J. Gaston, N. Gedge, G. Geiger, G.R. Gervis, R.G. Gibbs (6 plots), Gibraltar Point Bird Observatory, C. Gibson, T. Gibson (Dumfries), T. Gibson (Derbys) (2 plots), Miss B. Gillam MBE *et al* (4 plots), Mrs B. Gilling, C.H.P. Gillow, D.J. Girling, D. Given, D.J. Glaves, G.J. Glover, D.E. Glue (11 plots), P.F. Goodfellow (2 plots), K.J. Goodrich, G.R. Goodway, Mrs M.G. Gordon (2 plots), R. Gosden, D. Gosney, M.G. Gotts, J. Gould, J. Gowerlock, G. Goyder, Major N.J.O. Graham, K.R. Grant, Mrs P.I. Grant (2 plots), Mrs S. Grant, D.B. Gray, G.H. Green, Dr G.P. Green, G.W. Green, M. Green (2 plots), R.R. Green, R. Greenwood, J. Gregg, Mrs J. Gregory, W. Gregory, H.E. Grenfell, D. Griffin, A. Griffiths (2 plots), C.N. Griffiths, R.D. Griffiths, E. Gunstone, M. Guppy, J. Gurr, G.H. Gush (2 plots), A.C. Gutteridge, Miss R. Gyle-Thompson, Dr E.G. & G.G. Gynn.

P.S. Hackett, M. Hackston, T.G.B. Hackston, Mrs P.K. Hadley, D. Hale, A.G. Hall, N.A. Hall, S. Halton, H.W. Hamar, B.G. Hamblin, L.I. Hamilton, Mrs R. Hamilton, T. Hamlett, F.W. Hammond (2 plots), M. Hammond, A. Hancock, J. Hancox, K.D. Hand, D.M. Hanford, J.A. Hardman, J. Hardy *et al*, A.F. Harris, F. Harris, Dr M.P. Harris, H.J. Harrison, Dr J.G. Harrison, P. Harrison (2 plots), J.M. Harrop, Mrs G.D. Harthan, A. Hartley, J. Hartley, R. & J. Harvey, W.G. Harvey, R.H. Hatton, B.F. Hawkes, D.A. Hawkins, H. Hawkins, I. Hawthorn (3 plots), R.J. Haycock *et al* (4 plots), N. Hayes *et al*, L. Hayward, P.H. Hazle, C.G. Headlam, A. Heaton, M.J. Helps, L.G. Hemmings, A.C.B. Henderson (2 plots), A.J.K. Henderson (2 plots), Miss M. Henderson, C. Hendry, Mrs J. Henton, Mrs D.E. Hewitt, P.J. Hewitt, Mrs J.M. Heynes, R.A.O. Hickling (2 plots), A. Hickman, B. Hickman, J.A. Hicks, Mrs D. Hilder, Mrs I. Hildred, B.A.G. Hill, G.B. Hill, P.A. Hill (3 plots), P.M. Hill, R.B. Hillier, A. Hind, R.D. Hind (3 plots), C. Hindle, Miss J.C. Hindley, D. Hird, T.G. Hiscock (2 plots), R.L. Hockin, S. Hodgkin, F. Hodson, H. Hodson (2 plots), Mrs P.M. Hoggett, M.Y. Holdsworth, P.K. Holland, M. Hollings, G.StJ. Hollis, D.P. Holmes, J.R. Holmes (2 plots), L. Holmes, J.W. Holt, D.T. Holyoak, Homefield Bird Group (6 plots), W.E. Hopkins, W.J.H. Hopkins, Brig. J.A. Hopwood, A. Horder, Mrs C. Horton, J.W. Howie, A.C. Hubbard, Mrs A. Hughes OBE (4 plots), I.G. Hughes, J.A. Humphrey (2 plots), Dr A.J. Hunt, M.R. Hunt, J.R. Hunter (2 plots), Mrs R.S. Hunter, G. Hutchinson, P. Hutchinson.

A.E. Ingleby, M.P. Ingram, Mrs C. Inskipp (née Robinson), Dr H. Insley, Mrs J. Irvine (5 plots), R.F. Irvine. W.S. Jacklin, P. Jackson (2 plots), R. Jackson, G.R. Jacobs (2 plots), M. Jacoby, L.T. James, W. James, M.B. Jeeves, Dr A.R. Jennings, T.J. Jennings, Lt.Com. D.H. Johnson, Dr H.M. Johnson T. Johnson, A.J. Johnston, A. Johnstone, H. Johnstone, A.D. Jones, Miss E.B. Jones, J.B. Jones, J.M. Jones (2 plots), K. Jones (2 plots), R. Jones, W.E. Jones, Mrs E.M. Judson, W.J. Julyan.

M. Kaemena, A.S. Keith, M. Kemp, Miss C.V. Kendall, T. Kent, L.E. Kerridge, N.A. Kerridge, T.P. Kerridge, M. Ketcher, R.H. Kettle (3 plots), J.G. Keylock, R. Keymer, K.P. Keywood, J. Kieser (2 plots), C. Kightley, P.J. Kightley, Mrs A. Kinahan (née Williams) (2 plots), King Edwards School Natural History Society (Birmingham), D.J. King, P. Kingsbury, P. Kirmond, P.G. Kitchener, Miss P.F. Kite, D. Knight, Dr J.T. Knowler, P.J. Knowling, D. Kramer (2 plots).

L. Lacey-Johnson, Mrs E. Lack, Dr P.C. Lack, P. Lackie, R. Lambert *et al*, R.J. Lanaway, W.N. Landells, Mrs E. Lang-Brown, Dr D.R. Langslow, H. Larsen, J.O. Latham, R.C. Laugher (3 plots), A. Laws, Miss V.M. Leather (2 plots), D. Lee, Mrs M.B. Lee, C. Lees, D.A. Lees, R.D. Lees, Leicestershire & Rutland Ornithological Society, Leighton Park School, H.N. Lemon *et al*, D. Leroux (2 plots), R. Leslie (2 plots), R.K. Levett, Miss R.F. Levy (3 plots), L.R. Lewis, Mrs M. Lewis, R. Lidstone-Scott, Miss P.B. Lind (4 plots), P.A. Linger, D.J. Lister, G. Litch, D.I. Little *et al* (2 plots), R. Little (2 plots), Liverpool RSPB Group (3 plots), A.J.E. Lloyd, J. Lloyd, J.W. Lock, D.F. Lodge, Lt.Col. W.M. Logan-Home, P.D.R. Lomas, G. Longrigg (2 plots), J. Lord, R.J. Louch, J.D. Lough (2 plots), G. Lowe, M.I. Lowman (2 plots), R.M. Lucas, Mrs B. Lumsden, P.H. Lunn, N. Lusmore, Miss R. Lyon.

D. Macdonald (2 plots), M.A. Macdonald, R.H. Macdonald, Mrs M.K. Macduff-Duncan, A. Maciver (2 plots), Miss E.M. Maddock, A. Malein, P.D. Mann, R. Mann, Mrs A. Mansell, Mrs D. Mansell, P. March, J.H. Marchant (2 plots), D.S. Marshall (2 plots), J.R. Marshall, Miss C.A. Martin, D. Martin, G.K. Martin, Mrs J.P. Martin, P. Martin, M.E. Massey, Mrs S.F. Matthews (2 plots), Mrs W.A. Mattingley, Miss E. Maughan, G.P. Mawson, J. Maxwell, R.H. May, K.W. Maycock (2 plots), J. McCowen, P. McDougall, P. McGill, C.R. McKay, D. McKay, Dr K. McKay (2 plots), J.N. McKelvie, E.D. McMillan, Dr D.A.C. McNeil (9 plots), C.J. Mead, A. Meakin, C. Measures, Mrs M. Meek, H.G. Mellar, W.D. Melluish, T.J. Mendham, W.E. Merrill, B.E. Messent, K.A. Miles, A.R. Miller (2 plots), C. Miller, T.I. Mills, Mrs L.M. Milner, Milton Keynes Natural History Society, J.G. Milton, L.J. Milton, R.D.P. Milwright, R. Missin (3 plots), Miss S.J. Monk, D.J. Montier, B.J. Moody, Mrs B.A. Moore *et al* (2 plots), H.B. Moore, B.D. Moreton (2 plots), J.H. Morgan, R.A. Morgan, T.A. Morgan, Mr & Mrs B.J. Morris, I.W. Morris, N.J. Morris, Mrs S. Morrison, Dr D. Moss (17 plots), M. Moss, P. Moule (2 plots), Miss L. Mousley *et al*, N. Muddeman, B.J. Mulford, J.R. Mullins (2 plots), Major G.F.A. Munns, C. Murdoch, J.M.W. Murphy, N.J. Musgrove.

R.G.W. Nairn (5 plots), A.H. Nash, A.J. Nash (2 plots), F.J. Nattrass, Dr A.K. Naylor, B. Neath, W.N.A. Nelson (2 plots), L.R.S. Newman, C.D. Newton, Mrs E. Newton, Deaconess M. Newton, S.C. Nichols, J.R. Nicholson, P. Nicholson, Mrs P.E.W. Nicholson, B. Nightingale, J. Niles, J. Nixon, S. Noble, Dr D. Norman, R. Norman, J.A. Norton, Mrs L.E. Nottage, S.R. Nutman.

G.F. Oates, E.C. Offord (5 plots), D. Ogle, Dr J.R. Ogle, C. Ogston, J.C.C. Oliver, M.F. Oliver (2 plots), Omagh Wildbird Society, D. Onley, A.J. Osborne, J. O'Sullivan, D.L. Ovenden, R. Overall, Mrs E. Owen, T.R.M. Owen, N.W. Owens, Oxford Ornithological Society.

K.H. Palmer, K.W. Palmer, S.M. Palmer, D. Paradise, A. Parker, D. Parker, T.N. Parker, R. Parkinson, D. Parr (6 plots), F.G. & A.M. Parsons, J. Pattinson, G. Peacock, Mrs G.M. Peall, D.A. Pearce, Mrs E.M. Pearce, W. Pearce, P. Pearson, R.M. Pearson (Hants) (2 plots), R.M. Pearson (Herts) (2 plots), K. Peart (2 plots), I.R. Peill, M.J. Penistan (2 plots), Miss D.A. Phillips, Rev. J.S. Phillips, Mrs R. Phillips, M. Phillips-Price (2 plots), P.H. Phillipson *et al* (2 plots), R.H. Pickering (2 plots), B.P. Pickess, A. Pickup, Dr D.J. Pickup, Dr M.W. Pienkowski, A. Piersene, N. Pinchbeck, N. Pinder, Dr R.S. Pitcher *et al*, S. Pointing, J.D. Pollard, Mrs B. Poloniecka, Dr D.E. Pomeroy, R. Pooley (2 plots), R.F. Porter (2 plots), B.C. Potter, J. Potter (2 plots), P.M. Potts, F.J. Poynter (2 plots), T. Poyser, A.J. Prater (2 plots), M. Pratley, Dr S.R.D. da Prato, R. Pratt, M.V. Preece (2 plots), Miss M.E. Price *et al* (2 plots), Mrs M. Price, A.D. Priestley, Dr M. Prime, D. Prince, P. Prince, R. Proctor, I. Puckrin, Mrs J. Pullein, D.M. Putman, L.W. Pygott.

F.W.P. Radford, J.L. Raincock, Miss M. Ralph, R.J. Ramsay, W.T.C. Rankin, Mrs S. Ratcliffe, C.P. Rawcliffe, M.J. Raynor, C.H. Redfern, G.H. Redfern, K. Redshaw, Dr T.M. Reed (5 plots), F.C. Reeves (2 plots), Mrs A. Remfry, D. Reynolds, F.L. Reynolds, Mr & Mrs C. Rice, N.J. Riddiford, G. Riddle, M.J. Ridley, W.J. Rielly, J. Robbins (9 plots), J.S. Roberts, P. Roberts, P.J. Roberts, R.D. Robertson, M. Robertson, R.W. Robinson, A. Robson, R.W. Robson, Miss H.C. Rodgers *et al*, M.H. Rogers, M.J. Rogers, Miss S.M. Rogers, D. Rook, D.R. Rose (2 plots), Mrs C. Ross, M.J. Rossor (2 plots), G. Rothwell, S. Rowlands, P.C. Roworth (2 plots), F.N. Royle-Bantoft, Mrs J. Royston, Rufford Wildlife Study Group, Mrs A. Russell (2 plots), M.J. Rymer.

B.L. Sage, R.F. Sanderson (3 plots), Sandwich Bay Bird Observatory, D.R. Saunders, B. Savage, C.E.V. Saxton (2 plots), N. Scarfe, L. Schofield, A. Scott, D.J. Scott, Miss A.P.M. Scott (2 plots), K. Scott, R.E. Scott, L.G. Scudder, M. Seaman, D. Seaward, H.J.C. Seymour (2 plots), N.W. Shane, Dr J.T.R. Sharrock, Mrs A. Shaw, D.L. Shaw, G. Shaw, D. Shelton, P.J. Shepheard, Sherborne School (2 plots), Mrs M.E. Shimeld (2 plots), P. Shooter, D.I. Short, Mrs J. & Miss K. Shotton, M.F. Shotton, M. Shrubb, J. Sidey, N. Sills (3 plots), J.R. Simms, D.W. Simpson, G. Simpson (2 plots), T. Simpson, H.P. Sitters, Skokholm Bird Observatory, F.M. Slater, P. Slater, F.C. Smale, D.R. Smart, J.B. Smart (2 plots), A.S.C. Smith, D. Smith,

D.A. Smith, D.E. Smith, Dr A.H.V. Smith, E.C. & M. Smith (2 plots), F.R. Smith, G.P. Smith, Miss J. Smith, Mr & Mrs K.R.R. Smith, M.C.G. Smith, P. Smith, P.A. Smith, R. Smith, R.W.J. Smith (2 plots), T.C. Smith (2 plots), I. Snape, Mrs B.K. Snow, Dr D.W. Snow (3 plots), P. Solly, South-East Cheshire Ornithological Society, Southampton Natural History Society, J. Sparrow, J.R. Spencer, Miss M. Spooner, Dr G.H. Spray, R. Squires (2 plots), Miss J. Stacey, J.F. Stamp, S. Stanbury, Dr & Mrs R. Stanford, Mrs M.M. Stansfield, J.N. Stedman, Dr D.T. Steel, R.D. Steele, J.B. Steer, Mr & Mrs E. Stephens (2 plots), B. Stevens, Mrs V.R. Stevens, J.A. Stevenson, A. Stewart, G. Stewart *et al*, Dr C.H. Stewart-Hess, C. Stoate (2 plots), B.A. Stoker, Mrs V.B. Stokes *et al*, T. Stone, A.L. Stonell, M. Stott, Stowe School Natural History Society, R. Strachan (2 plots), P.J. Strangeman (2 plots), R. Stratford, J.A. Strutt (2 plots), W. Stuart-Best, P. Stuttard (4 plots), Dr J.D. Summers-Smith (2 plots), Mrs M. Summers-Smith, Surbiton & District Bird Watching Society (2 plots), R.L. Swann (3 plots), D.W. Swindells, A. Sykes, Dr J.B. Sykes.

R.E. Tallack, J. Tallowin, B.S. Taylor, Mrs C.P. Taylor, D. Taylor, G. Taylor, I. Taylor, Miss M.M. Taylor, P.B. Taylor, Lady R.G. Taylor (3 plots), S.M. Taylor (3 plots), C.F. Tebbutt, W. & A. Telford, J.H. Terry, J. Tester, Thanet Natural History Society (7 plots), B. Thomas, G.M. Thomas, S.R. Thomason, B. Thompson, M.H. Thompson (2 plots), R.L. Thompson, W.A. Thornhill, A.W. Thorpe, A.F.M. Thrower, A.F. Tilt, W.D. Todd, Dr L. Tomiałojć, R.J. Tomlin (3 plots), Mrs J. Tory, F.A. Tovery, M.J. Townsend, B. Townson (2 plots), P. Toynton (2 plots), Mrs S.M. Tracey, F.R. Traynor (2 plots), J.E. Treganna (2 plots), N.S. Trout, M. Trubridge, Mrs M. Tugendhat (5 plots), J. Tully, E.L. Turner, M.G. Turner, P.C. Turner, Dr S.J. Tyler (2 plots).

L. Ullock, Mrs R. Upton, G.G. Ushaw.

Vale of White Horse RSPB Group, V. Veal, Mrs G.A. Vowles (3 plots).

J. Waldon, J. Walford, Mrs B.T. Walker, Miss B.W. Walker, M.J. Wallace (2 plots), C.S. Waller, Mrs M. Waller, O.H. Wallis, A.P. Walmsley, M. Walter, J. Walton, Mrs J. Walton (3 plots), J.W. Walton, G.B. Warboys, A.B. Warburton (2 plots), S.W. Warburton, E. Ward, I. Ward, D.M. Warden, D.W. Warner, J.P. Warren, G.J. Warrilow, P.M. Warrington, A.B. Wassell, G. Waterhouse, B.R. Watmough, Dr G.L. Watson (4 plots), A.R. Watts, C.E.D. Watts, R. Weatherhead, D. Weaver, G.R. Webb, P.G. Webb, G.L. Webber, J. Webber (2 plots), Miss M. Weedon, Mrs M. Weir, D.T. Wellman, J. Wells, J.D. Wells, R. West, R.W.H. West, Weston-Super-Mare Grammar School for Boys, W.E. Weyman, P. Whaley, P.D. Whalley, Mrs J.A. Whatmough (5 plots), B.M. Wherrett, C.R. Wheway, F. Whitaker, Mr & Mrs G.J. Whitby (2 plots), D. White, D.M. White, S.L. White, B. Whitehall, A.A.K. Whitehouse (2 plots), M.H. Whitmore (2 plots), P.A. Whittington, G.F. Whitwell (3 plots), J.P. Widgery, T. Wiggington (2 plots), W.H. Wild, Mrs J. Wilder, Dr A.O.M. Wilkie, D. Wilkins, Mrs M. Wilkinson, M.J. Wilkinson, R.B. Wilkinson, E.J. Williams, G. Williams, H. Williams, J.H.G. Williams (2 plots), J.W. Williams, Mrs M. Williams, R.F.V. Williams, K. Williamson (18 plots), R.L.C. Williamson (3 plots), N. Willis, Mr & Mrs A.C. Willson (4 plots), R.J. Wilmshurst (6 plots), D. Wilson, G.O. Wilson, J. Wilson (Lancs) (2 plots), J. & B. Wilson, Winchester College Natural History Society, J. Winterbottom, E.J. Wiseman (3 plots), D. Woobery, A. Wood, C.R. Wood, Dr J.B. Wood (2 plots), J.C. Wood, J.H. Wood (2 plots), Mrs R. Woodell (2 plots), D.L. Woodfall (2 plots), Miss S.M. Woodman (2 plots), R.W. Woods (2 plots), Miss C. Wooldridge, D. Worsfold, B. Wright (2 plots), C. Wright, Mrs D.B. Wright (2 plots), M.R. Wright (2 plots), M.W. Wright, T. Wyatt, I. Wyllie, Ms F. Wynmclean.

W.B. Yelland, A. Young, G.H.E. Young (2 plots) and J. Young.

Contributors to the Waterways Bird Survey, 1973-1988

C. Acheson, G.A. Acheson, J.R. Alderton, B. & R. Allen, J. Allen, W.N. Anderton, Miss M. Andrews, M.S. Andrews, R. Appleton, R.J. Arthur, J.C. Badcock, C.W. Bailey (2 plots), Dr D. Baines, Miss H. Baker, J.J. Baker, N.E. Baker *et al*, Banbury Ornithological Society (2 plots), S. Banks, Dr R.A. Bantin, Mrs C.F. Barber, J. Barber, G. Barrell, J.W. Barrington, Mrs M. Barrington, D.H. Barthram, C.J. Bastion, D.J. Bates, N.T. Baylis, G. Beasley, A.J. Booth, P. Booth, J.J. Boswell, P.G. Boxall, A.T. Bramhall, Mr & Mrs R. Bramhall, A. Bramley *et al*, Dr A. Brian, Dr K.B. Briggs, D. Bristow, Mrs S.F. Brunstrom, N.J. Bucknell, N. Burgess, P.M. Burnham, D. Butterfield, D. Campbell, Ms L. Campbell, R. Campbell, T.D. Carruthers, P. Carter, Mrs F. Cave, Mrs A.M. Challenger, Mr & Mrs C. Chester, N.E. Christian, G. Clark, J.E. Clark, T.R. Cleeves *et al*, J. Coffey, S.W. Cole, D.A. Coleman, Mrs C.W. Collins, W. Collinson, R. Cordery, M.W. Crabtree, Mrs D. Crane and family, Miss D.I. Crisp, Dr J.P. Cullen.

T.J. Davis, Miss G.E. Davison, M. Dent, I.H. Dillingham, J.M. Dodgson, E. Dorman, A. Dowell, G.A. Down *et al*, M.J. Doyle, F. Drake, D.G. Duggan, East Lothian Field Naturalists' Group (3 plots), Miss J. Eastmead, Mr & Mrs C. Edwards, S. Elcoate, O. Elidir, D. Elliott, N.E.G. Elms, R.E. Enoch, Essex Naturalists' Trust, M.R. Evans, M. Farmer *et al*, J.L. Figueiras, I.H. Findlay, Mrs G. Finney, C. Fisher, S. Fisher, J.T. Fletcher, G.W. Follows, S.W.B. Foss, Mrs P.S. Foxcroft, N.C. Frampton, M.W. Freer, Dr N.A. French, J. Friese, Ms A.C. Fryer, Dr H.W.C. Fuller, Mr & Mrs K. Garner, D.R. Gaskell, M.J. Gee, S. Gibson, W. Girling, A.C. Goodwin, D.J. Gordon, Mrs H. Gould, J. Gould, N.J.O. Graham, H.P. Grainge, M. Green, A. Gretton, G.D.O. Grieve, J. Gulliver, Dr I.R. Hainsworth, J.J. Hall, M. Harrison, Mr & Mrs G. Haw, K.W. Henshall, Cpl. K. Heron, R.A.O. Hickling, D.W. Hildred, B.J.N. Hill, C.M. Hind, A. Hinde, R. Holbeach, Mrs E. Hollands, M. Hollands, M. Holmes, J. Hornbuckle, R.J. Hubble, Lt.Col. P.J. Hubert OBE, G.W. Hudson (2 plots), Mr & Mrs B. Ingleby, I. Jackson, J. Jackson, G.C.D. James, D.C. Jardine, Miss M.R. Jellicoe, Dr H.M. Johnson, B.A. Jones, Mrs J.L. Jones, P. Jones, R.J. Jones, A.W.L. Joss.

A. Keatley, P.R. Kennedy, L.E. Kerridge, J.S. Kirby, J.P. Kirkby, R. Knight, R.A. Knock, P.J. Knowling, Lancaster & District Bird-Watching Society (24 plots), R.J. Lancey, J.J. Latham, P. Lawrence, Miss P.E. Lawrenson, D.A. Lee, R. Leslie, Mrs M.F.T. Leybourne, Mrs M. Lloyd, Dr L. & Mrs M.M. Lloyd-Evans, J.W. Lock, C. Loynes, H.F. Lyttle, Mrs M. MacKnight, A.C. Manley, Brother N. Marsh, R.G. Marsh, F.B. Martin, D. Matthews, Mr M.E. Matthews, Miss L. McConnell, D. McEwen, Mrs I.W. McLaren, Lt.Col. J.S. McLaren, Ms F.E. McLean, Dr D.A.C. McNeil, Miss S. Merlen, Mrs B.A. Moore, P.A. & A. Moran, Miss V.A. Morris, K. Morton, G.S. Motley, Miss C. Mulford, Dr P.I. Munro, K. Murphy, Lt.Col. J.R. Neighbour, Mrs E.R. Newton, Commander A.Y. Norris, North Wales Naturalists' Trust, J.E. Nunn, P. O'Brien, J. O'Connor, Dr R.J. O'Connor, D.J. Odell, M.F. Oliver, Miss J. Owen, Mrs J. Packwood, D.I. Page, J. Pain, B. Parker, Mrs M. Patterson, Miss A.A. Paul, B. Peacock, J.R. Pendle, A.C. Piper, E. Playle, Mrs A. Poole, P.M. & A. Potts, Mrs E.S. da Prato, R. Pyefinch, F.W.P. Radford, P.J. Raven, E.J. Redshaw, A. Renshaw, Miss C.L.C. Richards, R.A. Richards, D.F. Richardson, M.J. & P.I. Richardson, J. Ridley, Mr & Mrs D. Robertson, W. Robson, Mrs C. Ross, M.B. Ross, M.G. Rowan, K. Royles, J. Rushforth, M.D. Russell.

284

K. Sanderson, P.M. Scanlan, F.H.F. & M.J.F. Schofield, P. Schofield, Miss E.M.P. Scott, Sedbergh School, P. Senkans, J. Sharman, Dr J.T.R. Sharrock, G. Shaw, Sheffield Bird Study Group (14 plots), S. Shepherd, Mrs M.E. Shimeld, I.J. Simper, H. Simpson, K. Slater, C. Slator *et al*, R.A. & J. Slaughter, D.J.W. Smith, D.P. Smith, Miss F. Smith, G. Smith, R.L. Sorrell, J. Speller, D.E. Stainer, Miss E. Stainthorpe *et al*, Commander J.H. Stenning, J. Stevens, B. & J. Stigant, Mrs J.C. Stratford, Surrey Bird Club (13 plots), D. Swann, J. Swinfen, Mrs D. Tassell, Mrs C.C. Taylor, Mrs C.P. Taylor, Dr G.K. Taylor, Mrs R. Taylor, D. Teece, D.L. Thomas, G. Thomas, I. Tidmarsh, J.D. Tinkler, G. Todd, R.J. Tomlin, Mrs M. Trayner, N.S. Trout, T.J. Tubby, Dr S.J. Tyler, Ulster Trust for Nature Conservation, M.B. Vickers, Mr & Mrs R.S. Vowles, J. Wakefield, M.J. Waldron, D. Walkingshaw, K. Walls, P. Warden, D.W. Warner, P.S. Watson, R. Weatherhead *et al*, A.J. Weir, R.C. Welland, D. Whelan, A.A.K. Whitehouse, W. Whitmarsh, R.W. Whitworth, E.H. Williams, G. Williams, K. Williamson, Mrs E. Wilson, G. Wilson, J.F. & A.M. Wilson, R. Wimpress, K.W. Wood, N.J. Woodcock, C.B.J. Woodhams, K. Woods *et al*, Workers' Educational Association (Bucks) (3 plots), C.E. Wright, M.B.R. Wright, C. Yeates, Young Ornithologists' Club (Edinburgh Group) and R.E. Youngman.

Appendix 2. Longest-running CBC and WBS plots

Long-running plots are very valuable because they give continuity and reduce the problems of changes in the structure of the plot sample. We would like to commend the following observers for their long service on the same census plot, or in some cases for maintaining long-running plots begun by or handed on to others.

The CBC plots listed are those which have been covered at least twenty times, and the WBS plots those censused in ten or more seasons. They are ranked in the order of number of years in which a census was made, up to the end of 1988. Counts at several of the sites have now been discontinued, with no further censuses planned. A plus (+) indicates that a census for 1989 is awaiting analysis at BTO headquarters. Censuses with 19+ years (CBC) or 9+ years (WBS) are listed because, at the time of publication, they too have reached the criteria for inclusion.

Common Birds Census

Years	Habitat	Hectares	County		Observer	Years covered
28+	farm	81.0	Nottinghamshire		W.S. Jacklin	1961-88
28+	wood	29.6	Berkshire		P.D. Mann	1961-88
27+	farm	99.6	Norfolk		A.L. Bull	1962-88
26+	farm	121.9	Berkshire		J. Field	1962-88
26+	farm	73.1	Oxfordshire		Mrs M.G. Gordon	1962-88
26+	wood	57.9	West Sussex		R.J. Wilmshurst	1963
				then	R.L.C. Williamson	1964-88
25+	farm	93.6	Gr Manchester		J.M. Butterworth	1964-88
25+	farm	56.9	Hertfordshire		BTO staff (Pendley Farm)	1964-88
25+	wood	25.3	Shropshire		T.W. Edwards	1964-88
25+	wood	18.2	Buckinghamshire		A.A.R. Butler	1964-88
25+	farm	91.9	Leicestershire		Leics & Rutland O.S.	1964-88
25	farm	60.8	Kent		G.H. Redfern	1962-86
24+	farm	94.3	Cleveland		Dr J.D. Summers-Smith	1962-88
24+	farm	56.6	Lincolnshire		G. Atkin	1965-88
24+	wood	21.9	Dorset		J.G. Keylock & R.C. Branwhite	1965-88
23+	farm	44.5	Somerset		R.C. Branwhite	1966-88
23+	wood	6.1	Essex		K. Costar et al	1966-88
23+	farm	49.6	Derbyshire		Miss H.C. Rodgers et al	1966-78
				then	Mrs B.A. Moore et al	1979-86
				and	Mrs V.B. Stokes et al	1987-88
23	wood	16.2	Surrey		Dr G. Beven et al	1961-84
22+	farm	40.5	Northumberland		L. Charlton	1967-88
22+	farm	117.8	Tayside		RSPB (Vane Farm)	1967-88
22	farm	103.6	Wiltshire		Miss B. Gillam et al	1962-83
22	farm	55.7	Surrey		P.J. Hewitt	1961-82
21+	farm	100.0	Lancashire		E. Ward	1968-88
21+	wood	6.7	Buckinghamshire		Mrs R. Woodell	1968-88
21+	wood	16.2	Kent		RSPB (Northward Hill)	1966-88
21	farm	89.1	Cumbria		R.W. Robson	1961-76
				then	G. Longrigg	1978-83
21	farm	64.4	Dorset		W. Stuart-Best	1963-83
20	special	43.3	Dorset		B.P. Pickess	1966-85
20	special	106.5	Nottinghamshire		B.D. Bell & T. Kent	1964
				then	K.J. Corbett et al	1966-82
				and	N. Hayes et al	1983-84
20	special	18.2	Hampshire		R.J. Carpenter	1969-73
				then	B.S. Duffin et al	1974-88
20	farm	51.8	Devon		Brig. J.A. Hopwood	1965-84
20	farm	125.5	Gloucestershire		Mrs P.K. Hadley	1962-81
19+	farm	53.7	West Glamorgan		D.M. Hanford	1967-82
				then	B.E. Messent	1985-88
19+	farm	55.3	Down		J. Forsyth et al	1970-88
19+	special	10.1	Buckinghamshire		D. Bodenham & D.E. Glue	1970-88
19+	farm	31.8	West Yorkshire		L.W. Pygott	1970-88
19+	special	36.1	Oxfordshire		Banbury Orn. Soc.	1970-88
19+	wood	45.4	Kent		D.E. Smith	1970-88
19+	wood	15.3	Durham		S.J.H. Allen	1970-88
19+	farm	120.2	Tyne & Wear		L.J. Milton	1970-88

Waterways Bird Survey

Years	Length (km)	County	Observer	Years covered
15+	4.3	Antrim/Down	C.W. Bailey	1974-88
15+	5.6	Antrim/Down	C.W. Bailey	1974-88
15+	4.8	Derbyshire	Sheffield BSG	1974-88
15+	5.0	Lancashire	Lancaster & District BWS	1974-88
15+	5.3	Lancashire	A.E. Ingleby	1974-79
			then Lancaster & District BWS	1979-88
15	3.8	South Yorkshire	Sheffield BSG	1974-88
14+	3.1	Derbyshire	Sheffield BSG	1974-88
14+	5.9	Derbyshire	Sheffield BSG	1974-88
14+	5.4	Derbyshire	Sheffield BSG	1975-88
14+	4.2	South Yorkshire	Sheffield BSG	1975-88
14+	3.6	Derbyshire	Sheffield BSG	1974-88
14+	5.8	Cambridgeshire	J.J. Hall	1975-88
14+	6.1	Oxfordshire	Banbury Orn. Soc.	1975-88
14	5.5	North Yorkshire	Mrs M.E. Shimeld	1974-77
			then D. Barthram	1978-87
14	4.4	Derbyshire	Sheffield BSG	1974-88
13+	3.3	Powys	Mrs J. Packwood	1976-88
13+	3.1	Lancashire	Lancaster & District BWS	1975-88
13+	4.9	Lancashire/Cumbria	Lancaster & District BWS	1975-88
13	5.5	Derbyshire	Sheffield BSG	1974-87
12+	3.5	Lancashire	D.E. Stainer	1977-80
			then J. Jackson & Mrs C.F. Barber	1981-88
12+	3.6	Lancashire	Lancaster & District BWS	1976-88
12+	4.4	South Yorkshire	Sheffield BSG	1973-88
12+	4.6	Lancashire	Lancaster & District BWS	1976-88
12	5.6	Down	H.F. Lyttle	1975-86
11+	5.2	Dumfries & Galloway	G. Shaw	1977-88
11+	6.6	Tayside	Mrs M.E. Shimeld	1978-88
11+	5.3	Surrey	W. Girling	1977-88
11+	3.6	South Yorkshire	Sheffield BSG	1977-88
11	6.0	West Sussex	Miss E.M.P. Scott & Miss C.L.C. Richards	1975-85
11	3.8	Hampshire	F.W.P. Radford	1975-84
10+	3.5	Berkshire	N.J. Bucknell	1979-88
10+	6.0	Leicestershire	Dr D.A.C. McNeil	1979-83
			then N. Burgess *et al*	1984-88
10+	4.9	Hertfordshire	Miss H. Baker	1979-88
10	4.8	Lothian	M.J. & P.I. Richardson	1976-86
9+	5.0	Lincolnshire	E.J. Redshaw	1980-88

287

Appendix 3. Summaries of plots used in the index calculations

The tables in this Appendix show various parameters of the CBC and WBS index samples that are kept under surveillance for any evidence of shifts in the way habitats are sampled. Please refer to Chapter 2 for discussion of these figures.

Notes

1. In Tables A1-A4, plots described as new are those not used, for one reason or another, in the previous index comparison. They include long-running plots for which full coverage was not continuous. In 1963-64, 11 woodland plots were used in the all-habitats index, but the woodland index did not begin until the following year (Table A2).

2. In Tables A5-A8, the figures given are the percentages of the total number of plots in each region. For the CBC, English regional boundaries follow post-1974 county boundaries (see Figure 2.1). The following counties are assigned to each region: SOUTHERN ENGLAND Avon, Berkshire, Cornwall, Devon, Dorset, Hampshire, Isle of Wight, Kent, Greater London, Somerset, Surrey, West Sussex, East Sussex, Wiltshire; EASTERN ENGLAND Bedfordshire, Buckinghamshire, Cambridgeshire, Essex, Hertfordshire, Leicestershire, Lincolnshire, Norfolk, Northamptonshire, Nottinghamshire, Oxfordshire, Suffolk; WESTERN ENGLAND Cheshire, Derbyshire, Gloucestershire, Hereford & Worcester, Shropshire, Staffordshire, Warwickshire, West Midlands; NORTHERN ENGLAND Cleveland, Cumbria, Durham, Humberside, Isle of Man, Lancashire, Greater Manchester, Merseyside, Northumberland, North Yorkshire, South Yorkshire, West Yorkshire, Tyne & Wear. WBS regions in Table A8 follow pre-1974 boundaries, but are very similar (see Figure 2.3).

3. The categories of WBS plots, as used in Table A10, are defined fully by Marchant & Hyde (1979). A fast river is one with a gradient usually greater than 5 m/km, and in a shallow or steep-sided valley, while a slow river usually has a gradient of less than 5 m/km and lies in a broad valley or crosses fairly level country.

Table A1. Summary of farmland plots used for calculating indices, 1962-1988.

	No. of plots used	Mean area (ha)	No. of new plots	Mean area of new plots (ha)
1962-63	35	88.4	35	88.4
1963-64	55	89.8	28	90.0
1964-65	74	86.2	33	82.5
1965-66	92	77.0	33	60.6
1966-67	84	77.3	16	65.2
1967-68	79	76.8	14	71.1
1968-69	90	72.2	31	65.9
1969-70	82	73.0	14	72.8
1970-71	85	79.9	19	96.2
1971-72	87	76.2	17	66.0
1972-73	79	74.5	10	76.9
1973-74	79	75.8	14	80.5
1974-75	85	73.6	18	62.5
1975-76	83	72.3	12	59.8
1976-77	89	68.2	14	46.4
1977-78	98	70.4	19	92.1
1978-79	98	69.1	20	81.2
1979-80	87	68.0	10	87.2
1980-81	79	65.6	13	72.1
1981-82	77	70.1	12	89.3
1982-83	83	71.7	18	68.6
1983-84	72	72.2	8	78.3
1984-85	76	69.0	14	58.1
1985-86	79	74.5	16	88.6
1986-87	80	71.9	12	66.5
1987-88	82	72.9	13	77.2

Table A2. Summary of woodland plots used for calculating indices, 1963-1988.

	No. of plots used	Mean area (ha)	No. of new plots	Mean area of new plots (ha)
1963-64	11	16.7	—	—
1964-65	25	18.7	25	18.7
1965-66	42	18.3	25	17.8
1966-67	48	17.8	16	17.1
1967-68	40	18.6	8	17.4
1968-69	43	17.0	11	13.7
1969-70	43	21.1	6	44.5
1970-71	51	18.0	19	17.7
1971-72	49	18.7	12	15.4
1972-73	47	16.9	11	10.0
1973-74	46	17.7	9	18.1
1974-75	54	16.7	14	16.0
1975-76	65	17.3	23	17.9
1976-77	76	16.5	22	16.6
1977-78	76	18.2	20	17.8
1978-79	79	18.6	15	18.5
1979-80	91	19.6	24	23.4
1980-81	91	19.4	15	17.7
1981-82	81	20.7	17	24.9
1982-83	82	19.5	12	19.4
1983-84	85	19.1	14	18.2
1984-85	80	20.3	10	23.3
1985-86	83	19.8	9	16.8
1986-87	82	20.5	6	21.7
1987-88	76	20.8	5	25.8

Table A3. Summary of "special" areas contributing to the all-habitats indices, 1963-1988.

	No. of plots used	Mean area (ha)	No. of new plots	Mean area of new plots (ha)
1963-64	7	97.9	7	97.9
1964-65	18	79.2	13	66.4
1965-66	25	52.8	16	31.4
1966-67	30	47.5	13	50.4
1967-68	25	39.0	5	21.0
1968-69	24	46.3	7	48.2
1969-70	24	44.9	7	47.5
1970-71	31	43.1	13	36.7
1971-72	27	47.3	9	36.7
1972-73	27	55.3	13	49.5
1973-74	29	49.3	11	33.8
1974-75	44	46.1	21	38.8
1975-76	52	41.0	21	33.9
1976-77	51	39.0	15	34.8
1977-78	55	43.4	14	47.6
1978-79	62	42.0	17	32.1
1979-80	74	38.7	24	38.0
1980-81	73	37.8	14	32.5
1981-82	71	37.2	19	29.6
1982-83	65	35.9	9	39.5
1983-84	39	39.3	7	25.5
1984-85	37	34.0	8	28.2
1985-86	30	34.2	1	17.6
1986-87	18	37.2	0	—
1987-88	22	32.8	6	36.1

Table A4. Summary of plots used for calculating WBS indices, 1974-1988.

	No. of plots used	Mean length (km)	No. of new plots	Mean length of new plots (km)
1974-75	45	4.64	45	4.64
1975-76	54	4.54	32	4.71
1976-77	53	4.92	22	5.04
1977-78	50	4.92	10	4.78
1978-79	51	5.03	10	4.83
1979-80	52	4.88	16	4.63
1980-81	48	4.78	7	4.21
1981-82	76	4.93	43	4.92
1982-83	66	4.65	19	4.37
1983-84	67	4.63	18	4.56
1984-85	73	4.80	21	4.90
1985-86	84	4.78	24	4.41
1986-87	82	4.80	16	4.54
1987-88	81	4.65	15	4.51

Table A5. Geographical distribution of plots used in the farmland index, 1962-1988.

	Southern England	Eastern England	Western England	Northern England	Wales	Scotland	Northern Ireland
1962-63	26	17	26	17	9	6	0
1963-64	31	24	15	16	9	6	0
1964-65	22	28	19	12	8	11	0
1965-66	21	37	15	12	5	10	0
1966-67	23	37	13	13	4	11	0
1967-68	25	33	15	11	4	11	0
1968-69	27	31	12	14	4	11	0
1969-70	23	34	12	16	6	9	0
1970-71	26	35	11	14	5	8	1
1971-72	26	37	12	15	2	6	2
1972-73	27	37	11	17	1	5	3
1973-74	24	35	13	18	1	6	3
1974-75	22	37	14	18	1	6	2
1975-76	23	36	13	16	2	7	2
1976-77	23	34	16	17	2	6	3
1977-78	25	32	15	15	5	5	3
1978-79	30	29	13	14	6	5	3
1979-80	26	33	10	17	5	5	3
1980-81	27	33	10	17	5	4	5
1981-82	29	34	8	16	7	4	4
1982-83	27	27	13	17	7	5	5
1983-84	29	28	11	14	7	6	6
1984-85	29	28	12	15	5	7	5
1985-86	27	30	14	18	5	3	4
1986-87	30	29	13	18	5	4	3
1987-88	26	33	12	15	5	6	4

Table A6. Geographical distribution of plots used in the woodland index, 1964-1988.

	Southern England	Eastern England	Western England	Northern England	Wales	Scotland	Northern Ireland
1964-65	44	24	12	12	0	8	0
1965-66	45	26	7	12	0	10	0
1966-67	42	25	15	6	6	6	0
1967-68	40	25	10	13	5	8	0
1968-69	44	28	5	7	7	9	0
1969-70	47	26	5	7	9	7	0
1970-71	55	24	6	8	2	6	0
1971-72	45	31	6	6	4	6	2
1972-73	45	34	6	6	2	4	2
1973-74	48	24	7	9	7	4	2
1974-75	48	24	6	11	6	6	0
1975-76	49	20	5	17	2	6	2
1976-77	45	22	3	16	1	12	1
1977-78	43	26	7	16	3	4	1
1978-79	44	28	11	9	3	4	1
1979-80	40	29	9	11	1	10	1
1980-81	35	30	9	14	2	9	1
1981-82	40	28	9	11	4	7	1
1982-83	43	26	6	14	4	6	1
1983-84	43	27	8	10	5	6	1
1984-85	42	28	8	10	4	8	1
1985-86	38	31	6	11	4	9	1
1986-87	41	30	6	10	5	7	1
1987-88	41	29	5	8	5	9	1

Table A7. Geographical distribution of plots used in the all-habitats index, 1963-1988.

	Southern England	Eastern England	Western England	Northern England	Wales	Scotland	Northern Ireland
1963-64	30	23	14	15	11	7	0
1964-65	30	26	15	11	9	10	0
1965-66	32	31	11	11	6	8	1
1966-67	31	32	12	11	6	8	1
1967-68	31	29	13	13	6	9	1
1968-69	34	28	10	12	7	9	1
1969-70	33	30	9	13	7	7	1
1970-71	40	29	8	12	3	6	2
1971-72	35	33	9	12	4	5	3
1972-73	33	33	9	14	2	6	3
1973-74	32	31	9	16	4	6	3
1974-75	32	31	10	14	3	8	3
1975-76	35	29	10	15	2	8	3
1976-77	34	28	10	16	1	8	2
1977-78	35	28	10	16	3	6	3
1978-79	38	27	10	12	4	6	3
1979-80	34	29	8	14	3	10	3
1980-81	32	31	7	14	4	9	4
1981-82	36	31	7	12	4	7	3
1982-83	36	27	7	14	6	7	3
1983-84	37	26	8	12	6	7	4
1984-85	38	26	8	12	5	9	3
1985-86	36	28	8	14	4	6	3
1986-87	37	28	8	14	5	6	2
1987-88	35	30	8	12	5	7	2

Table A8. Geographical distribution of plots used in the WBS index, 1974-1988.

	Southern England	Eastern England	Western England	Northern England	Wales	Scotland	Northern Ireland	Eire
1974-75	11	22	29	27	4	2	4	0
1975-76	13	24	13	28	2	9	11	0
1976-77	19	23	11	28	6	6	8	0
1977-78	20	16	18	28	4	4	10	0
1978-79	20	22	12	29	2	8	8	0
1979-80	12	29	13	27	4	8	8	0
1980-81	15	25	13	29	4	8	6	0
1981-82	22	22	12	22	4	12	5	0
1982-83	21	18	12	27	5	11	6	0
1983-84	18	21	12	30	0	12	6	2
1984-85	19	21	11	27	5	10	5	1
1985-86	18	23	15	21	6	11	5	1
1986-87	20	20	13	27	7	9	5	0
1987-88	17	15	17	27	9	9	5	1

Table A9. Habitat composition of CBC plots used in the all-habitats index, 1963-1988.

	Farmland		Woodland		"Special"		All
	No.(%)	Area (%)	No.(%)	Area (%)	No.(%)	Area (%)	Area (ha)
1963-64	75	85	15	3	10	12	5808.7
1964-65	63	77	21	6	15	17	8273.2
1965-66	58	77	26	8	16	14	9173.9
1966-67	52	74	30	10	19	16	8779.4
1967-68	55	78	28	10	17	13	7784.0
1968-69	57	78	27	9	15	13	8343.3
1969-70	55	75	29	11	16	14	7973.1
1970-71	51	75	31	10	19	15	9049.3
1971-72	53	75	30	10	17	14	8819.5
1972-73	52	72	31	10	18	18	8170.5
1973-74	51	73	30	10	19	17	8232.0
1974-75	46	68	30	10	24	22	9178.4
1975-76	42	65	33	12	26	23	9257.1
1976-77	41	65	35	13	24	21	9321.0
1977-78	43	65	33	13	24	22	10667.0
1978-79	41	62	33	14	26	24	10845.7
1979-80	35	56	36	17	29	27	10548.6
1980-81	33	53	37	18	30	28	9702.6
1981-82	34	56	35	17	31	27	9713.7
1982-83	36	60	36	16	28	24	9885.2
1983-84	37	62	43	19	20	18	8357.3
1984-85	39	65	41	20	19	15	8126.5
1985-86	41	69	43	19	16	12	8555.2
1986-87	44	71	46	21	10	8	8101.8
1987-88	46	72	42	19	12	9	8276.5

Table A10. Habitat composition of plots used in the WBS index 1974-1988.

	Fast river		Slow river		Canal		Canal/river		Other		Total
	No. (%)	Length (%)	No. (%)	Length (%)	No. (%)	Length (%)	No. (%)	Length (%)	No. (%)	Length (%)	Length (km)
1974-75	38	39	49	50	9	7	4	4	0	0	208.6
1975-76	24	23	54	55	19	18	2	2	1	2	245.2
1976-77	21	20	51	52	21	20	6	6	2	2	260.5
1977-78	24	21	52	54	14	14	8	9	2	2	246.2
1978-79	27	25	53	54	10	10	8	9	2	2	256.5
1979-80	25	25	54	53	15	15	4	5	2	2	253.7
1980-81	29	29	58	56	8	10	4	5	0	0	229.6
1981-82	20	20	57	55	18	19	5	6	0	0	374.4
1982-83	23	20	50	50	21	24	6	6	0	0	306.6
1983-84	28	26	48	46	21	25	3	3	0	0	309.9
1984-85	26	24	51	48	19	23	4	5	0	0	350.4
1985-86	27	26	51	49	17	20	4	4	1	1	401.4
1986-87	26	26	54	49	15	18	6	7	0	0	393.8
1987-88	25	25	57	54	14	15	5	6	0	0	376.9

Appendix 4. Table of abundance for British breeding birds

This Table includes estimates of abundance for all British breeding species, and thus includes those seabirds and rarities (under 50 pairs) which were omitted from the main text. Species which breed irregularly in Britain are included only if they have nested here at least once since 1970; cases of hybridisation are excluded. In all, 228 species are listed.

The principal sources used in compiling this Appendix are: the BTO Breeding and Wintering Atlases (Sharrock 1976, Lack 1986); Hudson & Marchant (1984), a general survey which includes revised estimates for common species derived from CBC sample densities; Owen *et al* (1986) for waterfowl; Piersma (1986) for waders; Stroud *et al* (1989) for a range of species of conservation concern, including various seabirds; Spencer *et al* (1988, 1989) for rarities monitored by the RBBP; and the systematic sections of the present book, where additional references are cited for single-species studies.

All figures refer to Britain, rather than to the United Kingdom or to Britain and Ireland, and to breeding pairs unless otherwise stated. Territories or breeding females are the units where these are more appropriate to a species' breeding biology. In general, only scarce species and some colonial ones have been censused reliably. For most species tabulated, the figures should be regarded as only very approximate. For this reason, the Table is split into sections, and species in each section are listed taxonomically rather than in an attempted numerical ranking. Some figures are more imprecise than others, and these are enclosed in brackets. These include instances where a combined British and Irish total given by Sharrock (1976) or Lack (1986) has been reduced to its British component using a factor based on the distribution of occupied 10-km squares between Britain and Ireland at that time.

(a) *at least 500,000 pairs* (27 species)

Fulmar	525,000-530,000	Willow Warbler	2½ million
Pheasant	(3-3½ million females)	Goldcrest	500,000-600,000
Guillemot	500,000	Coal Tit	500,000-700,000
Puffin	550,000	Blue Tit	3½ million
Woodpigeon	2½ million	Great Tit	2 million
Skylark	2 million	Rook	850,000-860,000
Swallow	500,000	Carrion Crow	(800,000-1 million)
Meadow Pipit	1-1½ million	Starling	(3-5 million)
Wren	3-3½ million	House Sparrow	(4-4½ million)
Dunnock	2 million territories	Chaffinch	5 million
Robin	3½ million	Greenfinch	800,000
Blackbird	4½-5 million	Linnet	(600,000-700,000)
Song Thrush	1½ million	Yellowhammer	1½ million
Blackcap	800,000		

(b) *50,000-500,000 pairs* (49 species)

Manx Shearwater	(230,000-240,000)	Tree Pipit	100,000
Storm Petrel	(50,000-100,000)	Yellow Wagtail	(80,000-100,000)
Gannet	158,000-160,000	Pied Wagtail	300,000
Mallard	(50,000-100,000)	Redstart	140,000
Kestrel	70,000	Wheatear	(50,000-60,000)
Red Grouse	(200,000-400,000)	Mistle Thrush	300,000
Red-legged Partridge	(100,000-200,000)	Sedge Warbler	(150,000-200,000)
Grey Partridge	(200,000-400,000)	Reed Warbler	40,000-80,000
Moorhen	(200,000-225,000)	Whitethroat	400,000-500,000
Coot	(40,000-70,000)	Garden Warbler	200,000
Lapwing	200,000-225,000	Chiffchaff	400,000-500,000
Black-headed Gull	(150,000-200,000)	Spotted Flycatcher	200,000
Lesser Black-backed Gull	70,000	Long-tailed Tit	200,000 territories
Herring Gull	(200,000)	Marsh Tit	(120,000-140,000)
Kittiwake	490,000	Willow Tit	50,000-100,000
Arctic Tern	80,000	Treecreeper	200,000-250,000
Razorbill	(75,000-100,000)	Jay	(80,000)
Rock Dove/Feral Pigeon	(80,000-100,000)	Magpie	(300,000-400,000)
Stock Dove	100,000	Jackdaw	(350,000-400,000)
Collared Dove	100,000	Tree Sparrow	(260,000)
Turtle Dove	(75,000-100,000)	Goldfinch	250,000-300,000
Tawny Owl	50,000-100,000	Redpoll	140,000-150,000
Swift	70,000-80,000	Bullfinch	300,000-350,000
Sand Martin	300,000-500,000	Reed Bunting	400,000
House Martin	(250,000-450,000)		

(c) 5000-50,000 pairs

		(45 species)	
Little Grebe	(7000-13,000)	Sandwich Tern	14,000-15,000
Leach's Petrel	(5000-10,000)	Common Tern	12,000
Cormorant	6200	Black Guillemot	(10,000-15,000)
Shag	36,000	Cuckoo	(15,000-22,000 females)
Grey Heron	9500-9600	Little Owl	7000-14,000
Shelduck	12,000	Green Woodpecker	10,000-15,000
Tufted Duck	7000	Great Spotted Woodpecker	30,000-40,000
Eider	15,000-25,000	Rock Pipit	(35,000-40,000)
Sparrowhawk	25,000	Grey Wagtail	(17,000-34,000)
Buzzard	12,000-15,000	Dipper	(20,000-22,000)
Black Grouse	(10,000-15,000 females)	Whinchat	(18,000-35,000)
Oystercatcher	33,000-43,000	Stonechat	(10,000-20,000)
Ringed Plover	8450-8500	Ring Ouzel	(8000-15,000)
Golden Plover	23,000	Grasshopper Warbler	(10,000-18,000)
Dunlin	9900	Lesser Whitethroat	50,000
Snipe	30,000	Wood Warbler	16,000-18,500
Woodcock	(15,000-35,000 females)	Pied Flycatcher	(40,000)
Curlew	33,000-38,000	Nuthatch	50,000
Redshank	30,000-33,000	Siskin	(14,000-28,000)
Common Sandpiper	17,000-20,000	Twite	(17,000-34,000)
Great Skua	7900	Hawfinch	5000-10,000
Common Gull	47,000	Corn Bunting	30,000
Great Black-backed Gull	18,000-20,000		

(d) 500-5000 pairs

		(35 species)	
Red-throated Diver	1200-1500	Little Ringed Plover	610-630
Great Crested Grebe	(3000-5000)	Dotterel	850
Mute Swan	3100-3200	Greenshank	1500-1600
Greylag Goose	(2000)	Arctic Skua	3400
Canada Goose	(4000-5000)	Little Tern	2400-2500
Mandarin Duck	(2000-3000)	Barn Owl	4400
Gadwall	600	Long-eared Owl	(2000-6000)
Teal	3000-4500	Short-eared Owl	(1000-10,000)
Shoveler	1000-1500	Nightjar	1800-2100
Red-breasted Merganser	1500-2000	Kingfisher	(4000-6000)
Goosander	1000-1300	Lesser Spotted Woodpecker	3000-6000
Merlin	550-650	Nightingale	4000-5000
Peregrine	750-1000	Dartford Warbler	600
Ptarmigan	(3000-5000)	Bearded Tit	590-600
Capercaillie	(500-1000 females)	Crested Tit	900
Golden Pheasant	500-1000	Raven	(3500-4000)
Water Rail	(1500-3000)	Common Crossbill	(500-5000)
Corncrake	550-600		

(e) 50-500 pairs

		(32 species)	
Black-throated Diver	150-155	Quail	50-600
Slavonian Grebe	70-80	Lady Amherst's Pheasant	100-200
Egyptian Goose	(80-100)	Avocet	385
Wigeon	300-500	Stone-curlew	135-155
Garganey	40-90	Black-tailed Godwit	40-80
Pochard	200-300	Whimbrel	460-470
Common Scoter	100-115	Roseate Tern	300-330
Goldeneye	85-90	Ring-necked Parakeet	(100-150)
Ruddy Duck	(350-400)	Woodlark	200-230
Red Kite	50-60	Black Redstart	80-110
Marsh Harrier	60 females	Redwing	40-80
Hen Harrier	400-450 females	Cetti's Warbler	185-190
Goshawk	100	Firecrest	80-100
Golden Eagle	425	Chough	300
Osprey	50-60	Scottish Crossbill	300-400
Hobby	500	Cirl Bunting	60

(f) *0-50 pairs*

(40 species)

Great Northern Diver	0-1	Red-necked Phalarope	12-20
Red-necked Grebe	0-2	Mediterranean Gull	1-4
Black-necked Grebe	26-35	Little Gull	0-2
Bittern	22-25	Black Tern	0-1
Little Bittern	0-1	Snowy Owl	0-2
Whooper Swan	2-4 (feral)	Hoopoe	0-2
Pintail	20-30	Wryneck	1-10
Red-crested Pochard	5-10 (feral)	Shore Lark	0-1
Scaup	0-3	Bluethroat	0-1
Honey Buzzard	10-20	Fieldfare	1-7
White-tailed Eagle	6-10	Savi's Warbler	10-20
Montagu's Harrier	7-10	Marsh Warbler	10-20
Spotted Crake	5-20	Golden Oriole	10-30
Black-winged Stilt	0-1	Red-backed Shrike	3-10
Kentish Plover	0-1	Brambling	1-3
Temminck's Stint	4-6	Serin	1-5
Purple Sandpiper	2-3	Parrot Crossbill	0-3
Ruff	2-10 females	Scarlet Rosefinch	0-1
Wood Sandpiper	2-5	Lapland Bunting	0-15
Spotted Sandpiper	0-1	Snow Bunting	5-15

Appendix 5. Scientific names of species mentioned in the text

The list below gives the scientific names of plant and animal species (and other taxonomic categories) mentioned in the text.
Those birds for which population trends are discussed separately, either in the main systematic section or under *Additional
species*, are omitted: to find scientific names of these, please refer to the index and the relevant species text.

Plants

alder	*Alnus glutinosa*	oak	*Quercus robur*
ash	*Fraxinus excelsior*	pine	*Pinus* spp.
beech	*Fagus sylvaticus*	rhododendron	*Rhododendron ponticum*
birch	*Betula* spp.	reed	*Phragmites australis*
bracken	*Pteridium aquilinum*	Scots pine	*Pinus sylvestris*
bramble	*Rubus* spp.	sessile oak	*Quercus petraea*
chickweed	*Stellaria* spp.	Sitka spruce	*Picea sitchensis*
common fumitory	*Fumaria officinalis*	spear-plumed thistle	*Cirsium vulgare*
damson	*Prunus* spp.	spruce	*Picea* spp.
dock	*Rumex* spp.	sweet chestnut	*Castanea sativa*
elm	*Ulmus* spp.	sycamore	*Acer pseudoplatanus*
fat hen	*Chenopodium album*	thistle	*Carduus, Cirsium* spp.
gorse	*Ulex europaeus*	wild cherry	*Prunus avium*
heather	*Calluna, Erica* spp.	willow	*Salix* spp.
hornbeam	*Carpinus betulus*	willow herb	*Epilobium* spp.
larch	*Larix* spp.	wych elm	*Ulmus glabra*
meadowsweet	*Filipendula ulmaria*	yew	*Taxus baccata*
Norway spruce	*Picea abies*		

Birds

Arctic Skua	*Stercorarius parasiticus*	Manx Shearwater	*Puffinus puffinus*
Arctic Tern	*Sterna paradisaea*	Marsh Warbler	*Acrocephalus palustris*
Bittern	*Botaurus stellaris*	Mediterranean Gull	*Larus melanocephalus*
Black Guillemot	*Cepphus grylle*	Montagu's Harrier	*Circus pygargus*
Black Tern	*Chlidonias niger*	Parrot Crossbill	*Loxia pytyopsittacus*
Black-headed Gull	*Larus ridibundus*	Pintail	*Anas acuta*
Black-necked Grebe	*Podiceps nigricollis*	Puffin	*Fratercula arctica*
Black-winged Stilt	*Himantopus himantopus*	Purple Sandpiper	*Calidris maritima*
Bluethroat	*Luscinia svecica*	Razorbill	*Alca torda*
Brambling	*Fringilla montifringilla*	Red-backed Shrike	*Lanius collurio*
Chukar	*Alectoris chukar*	Red-crested Pochard	*Netta rufina*
Common Gull	*Larus canus*	Red-necked Grebe	*Podiceps grisegena*
Common Tern	*Sterna hirundo*	Red-necked Phalarope	*Phalaropus lobatus*
Common Turkey	*Meleagris gallopavo*	Roseate Tern	*Sterna dougallii*
Cormorant	*Phalacrocorax carbo*	Ruff	*Philomachus pugnax*
Fieldfare	*Turdus pilaris*	Sandwich Tern	*Sterna sandvicensis*
Fulmar	*Fulmarus glacialis*	Savi's Warbler	*Locustella luscinioides*
Gannet	*Sula bassana*	Scarlet Rosefinch	*Carpodacus erythrinus*
Golden Oriole	*Oriolus oriolus*	Scaup	*Aythya marila*
Great Black-backed Gull	*Larus marinus*	Serin	*Serinus serinus*
Great Northern Diver	*Gavia immer*	Shag	*Phalacrocorax aristotelis*
Great Skua	*Stercorarius skua*	Shore Lark	*Eremophila alpestris*
Guillemot	*Uria aalge*	Short-toed Treecreeper	*Certhia brachydactyla*
Herring Gull	*Larus argentatus*	Snow Bunting	*Plectrophenax nivalis*
Honey Buzzard	*Pernis apivorus*	Snowy Owl	*Nyctea scandiaca*
Hoopoe	*Upupa epops*	Spotted Crake	*Porzana porzana*
Kentish Plover	*Charadrius alexandrinus*	Spotted Sandpiper	*Actitis macularia*
Kittiwake	*Rissa tridactyla*	Storm Petrel	*Hydrobates pelagicus*
Lapland Bunting	*Calcarius lapponicus*	Temminck's Stint	*Calidris temminckii*
Leach's Petrel	*Oceanodroma leucorhoa*	White-tailed Eagle	*Haliaeetus albicilla*
Lesser Black-backed Gull	*Larus fuscus*	Whooper Swan	*Cygnus cygnus*
Little Bittern	*Ixobrychus minutus*	Wood Sandpiper	*Tringa glareola*
Little Gull	*Larus minutus*	Wryneck	*Jynx torquilla*
Little Tern	*Sterna albifrons*		

Other animals

ant	*Formicidae*	mussel	*Mytilus edulis*
aphid	*Aphis, Hyalopterus* spp.	rabbit	*Oryctolagus cuniculus*
caddis fly	*Trichoptera*	red deer	*Cervus elaphus*
cockle	*Cerastoderma edule*	sheep	*Ovis aries*
earthworm	*Lumbricidae*	short-tailed vole	*Microtus agrestis*
field mouse	*Apodemus* spp.	spider	*Araneae*
fox	*Vulpes vulpes*	wood ant	*Formica rufa*
leatherjacket (a cranefly larva)	*Tipula paludosa*	zebra mussel	*Dreissena polymorpha*
mayfly	*Ephemeroptera*		

Index of bird species names

This index contains English names and scientific names (listed by genus only) of all bird species mentioned in the main text or in Appendix 4. References to species mentioned in the Foreword are omitted. Page numbers in bold type refer to the main text entries.